FOUNTAIN PENS
AND PENCILS

The Golden Age of Writing Instruments

George Fischler and Stuart Schneider

Revised Price Guide

4880 Lower Valley Rd. Atglen, PA 19310 USA

Title page photo:
WATERMAN #0504, ca. 1900-1905. Gold filled "Chased Filigree"
design overlay, eyedropper filled pen. There is no reference to this style of
pen in any catalogs.

This book is dedicated to Peggy and Michelle who have
supported us with patience, love, and guidance; and to
the memory of Alex Montgomery.

Published by Schiffer Publishing Ltd.
4880 Lower Valley Road
Atglen, PA 19310
Phone: (610) 593-1777; Fax: (610) 593-2002
E-mail: schifferbk@aol.com
Please write for a free catalog.
This book may be purchased from the publisher.
Please include $3.95 for shipping.
Try your bookstore first.

We are interested in hearing from authors
with book ideas on related subjects.

Revised price guide: 1998
Copyright © 1990 by George Fischler and Stuart Schneider.
Library of Congress Catalog Number: 89-63849.

Designed by Ellen J. (Sue) Taylor
ISBN: 0-7643-0491-7
Printed in the United States of America.

PARKER #11, ca. 1899-1910. Sterling silver cable chased design overlay, eyedropper filled taper cap pen.

Oh! Nature's noblest gift
My grey goose quill
Slave of my thoughts,
Obedient to my will.
Torn from thy parent bird
To form a pen.
That first mighty
Instrument of all men.

Byron

Acknowledgments

The authors wish to thank all the people whose enthusiasm about this project and about pen collecting made this book possible, and especially to thank those individuals and organizations who so generously shared their knowledge, pens, and photographs with us :

Peter Amis, Dr. Bernard Boal, Harry Bouras, Dr. Roberto Caffaro, Howard Edelstein, Bob Edison, Sam Elardo, Edward Fingerman, L. Michael Fultz, Pier Gustafson, Murray Hoffman, R.H. Johnson, James Krause, Barbara Lambert-A.T. Cross Pen Company, Donald Lavin, Gary Lehrer, Dr. Larry Liebman, Montblanc Pen Company, Boris Rice, Howard M. Rifkin, The Southern California Pen Collectors Club, Dr. Robert Tefft, Stewart Unger, Daniel Zazove. Handmade paper backgrounds by Marcia Meirowitz.

MONTBLANC #333, ca. 1935-1940. Black plastic twist filling pen.

Contents

MABIE, TODD, ca. 1932-1936. Swallow red marble plastic lever filling pen/pencil combination.

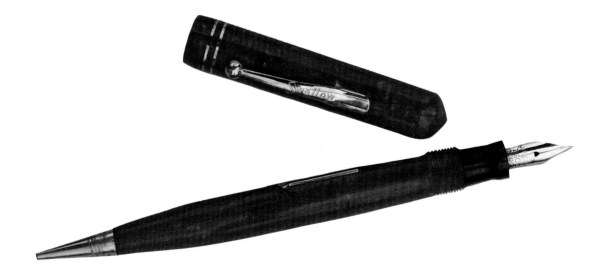

PARKER, ca. 1929 *Duofold* advertisement.

Introduction

This book is for all people using, owning or collecting fountain pens and their matching pencils. It will introduce the beginning pen collector to the hobby of pen collecting and answer questions asked by advanced pen collectors about the earliest and rarest of pens. It will help identify pens and provide the opportunity to examine many of the pens that were produced.

Fountain pen collecting is very rewarding. There are few hobbies that let one use the items every day that one collects. Fountain pens are a part of history. Presidents, authors, statesmen, scientists, lawyers, managers and secretaries, to name just a few, used fountain pens. The author, Mark Twain, not only used a fountain pen but publicly endorsed the Conklin *Crescent* and the Paul E. Wirt fountain pens. Twain stated, "I like the Conklin *Crescent* because it doesn't roll off the table when I put it down". Charles Lindbergh carried only a Waterman's pen on his solo flight across the Atlantic. Such famous personalities as Mickey Mouse, Popeye, Superman and Babe Ruth also loaned their names to fountain pens. General MacArthur made sure that the pens used to sign the Japanese surrender documents at the end of World War II were American Watermans and Parkers.

During that war, Parker *51's* were so rare in Europe, that soldiers could use them like currency, trading them for German lugers or a lady's favor. They were also rare in the States. Parker ran advertisements apologizing for the shortage of pens due to the war rationing. It is rather incredible that in the 1920s, more than half of America was illiterate. The fountain pen makers found that by making pens in bright colors, even those who could not read or write would buy them, carrying them in their front pocket to make it appear that they could.

Looking through this book, you will see the earliest pens, the finest pens and examples of hundreds of other pens. Every pen has its own personality. One writer may like the smooth, flexible point of a 1940s Eversharp *Skyline*, another the less flexible point found on the 1920s Parker *Duofold*. Left-handed writers like the rounded point of the 1930s Sheaffer or the ball tipped point of the Wahl, as "lefties" push a pen rather than pull it as they write. A signature will vary with each brand of pen used and within the decade that the pen was made.

Pens are very personal items. One may have 25 pens in a collection, yet 2 or 3 will be the favorites. Their balance is perfect, the nib glides over the paper, the weight changes ever so slightly, and people know by feel when they are about to run out of ink. The pen becomes an extension of one's hand and lets you write for hours without fatigue. A "good" pen writes from the moment it touches the paper and is tuned to let just the right amount of ink flow out. It does not "ink the fingers" (provided that it is cleaned out every so often and kept relatively full of ink).

An interesting note about fountain pens is that writers in each generation up to the advent of the ball point pen remember the pen they used in school. Once the ballpoint pen appeared, writing became homogeneous and the differences between pens faded.

There are great pens and not-so-great pens. If a pen appears here, it is either interesting, collectible, or a good example of that maker's pen. There are dozens of pens that were not illustrated, not because they were bad pens, but because illustrating every pen made would take a 10 volume encyclopedia. Look for yours among these pages.

The hobby of collecting fountain pens has grown tremendously and the focus of collecting has changed. The urge to have every pen made has been replaced by collectors seeking out one or two styles or lines of fountain pens. Pen repair and research of the manufacturer's activities

PARKER, 1928-1929.
Duofold Senior button filling pen and pencil set in moderne black & pearl Permanite.

has become a part of the hobby. Beginning collectors can no longer amass pens in the quantities that the early collectors could. Many once common pens, such as the Waterman #52, Parker *51* and Eversharp *Skyline* are now difficult to find. Collectors must work harder to find each new pen and of course, prices are rising. Almost any new collector/user, however, can put together a representative collection in a short time. A few collectors can show collections of 1500 pens, but the average collector has under 25.

Fountain pen makers produced over a million pens a year in the 1910s to the 1940s. The ballpoint pen arrived in 1945 and was eventually proven reliable (The first ones wrote for several weeks and then died). Millions of fountain pens were put in drawers and forgotten.

Four particular pen manufacturers are especially revered. Among the "big four" companies, the Wahl-Eversharp Pen Company is remembered for the Art Deco designs of the *Doric, Gold Seal,* and *Skyline* pens. Sheaffer Pen Company was known for its exclusive colors, such as bright jade green and the mother-of-pearl inlay, as well as the *Lifetime Balance* pen, *Triumph,* and *PFM*. The Parker Pen Company brings to mind the "Snake" pen, *Duofolds, Vacumatics,* and the *51*. A favorite among collectors is the L.E. Waterman Pen Company which consistently made the most attractive pens and had such hits as the "Safety" pen, and the *Ripple, Hundred Year,* and *Patrician* pens.

SHEAFFER, 1924-1929. *Lifetime,* jade green Radite, lever filling pen.
The first company to introduce a plastic pen, it created a revolution in the industry, forcing the other pen makers to introduce their own plastic pens, and spelling the end of hard rubber pens.

Chapter 1

Valuing Fountain Pens

Valuing older fountain pens can be approached several ways. The easiest method for a new collector is to compare the price of an older pen with a modern pen. The older pen should be valued at least equal to the new pen. Pen collectors, however, use a "supply and demand" valuation, or what would a willing buyer and a willing seller agree to as a value? An examination of the components of value are helpful.

A valuable pen is usually rare, but a rare pen is not always valuable. A rare pen, of which only one or two are known may not have the broad appeal of say the 1906 Parker "Snake" pen. There are more than twenty Parker "Snakes" in collections and yet the knowledgeable collector would jump at the opportunity to pick one up at a bargain price of $2,500, about one third of its present value. A 1940s *Superman* pen, of which there are only two known in collections, may sell for less than $250. Obviously, the rarity factor is not the main determinant of value.

Take the example of a collector who is attempting to find a certain pen for his collection. He values that pen many times higher than another person who already has one. That collector might be willing to pay $500 for one pen, but would he buy a second or a third at the same price? It depends upon who is buying, the availability, and how badly he wants that pen.

Terms Used in Describing Fountain Pens

Mint: No sign of use
Near Mint: Slight signs of use
Excellent: Imprints sharp, writes well, looks great
Extra Fine: One of the following: brassing, darkening, or some wear
Fine: Used, some parts are worn or darker
Good: Well used
Fair: A parts pen

HR	Hard rubber
ED	Eyedropper filler
LF	Lever filler
PF	Plunger without sac filler
PS	Plunger with sac filler
GFT	Gold plate or gold filled trim
NPT	Nickel trim
CPT	Chrome trim

Things to Consider When Valuing Fountain Pens

Condition: This is the most important criteria. A Parker *Duofold* "Deluxe", in Mint condition, may be worth 5 times one in Extra Fine condition. Damage to a cap or barrel is a major problem. A pen with a small crack in the cap or barrel may be worth one quarter as much as one without a crack. Repair is often possible, but to repair the pen, one needs parts or another pen with that part. Ask yourself if the price is still a bargain when you have to cannibalize another pen for parts.

SUPERMAN, ca. 1940. The rarest comic character fountain pen. This model features a decal of Superman with his name on the clip. An inexpensive pen, it originally sold for 59 cents. Superman did not lend his good name to just any pen, this Superman pen could only be purchased by one true of heart and willing to fight for truth, justice, and the American way.

Color: Tens of millions of pens were made in black, less were made in other colors. The quality of the color is also important. A perfect pen in a crisp, rich color may demand a premium over a standard, well-colored pen. The pens illustrated show good examples of color.

Working Condition: Pens should be in working condition if possible. While the collector who can put a pen in working order may not care if the pen needs cleaning and a new ink sac, most collectors would rather not do that job. During cleaning, the pen can be broken. If you are not sure what you are doing, have someone else put your pens in working order. Ideally you will find pens that have been repaired and are in working condition (new ink sac & cleaned). Plan to spend $10-$20 for cleaning and new ink sac.

Size: Collectors usually look for the largest versions of a pen. Lady's pens, the smaller pens with the ring on top, have remained undervalued. Many of these pens rival the men's pens for beauty and workmanship and certain colors are available only in lady's pens. Presently, more men collect fountain pens than women. Men want a pen that can be kept in a jacket or shirt pocket. Lady's pens were designed to be worn on à ribbon or kept in a pocket book. Good values abound in quality Lady's pens.

The standard size pen is 5.25″ (13.4 cm) to 5.5″ (14 cm) long when closed. Often the highest priced pens are the largest men's pens, all over 5.5 inches (14 cm) long when closed. Examples are the Waterman *#20* and *#58*, the Parker *Black* or *Red Giant*, large *Duofolds*, oversized *Vacumatics*, full-sized Sheaffers and Wahl-Eversharps. They can be compared with the most popular modern selling pen, the large Montblanc *Diplomat.* Many collectors simply want the biggest, high quality pen available.

Original Parts: Not all pens need to have original parts but they are very important to some people, especially Parker *Duofold* collectors. Parker *Duofolds* were originally made with the stiff *Duofold* nib and the "Christmas tree" feed. The later *Vacumatic* nib and feed were more flexible and wrote differently from the *Duofold* nib and feed. During the 1930s, pen stores often replaced the *Duofold* nib and feed with the *Vacumatic* nib and feed when making repairs. Also in the 1930s, Parker sold its remaining *Duofold* stock with the *Vacumatic* nib and feed. Although technically correct on the 1930s *Duofold* pens, a *Duofold* pen with *Duofold* nib and feed may sell for 25% more than the same pen with a *Vacumatic* nib and feed.

Early Pens, 1910 and before: Collectors are looking for the earliest pens made by the major pen manufacturers. Rarely do they expect to use them. Nevertheless, they should be in working condition to maintain value. When made by Waterman or Parker, the early pens, especially silver or gold covered, are more valuable than many of the later pens. As pen collecting has matured, collectors have rediscovered the early pen makers.

Novel Filling Systems: These normal sized, black pens often contain ingenious methods for making the pen more leak proof, easier to fill, or able to hold more ink. Some manufacturers were just trying to avoid patent infringement lawsuits while others thought they had a better idea. For example, Crocker, Sanford and a few other makers designed "blow filler" pens. You put the cap on the back end of the pen and blew into it. The air pressure compressed the sac and when you stopped blowing, the sac expanded drawing ink into the pen. Many innovative makers' pens are very collectible and can often be obtained at bargain prices.

COLLECTING TIPS

A fine collection of pens can be put together from today's modern pen makers. If you want to acquire the earlier models, you must work harder. Ask everyone you know who was in high school in the 1940s or before, visit the local antique shops and flea markets, run an advertisement in your local newspaper, exhibit your collection at the local library, visit older jewelry and stationery stores and ask if they have old stock of fountain pens, or join a local fountain pen club and attend a regional pen show.

A good starting place is your local antique shop. If they know that you are a pen collector, they may call you when they have pens. Unfortunately, antique dealers have a tendency to charge top price for the known pens, such as a Parker "Big Red", regardless of condition. The classic antique dealers phrase, "It's in the book at a much higher price than I am asking" instantly makes you want to collect pens that are not "in the book" (the dealers can rarely produce "the book" if you ask to see it).

In producing this book, we have tried to illustrate the pens that you most likely will see and the pens that you may never see in 20 years of looking. Also shown are pens that are interesting, unusual and fun to own. When deciding whether to buy a pen, remember that in a few years you will rarely regret paying too much for a pen that you own, but you will always regret having not bought a good pen when it was available.

PARKER, ca. 1892-1894. Black hard rubber hexagon barrel, eyedropper filled overfeed pen. This is one of the earliest Parker pens, the imprint simply reads: "Geo. S. Parker Fountain Pen 1892".

Chapter 2

A Brief History
of the Fountain Pen

The story of the fountain pen could not be told without a few words about its predecessor, the dip pen. Dip pens were used by the scribes of the Egyptian kings over 4000 years ago. Scribes used a sharp stick or goose quill shaved to a point and dipped in berry juice to keep inventory records or write a letter. An improvement on the quill was not made until the late 1700s with the introduction of the metal pen point in a plain or fancy holder. Reliable fountain pens were not perfected until the 1880s.

Today's collectors will tell you that Lewis E. Waterman is the father of the Fountain Pen. His pen was patented and then introduced in 1884. Actually, the idea and production of the fountain pen was begun in the early 1800s. The idea was simple. Put a reservoir of ink behind a pen point and one would no longer have to dip one's pen into the bottle of ink. As easy as it sounded, it was not easily put into practice. Several problems appeared immediately. The first was that if the reservoir was closed, the ink would not flow out of it, but if there was an opening in the reservoir, all the ink would flow out at once. Many ideas were proposed to solve the problem, but few worked as expected. In 1809, an inventor named Folsch patented a pen with a reservoir that contained a valve at the end. Theoretically, the ink would flow when the valve was opened a little and not flow when it was closed. Would the pen work as promised? It did not, as there was a second major problem: the ink.

Ink, as we know it today, is a space age product compared to ink in the early 1800s. Then the ink was a thick liquid containing a sludge of solids. Using it presented a minimal problem for the dip pen, but if this sludge stayed in the fountain pen for any length of time, the solids would settle out and clog the openings. Had L.E. Waterman produced his pen in the early 1800s, it would have failed miserably. Different inks were produced during the nineteenth century to solve the sludge problem. Dyes were tried, but they were not acceptable as the dye would be absorbed into the paper, creating blobs of ink rather than lines. The object was to have the ink dry quickly on top of the paper. Metals dissolved in acid seemed to produce a good ink, but it soon burned right through the paper and often through the skin.

By the 1860s, an ink was produced that was both permanent and reasonably safe. Water would not wash it away, nor would it fade with age. It was, however, highly corrosive to the steel pen points then in use. The only option was to use a metal that was not attacked by the ink. Gold was substituted, as it was impervious to the effects of the ink and dip pens with gold nibs became the preferred writing instrument. Gold being a soft metal, had a limited life expectancy as a nib, since the tip wore away quickly.

What was needed was a metal tip that a) was impervious to the corrosive ink; b) was hard enough to stand up to daily use; c) could be bonded to the gold; and d) be polished to a smooth finish. Iridium, a rare metal, was the material of choice. At the time, it was more expensive than gold and mined in very limited quantities. Iridium was produced as a powder and melted into tiny balls which were soldered to the gold point. The point was then slit by a very thin, high speed wheel to produce the iridium-tipped, gold nib.

By the 1880s, the technology necessary to produce a workable fountain pen had been perfected. Fountain pens were soon being produced by many makers including A.T.Cross, Mabie Todd, Paul E. Wirt, John Holland, Eagle, Caw, and others. These pens were a big improvement over the dip pen but they were not consistently reliable. If the pen was cooled or warmed or nearly empty, the ink could and often would blob out of the point and onto the paper. This "flow" problem was solved to a great extent by Lewis E. Waterman.

1891

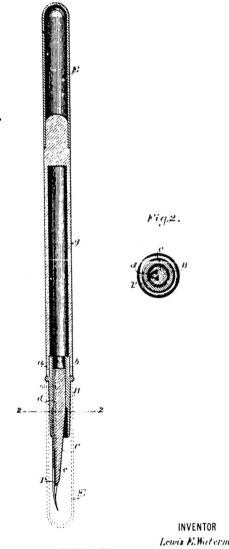

(No Model.)

L. E. WATERMAN.

FOUNTAIN PEN.

No. 293,545.   Patented Feb. 12, 1884.

Fig. 1.

Fig. 2.

WITNESSES

Wm A. Smith
Jas. S. Latimer

INVENTOR

Lewis E. Waterman.
By his Attorneys
Pope Edgcomb & Butler.

(Model.)

L. E. WATERMAN.

FOUNTAIN PEN.

No. 307,735.   Patented Nov. 4, 1884.

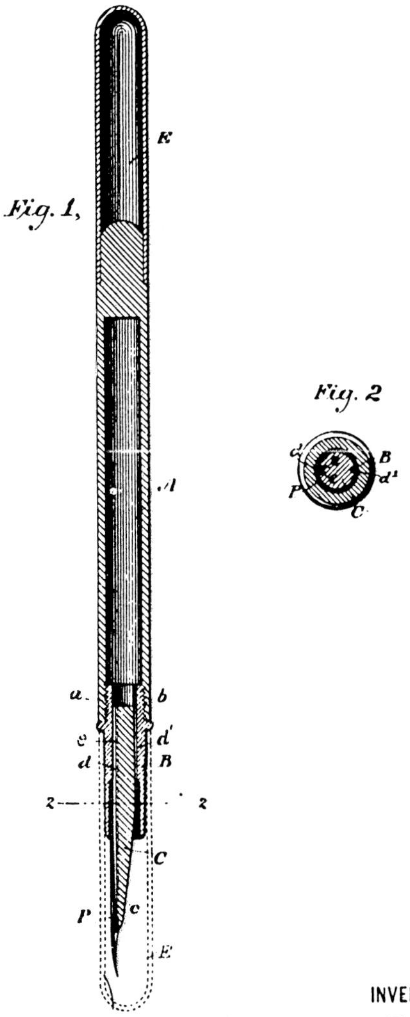

Fig. 1.

Fig. 2

WITNESSES

Wm A. Smith
Carrie E. Ashley

INVENTOR

Lewis E. Waterman.
By his Attorneys
Pope Edgcomb & Butler

Opposite page
WATERMAN #8, ca. 1885. Black hard rubber eyedropper filled pen. This pen illustrates the early two step section used only for the first couple of years of production. This example is one of the earliest Waterman's known. Straight cap pens,, which were the first style produced by Waterman were available with all the standard nib sizes and were made into the 1920s. The nib shown is a later replacement. $750-1250.

Chapter 3

The L.E. Waterman Pen Company

1884-Present

The oldest of the "Big Four" pen companies is the L.E.Waterman Pen Company of New York. Begun in 1884, using Lewis E. Waterman's patented (February 12, 1884) "Ideal" fountain pen, this company went on to become the largest American pen maker. Waterman started with his patent for an improved feed design. He knew that the simple channel in the "feed" from the ink reservoir to the nib had to serve two masters, the flow of ink out and the flow of air in. A way was devised for the air to enter the pen as the ink flowed out by cutting three razor thin slits in the bottom of the channel leading to the nib. Capillary action brought the ink to the nib's point and the channel now allowed air to enter the reservoir as needed. The pen was a success, and with Waterman's keen use of advertising, the Waterman Pen Company took off, producing some of the most attractive pens ever made, with designs in silver, gold and hard rubber.

Often there is a fairy tale-like story about how the giant, successful company started with a small, simple idea. Waterman's company was no exception. The Waterman fable goes something like this. Lewis E. Waterman was a struggling young insurance salesman. Once, when he was about to make a substantial sale, he had a terrible experience. He pulled out the contract for the customer to sign and after filling in all of the pertinent information, handed his pen to the customer to sign on the dotted line. When the pen touched the line, a blob of ink flowed from the tip of the pen and ruined the contract. Before he could prepare a new contract, the customer signed up with another company. Vowing to create a new, better fountain pen that would never suffer that problem again, he devised the Waterman's Ideal Pen. A good product and an aggressive sales campaign launched the company and helped it become the leading pen manufacturer. The truth was somewhat different.

Waterman's pen business began in 1883 in a small office at 136 Fulton Street in New York City. Pen parts were ordered from local jobbers and Waterman, who had been an insurance salesman, assembled and sold the pens. In March, 1884, Waterman and his best customer, Asa Shipman, formed a partnership known as the Ideal Pen Company and moved into Shipman's offices at 10 Murray Street. They increased production to about 200 pens that year. Waterman and Shipman, for whatever reason, dissolved the partnership in late 1884 with Waterman remaining at the Murray Street location until he could obtain a new manufacturing site.

Early in 1885, Waterman moved to 155 Broadway. To raise capital to pay off debts and expand production, Waterman formed the L.E. Waterman Pen Company, a corporation, on November 11, 1887. The Company's business grew at a slow but steady rate and the offices were moved to keep up with the expansion. It took over the offices at 157 Broadway in 1893, then moved to new quarters at 173 Broadway in 1902, and 191 Broadway in 1917.

Waterman found that there was a demand for a fountain pen with a guarantee. Either you liked your Ideal Fountain Pen or you were guaranteed a refund. Waterman's success had less to do with the fact that his pen was a good product than with Waterman's faith in, and use of advertising. He placed his pen before the public and hammered home the idea that his pen was better than all the rest.

The "New, Improved" Waterman Pen was promoted with testimonials such as these from 1891: "I find it the most satisfactory pen of its kind."—Chauncey M. Depew, President N.Y.C. & H.R.R.R.; "I have given up every other pen in its favor and have of late done all my writing with it."—Oliver Wendell Holmes, M.D.; "I have taken great comfort with my Ideal pen."—Harriet Ward Beecher.

WATERMAN gold nibs, ca. 1884-1899 by gold pen manufacturers. It should be noted that there are many variations in Waterman nibs besides those illustrated here. Left to right: ca. 1884-1890, the earliest style with crescent vent hole; ca. 1891-1894, a circular vent hole has been added to the nib; ca. 1892-1896, a star replaced the crescent and hole; ca. 1896-1897, a small star is imprinted on the nib which has the familiiar heart shaped vent hole; ca. 1897-1899, the large star imprint nib. Around the time of this last style, the Waterman numbering system came into use. All the nibs illustrated here were originally fitted to pens with the original Waterman three fissure feed.

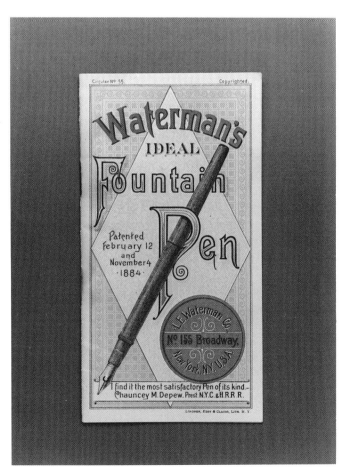

WATERMAN gold nibs, ca. 1900-1953. Left to right: ca. 1900-1907, small curved New York imprint nib; ca. 1907-1918, large curved New York imprint nib; ca. 1907-1918, straight line New York imprint; ca. 1918-1937, Registered U.S. Pat. Off. nib; ca. 1938-1953, Ideal 14k nib. There were also other nib styles which were used on specific pens, for example the "keyhole" nibs used on the #7 and #5 ripple pens, the *Hundred Year*, *Emblem*, and *Patrician* nibs used on those pens.

WATERMAN, ca. 1892. Catalog illustrating some early pens and available nib styles. $275-350.

Waterman flooded the media of his day with his message. An 1880s advertising vehicle was the trade card. These small, colorful cards advertising a product and telling where it could be obtained were given away by merchants and collected like baseball cards. Customers tried to collect the set of three or four which advertised Waterman's pens. Advertisements appeared in the popular magazines on a regular basis. Waterman followed up early sales with a letter asking for information about the sale. He also sent brochures to merchants telling them how to sell the Waterman Pen.

In 1901, when L.E.Waterman died at age 64, his company was selling over 1000 pens a day. The company exhibited at all major fairs and expositions such as the Saint Louis Exposition of 1904, advertising the "Dip-No-More" Waterman's pens. Waterman also saw the potential of selling outside this country. He travelled and promoted his pens in many countries and eventually had distribution outlets throughout the world.

Among the most jewelry-like of Waterman's pens were the early (1898-1915) eyedropper-filled pens with gold and silver overlays. Examples of many of these beautiful hand-finished pens are illustrated. Waterman also made attractive "Safety pens" with overlays, but the most beautiful of the Waterman "Safety pens" were "remade" in France, England, Germany or Holland. The foreign distributor would purchase the American pen and put their overlay of gold, silver or rolled gold (gold filled) on the pen. These overlays often incorporated enamels or featured dancing cherubs. Collectively they are referred to as the "Continental Safeties."

The company continued to make a variety of attractive pens and in 1923 introduced the *Ripple* pen. It was an immediate best seller. The Red and Black *Ripple* was a variation on the Red and Black "Mottled" or "Woodgrain" pen that Waterman had been making since about 1898. The *Ripple* hard rubber was made by H.P.& E. Day of Seymour, Connecticut and was exclusive to Waterman. This line of pens was made in almost every size, from #52 ½V to the largest #20. In 1924 and 1926 when Sheaffer and Parker began to make pens out of plastics, Waterman was successfully selling their *Ripple* pens and saw no need to immediately change to plastic.

In 1927 they introduced their #7 hard rubber *Ripple* pen. The #7 was approximately the size of a #55 pen with a colored band around the top of the cap. The color referred to the type of nib on the pen, for example red was a standard point. In 1928, Waterman produced hard rubber *Ripple* pens in three new colors, Rose *Ripple* —red and yellow, Olive *Ripple* —tan and black, and Blue-Green *Ripple*. The colored *Ripples* and the #7 were competing with the new plastic pens that were taking away sales from Waterman. It was time to introduce plastic to the Waterman line.

The first plastic pens were the *Patrician* (1929-1938), a large man's pen and the #94's (1930-1938). The advantage of plastic was that it could be made with fewer production steps, thereby saving money and it was available in many new colors. There were 6 colors in the *Patrician* line. Interestingly, the earliest black *Patrician* was made in hard rubber. The *Patrician* pens were not best sellers as the effect of the Depression cut sales. Toward the end of the life of the *Patrician* line, there were variations in clip placement and clip style. The variations are believed to exist because Waterman used whatever parts were on hand.

Another good-looking pen from Waterman was the plastic *#7* (1933-1938). It came in black and a striped design known as "Emerald Ray". The next plastic pen was the *Ink-Vue* (1935-1940). It was made to compete with the Parker *Vacumatic* and boasted a new filling system. These plastic pens used the lever filler system with the exception of the *Ink-Vue* that used a variation of the lever filler (see the section on the filling systems for details). The *Hundred Year* pen (1939-1946) designed by John Vassos, followed the *Ink-Vue*. Due to its being made of a new plastic that would not break, warp, shrink or twist, it was guaranteed for 100 years. Others models made during this period were the *Commando* (1942-1946), made during the war years and the *Emblem* pen (1946-1949) which was basically a *Hundred Year* pen without the guarantee.

In 1946, the Federal Trade Commission enjoined the pen companies from making unrealistic guarantees about their pens. All variations of "Lifetime" models were renamed and guarantees were changed to "for as long as you own the pen". Waterman's last interesting fountain pen, the *C/F*, made in Canada or France was introduced in 1954, but it could not save the American company which ceased manufacturing in 1958.

The fountain pen business stopped as the ball point pen became the popular writing instrument. Waterman USA was sold several times and is now, in 1989, a division of the Gillette Company. Today's Waterman pens are made in France.

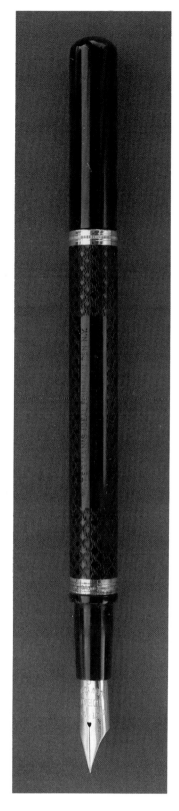

WATERMAN #6, ca, 1890-1895. Black chased hard rubber eyedropper filled pen with two gold filled bands, a very early pen. $400-600.

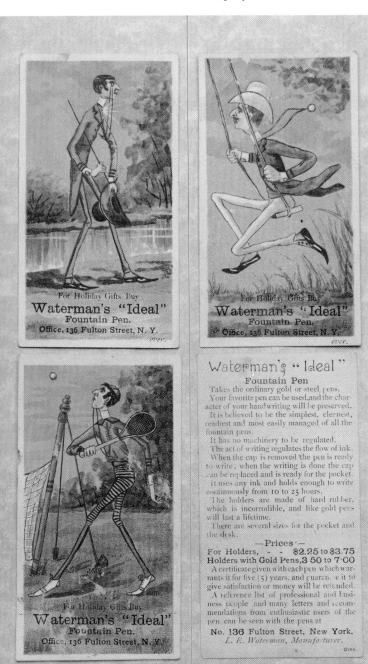

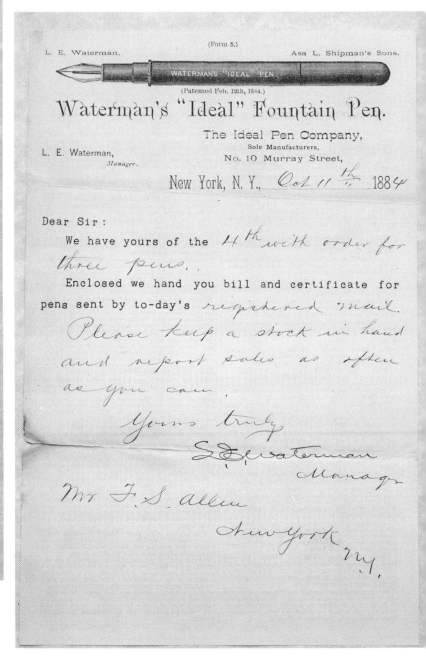

WATERMAN, 1884. Letter signed by L.E. Waterman as manager of the Ideal Pen Company.

WATERMAN, 1884 trade cards. The trade card was an early form of advertising typically with an amusing scene on one side, and advertising copy on the other. $150-225.

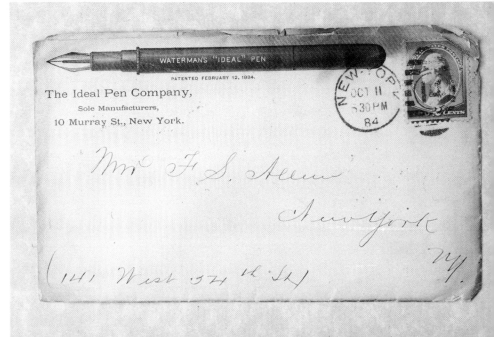

Waterman Numbering System

About 1898 Waterman began using a standard numbering system to describe its pens. This system was modified slightly in 1917 and lasted until the 1930s with exceptions creeping in after 1927. These numbers were stamped on the end of the pen as follows:

Hundreds column

2xx Sterling Silver barrel covered
3xx Gold barrel covered
4xx Sterling Silver barrel & cap
5xx Solid Gold barrel & cap
6xx Mother of Pearl (after 1917, two gold bands on barrel)
7xx One 14kt gold band on barrel
8xx One 14kt gold band on cap
9xx One 14kt gold band on top of cap
A zero before the Hundred's column means gold filled

Tens column

0x Straight cap
1x Cone cap
2x Taper cap
4x Desk pen (after 1917, Safety pen)
5x Lever filler
6x Lever filler w/slip cap
7x Eyedropper w/screw cap
8x Pump filler

Units column

This is the nib size

Additional Markings

½ indicates that the pen is thinner
V indicates that the pen is short
SF indicates Self Filler
S indicates Safety
P indicates Pump
POC indicates Pocket
PSF indicates Pocket Self Filler
X indicates Larger barrel than standard for that nib size
VP indicates Vest pocket

For example, a #0552½ indicates a thin, gold filled, lever filler pen with a #2 nib. A #404 is a silver, straight cap pen with a #4 nib, and a #58 is a lever filler pen with a #8 nib. About 1928, Waterman began making pens that did not use the above system such as #7's, #5's, #94's, #92's, and #32's.

Waterman Filling Systems

During the Waterman years, different systems were devised to improve the ease and neatness of filling the pen with ink. Some of the systems were extremely short-lived, making these pens hard to find and very desirable to the collector.

Eyedropper Filling, 1884-1928. The first and simplest system employed by Waterman was the eyedropper filling pens. The "section", composed of the nib, feed and collar, was unscrewed from the barrel and the barrel filled with ink from an eyedropper. It was, and still is unequaled in simplicity of function and design.

An advantage to this system was that the larger the pen and barrel, the more ink it would hold. The main drawback to this seemingly ideal filling system was the often times messy operation of refilling the pen and the requirement that the user have an eyedropper handy when the pen ran dry. Its practicality is evidenced by the fact that Waterman continued to feature

WATERMAN #504, ca. 1895-1910. Solid 14k gold "Repousse" design overlay, eyedropper filled pen, also made in silver. The black cap is a replacement. $8000-10000.

WATERMAN #26, ca. 1893-1898. Black chased hard rubber eyedropper filled pen with two gold filled bands. Note the early configuration of the nib. $400-500.

eyedropper filled pens long after most pens, including its own, were being made with other filling systems.

Pump Filling (1st style), 1899. The first improvement over the eyedropper filler was the 1899 pump filler. The end of the barrel was removed to expose a rod which was drawn up to pump in the ink. The pen was longer than a standard pen to accommodate the rod. It apparently did not work very well as Waterman abandoned it after a few months.

Pump Filling (2nd style), 1903-1926. This ingenious filling system, in theory should have worked very well, in practice, it did not. Filling was accomplished by holding the pen with the nib in the ink bottle, unscrewing the pump mechanism from the end of the barrel and then pumping up and down with short, half inch (1.3 cm) strokes. It contained a small weight attached through a hole in a piston which acted as a two way valve, closed on the upstroke to draw ink and open on the downstroke so as not to force the ink back out. From examination, it does not appear to be a very practical system although the pen would have held more ink than a pen with a sac.

The scarcity of these pens today indicates that it was not popular, although it continued to be shown in Waterman catalogs until 1925. Possible reasons for the continued advertising may be that there was a large supply of unsold stock or that Waterman wished to preserve certain patent rights to the design.

Safety Pen, 1907-1940s. The "Safety" pen sold very successfully. It was called a "Safety" pen because it was advertised not to leak in the pocket. The safety features were a nib and feed that retracted into the barrel of the pen when the bottom of the pen was turned, and a screw-on cap instead of a friction cap. The earliest models, designated "J" were fitted with friction caps. The inside of the cap acted as a plug to seal off the ink in the barrel. This pen was also an eyedropper filler and could create a flood of ink if it was opened upside down. More popular in Europe than the United States, it lasted until the 1940s in Europe and only the 1920s in the States.

Sleeve Filler, 1910-1915. In 1910 Waterman introduced the first practical non-eyedropper filled pen in the form of the sleeve filler. This was the beginning of the line of pens known as self-fillers and marked the appearance of two items still used in fountain pen filling systems: the rubber ink sac and the pressure bar. In this system a sliding sleeve covered an opening in the barrel. After sliding back the sleeve on the pen barrel the pressure bar was depressed, compressing the sac. Upon release, the sac expanded and ink was drawn in. Although this system functioned extremely well, one drawback was the large size of the sleeve. This made the pen uncomfortable to hold while writing. These pens are uncommon today.

Coin Filler, 1913-1914. The coin filler is one of the rarest filling systems found today. Like the sleeve filler, the pen had a rubber sac and pressure bar, but instead of a sleeve, the barrel had a slit into which you pushed a penny or the special Waterman Coin which came with the pen. It worked the same way as the sleeve filler but cut out several manufacturing steps such as making the sleeve and fitting it to the barrel. Rarely advertised, it was produced for only one year. Its short life is very puzzling as it worked so well, but it is possible that there may have been a legal problem due to the similarity to the Conklin *Crescent* filler system. It is rumored that Waterman licensed a filling system from Conklin and may have produced a crescent filler pen. To date, none have been found.

Lever Filler, 1915-1955. The most efficient self-filler was invented by W.A. Sheaffer in 1908 and later formed the basis of the Sheaffer Pen Company. It was a pen with a lever on the side of the barrel. Raising the lever pushed against a metal bar that compressed the ink sac. Waterman began selling lever filler pens in 1915. In the 1934 anniversary issue of the *Pen Prophet*, Waterman's publication for its dealers and distributors, the company claims to have introduced the lever system in 1913. There is however no mention of any Waterman lever filler pens in any catalogs or advertisements until June, 1915. How they obtained the patent is speculative. They may have changed the design enough from Sheaffer's patent to avoid patent infringement, licensed it from Sheaffer, or may have just used it, knowing that they were big enough to litigate Sheaffer into submission should they sue. Whatever the reason, the lever system eventually replaced all the previous Waterman filling systems and became the fountain pen industry standard.

Cartridge Filler, 1936-Present. Waterman introduced a pen which filled by means of a glass cartridge in 1936. The glass cartridge system had been used before by the Eagle Pen Company in 1890. Only made for a few years, very few of these early Waterman cartridge filled pens are found today. The next Waterman cartridge filler was made for the *C/F* pen in 1954. It used a plastic cartridge that slipped into the barrel and proved very successful until Waterman's last days as an American company.

Ink-Vue Filler, 1935-1940. The *Ink-Vue* pen was a variation on the lever filler, but was touted as one of the new sacless wonder pens of the 1930s. Basically a gimmick, the sac, depressed by a jointed lever, was used as a means of drawing ink into the sealed barrel. Rare today, their colors and designs are marvelous. Their function is considerably less so.

WATERMAN #2, ca. 1890. Black hard rubber eyedropper filled pen with two gold filled bands. This extremely early pen is fitted with a very rare early nib with star shaped vent hole, and unusually thin bands. $250-350.

WATERMAN #25, ca. 1893-1898. Black chased hard rubber eyedropper filled taper cap pen with early checked pattern on both the barrel and gold filled bands. Taper cap pens were available with #2 through #6 nibs. $250-350.

WATERMAN #2, ca. 1893-1900. Black hard rubber hexagon shape eyedropper filled pen. $650-850.

WATERMAN #24, ca. 1893-1900. Black hard rubber hexagon twist eyedropper filled pen. $1200-1400.

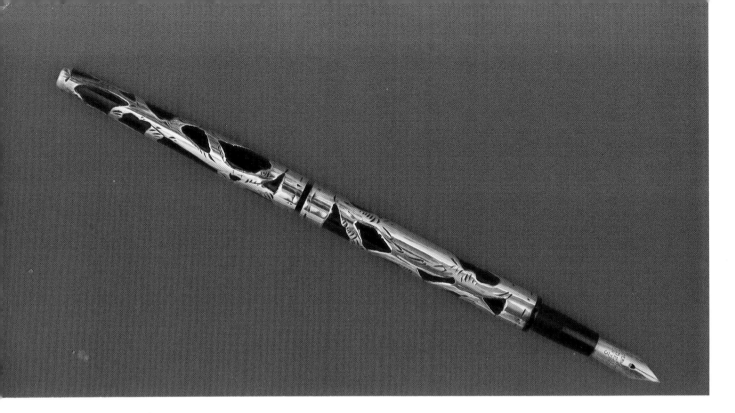

WATERMAN #424, 1898-1901. Sterling silver "Filigree" design overlay, eyedropper filled taper cap pen. This is the earliest example of a Filigree design overlay pen. $2000-2500.

WATERMAN #0502, ca. 1897. Gold filled "Chased" design overlay, eyedropper filled pen. This is a very early version of this design and varies slightly from the later version. $650-850.

WATERMAN #402, 1899-1920. Sterling silver "Chased" design overlay, eyedropper filled pen. This very popular design was also available in 14k gold and gold filled metal, and with a #4 nib. $750-1000.

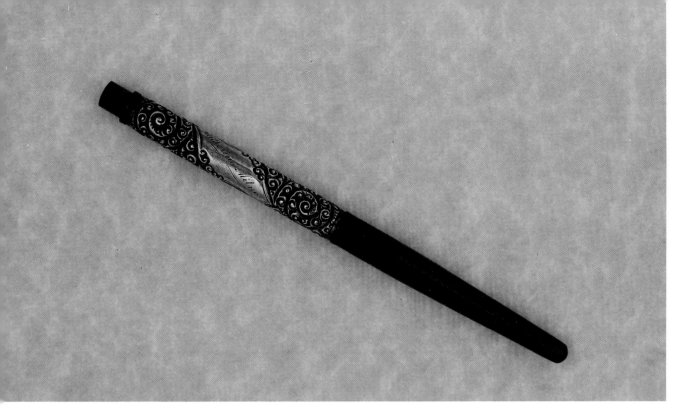

WATERMAN #224 $750-1000.

WATERMAN #0322, #224, 1899-1920. Gold filled, and sterling silver "Chased" design half overlay, eyedropper filled taper cap pens. Not shown but also available in 14k gold. $650-850.

WATERMAN #402, ca. 1896. Sterling silver "chased twist" design overlay, eyedropper filled pen. This is the only known example of this beautiful and unusual pattern and there is no reference to it in any catalogs. $4500-6000.

WATERMAN #2, ca. 1898. Black chased hard rubber eyedropper filled pen with two gold filled bands. $175-250.

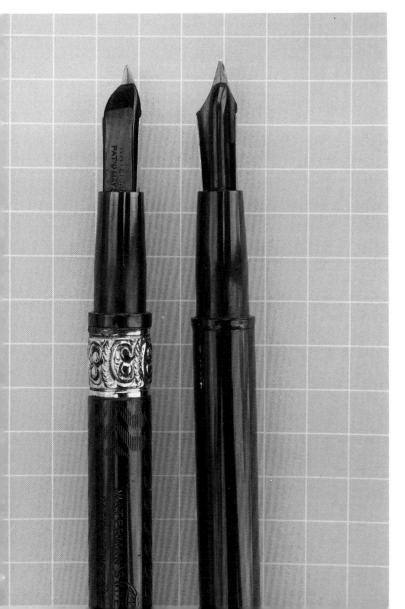

WATERMAN. Waterman "Spoon" feed ca. 1899 on the left compared to the early three fissure feed first developed by Waterman in 1883.

WATERMAN, ca. 1900. Illustration of some of the gold filled bands available on pens, Left to right: Crescent style, Chased style, narrow Crescent style.

WATERMAN #14, ca. 1898-1922. Red & black mottled, and red hard rubber eyedropper filled pens. The mottled hard rubber was succeeded in 1923 by the woodgrain and Ripple rubber. Although clips were not available on Waterman's until after 1905, they could be attached to older pens by returning them to the dealer. Cone cap pens were more commonly available in black or black chased hard rubber and with #2 through #10 nibs. Dark pen; $200-275. Orange pen; $300-500.

WATERMAN #402, ca. 1897. Sterling silver "chased engraved" design overlay eyedropper filled pen. This early pen is unusual in that the Waterman name is inscribed on the barrel of the pen. $2000-2500.

WATERMAN, c. 1910. Hard rubber eyedropper filled pens. Left to right: #12; $50-75, #14; $50-75, #15; $75-150, #18; $500-800, #20; $1250-1750.

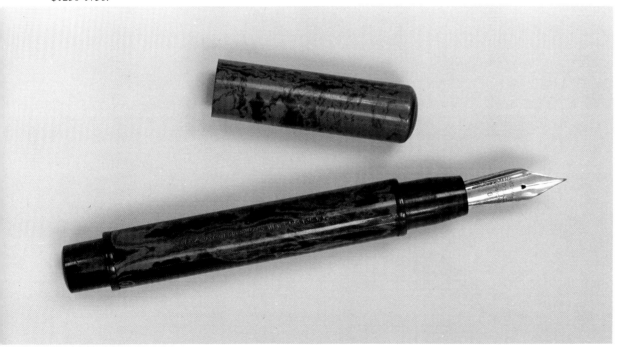

WATERMAN #8(?), ca. 1900. Red & black mottled hard rubber eyedropper filled pen. Although shown fitted with a #8 nib, this pen is substantially larger than other #8 pens seen. $5000-7500.

WATERMAN, ca. 1900-1910. Four styles of gold filled bands available on straight cap pens. Beginning in 1902, the "globe" imprint became standard on Waterman pens. This logo was taken from the emblem of the Pan-American Exposition of 1901 where Waterman pens won several awards.

WATERMAN #22, ca. 1893-1920. Black, and black chased hard rubber eyedropper filled taper cap pens. $200-250.

WATERMAN #20, ca. 1900-1915. Black hard rubber eyedropper filled pens illustrating the ventless type nib sometimes found on early models. The #20 was the largest standard production Waterman pen made. $1250-1750.

WATERMAN #20. Eyedropper filled pens. Left to right: Red ripple hard rubber POC pen, ca. 1923-1929, $2500-3000; red hard rubber pen, ca. 1900-1915, $3000-4000; red & black mottled hard rubber, ca. 1900-1915, $2750-3500.

WATERMAN #20, ca. 1910. Black chased hard rubber eyedropper filled pen with unusual 14k gold bands and clip. $1500-2000.

WATERMAN #0502, ca. 1902-1910. Gold filled "Patch" ("Puritan" after 1907) design overlay, eyedropper filled pen. Also available in sterling silver, and as a half covered taper cap pen. $2500-3000.

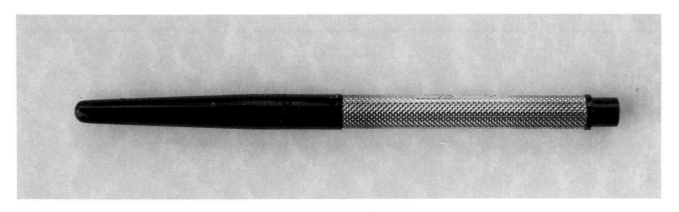

WATERMAN #324, 1900-1920. Solid 14k gold "Barleycorn" design half overlay, eyedropper filled taper cap pen. Not shown but available in silver, and gold filled metal, and with a #2 nib. $1000-1250.

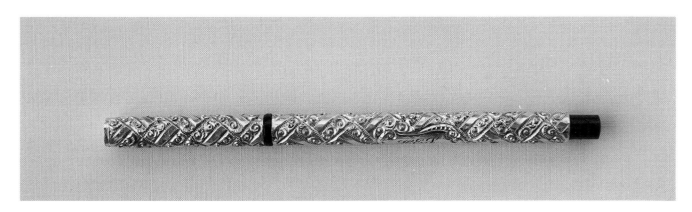

WATERMAN #0502, 1900-1920. Gold filled "Golph" ("Golpheresque") design overlay, eyedropper filled pen. Also made in silver, and 14k gold and with a #4 nib. $850-1000.

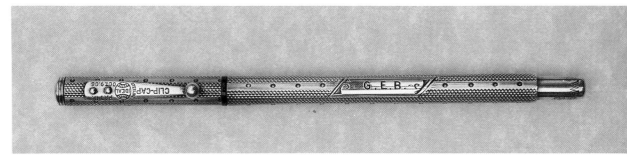

WATERMAN #402, ca. 1900-1915. Sterling silver "Line and Dot" design overlay, eyedropper filled pen with English hallmarks. This design was used exclusively on European pens. $850-1000.

WATERMAN #624, 1900-1915. Mother-of-pearl overlay, black hard rubber eyedropper filled taper cap pen. Also available with a #2 nib and with different gold filled band designs. $1000-1500.

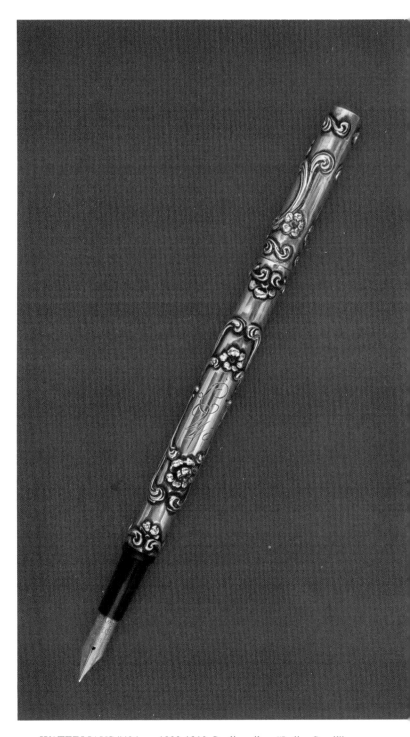

WATERMANS #404, ca. 1900-1910. Sterling silver "Indian Scroll" design overlay, eyedropper filled pen. Also available in 14k gold. $5000-6500.

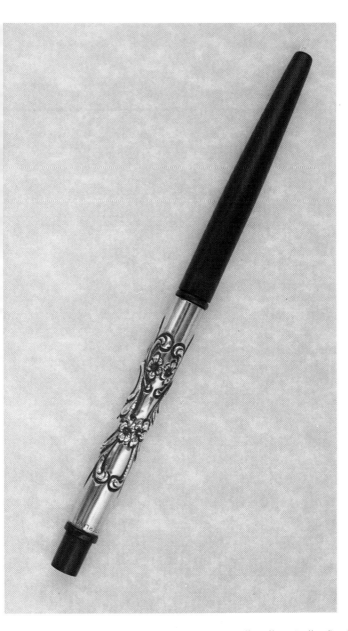

WATERMAN #0504, ca. 1900-1905. Gold filled "Chased Filigree" design overlay, eyedropper filled pen. There is no reference to this style of pen in any catalogs. $2750-4000.

WATERMAN #224, ca. 1900-1910. Sterling silver "Indian Scroll" design half overlay, eyedropper filled taper cap pen. $3000-4000.

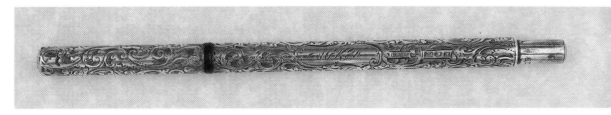

WATERMAN #402, 1905-1910. Sterling silver fancy etched design overlay, eyedropper filled pen with English hallmarks. $850-1000.

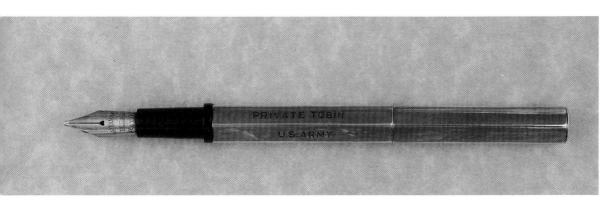

WATERMAN #404, ca. 1897-1904. Sterling silver overlay, hexagon shape eyedropper filled pen. Also made in 14k gold. $1250-1750.

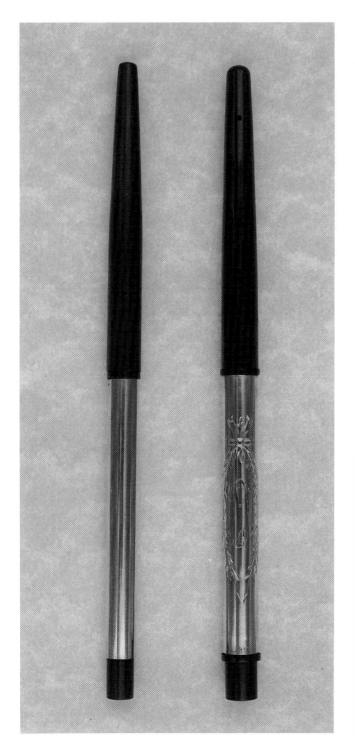

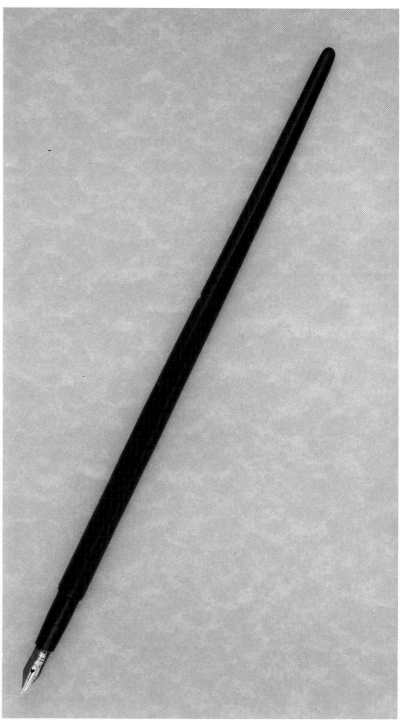

WATERMAN #324, ca. 1905-1920. Solid 14k gold half overlay, eyedropper filled pens in the plain, and "Wreath" designs. $850-1200.

WATERMAN #42, ca. 1900-1920. Black hard rubber eyedropper filled desk pen. $250-350.

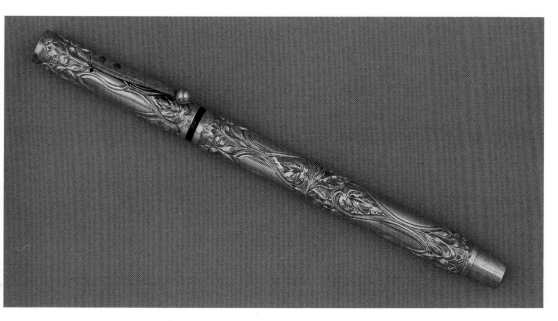

WATERMAN #0504, 1905-1920. Gold filled "Grecian Scroll" design overlay, eyedropper filled pen. Also made in sterling silver. $6500-8000.

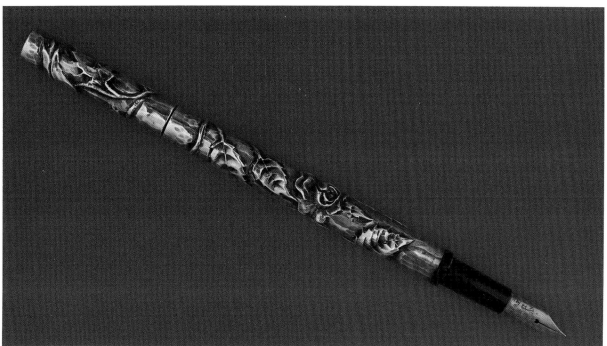

WATERMAN #404, ca. 1905-1915. Sterling silver "Heavy Rose" design overlay, eyedropper filled pen. $9500-12000.

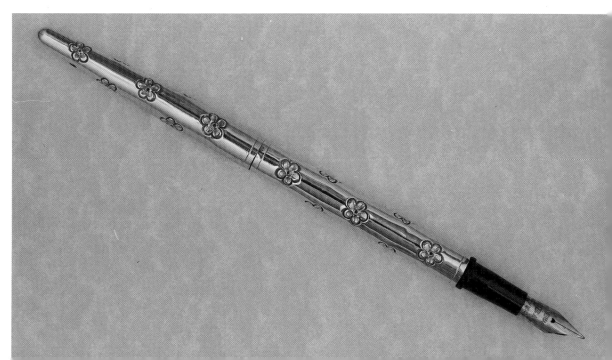

WATERMAN #0524, 1905-1915. Gold filled "Pansy" design overlay, eyedropper filled taper cap pen. $5500-7000.

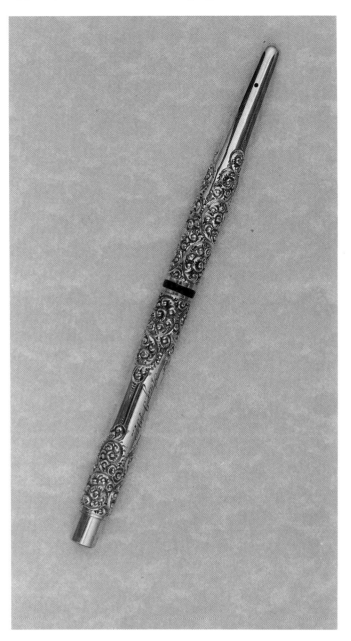

WATERMAN #524, 1900-1920. Solid 14k gold "Chased" design overlay, eyedropper filled taper cap pen. Also made in gold filled metal, and sterling silver and with #2 nib. $6500-7500.

WATERMAN #514, #412, ca. 1905. Solid 14k gold, and sterling silver unusual "Filigree" design overlay, eyedropper filled pens. #514, $650-850; #412, $1000-1250.

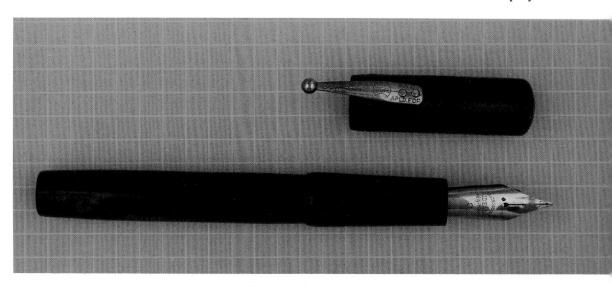

WATERMAN #18, ca. 1905-1910. Red & black hard rubber eyedropper filled pen with two part "Thimble" cap. This was a device for preventing the soiling of the fingers while writing. $850-1200.

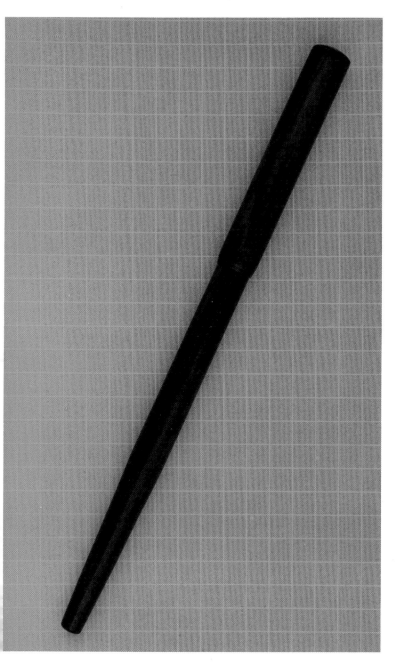

WATERMAN #44, ca. 1900-1915. Red & black mottled hard rubber eyedropper filled desk pen. $450-6000.

WATERMAN, ca. 1900-1920. Traveling ink bottle. $100-150.

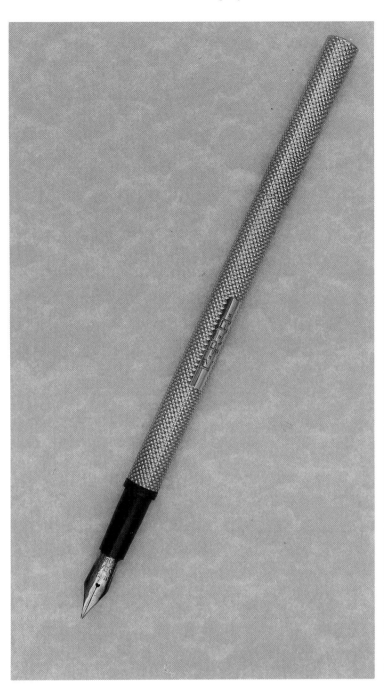 

WATERMAN #504, #402, ca. 1899-1920. Solid 14k gold, and sterling silver "Barleycorn" design overlay, eyedropper filled pens. This design was also made in gold filled metal. #504,$1500-2000; #402, $600-800.

WATERMAN #0322, ca. 1900-1920. Gold filled "Golph" design half overlay, eyedropper filled taper cap pen. $750-1250.

WATERMAN #612, #614, 1905-1915. Mother-of-pearl overlay black hard rubber eyedropper filled pens. $400-650.

THE AMERICAN STATIONER

The L. E. Waterman Company

of New York requests the pleasure of receiving you at their Booth

Waterman's Ideal Fountain Pen
at the
Louisiana Purchase Exposition

Cor. 7th & C Sts.
Varied Industries Bldg.

Make a Pilgrimage to the Shrine of the Dipnomores

EXPERT ATTENDANCE   BUREAU OF INFORMATION
RECEPTION ROOM FOR MEETING FRIENDS   CORRESPONDENCE DESK

WATERMAN, ca. 1904. Advertisement

WATERMAN #404, ca. 1905-1910. Sterling silver "Snake" design overlay, eyedropper filled pen. This design appeared in several company advertisements and in the 1908 Waterman catalog, always shown as a taper cap pen. The pen illustrated is the only known example of any Waterman "Snake" design pen. The snake design overlay was a popular one with manufacturers, the Parker version being the most well known. J.G. Rider, Wirt, and A.A. Waterman, among others also produced snake overlay pens. The L.E. Waterman design is by far the most beautiful and intricate of them all. $40000-50000.

WATERMAN #214, ca. 1905-1915. Sterling silver "Heavy Rose", and "Lily" half overlay, eyedropper filled pens. $5000-7000.

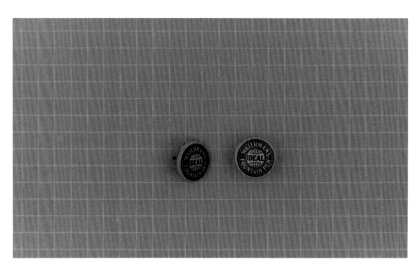

WATERMAN, ca. 1910 advertising thumbtacks. $35-55.

WATERMAN #504, ca. 1899-1920. Solid 14k gold plain design overlay, eyedropper filled pen. This pen was also made in gold filled metal, and sterling silver, and with a #2 nib. $1200-1400.

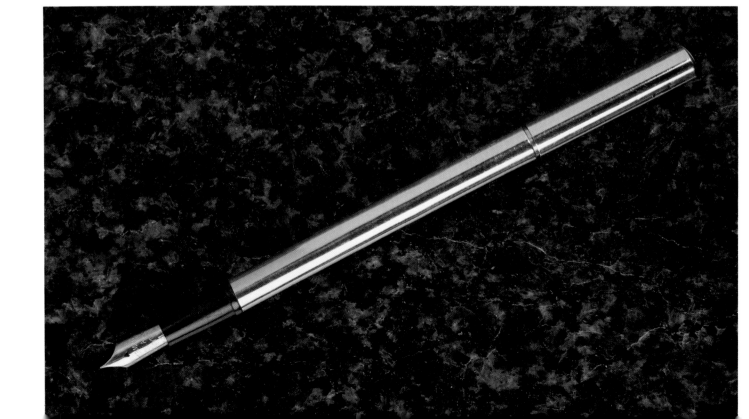

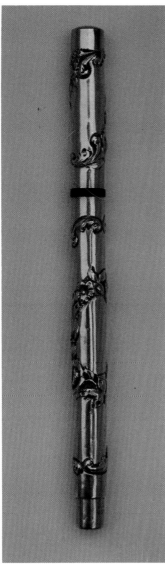

WATERMAN #514, ca. 1905-1915. Solid 14k gold "Colonial" design overlay, eyedropper filled pen. $1000-1250.

WATERMAN #502, ca. 1905-1915. Solid 14k gold "Rose" design overlay, eyedropper filled pen. $5000-6500.

WATERMAN #114 P, ca. 1903-1923. Sterling silver "Filigree" design overlay, pump filling pen. Waterman's pump filling mechanism does not appear to have been very popular based on the number surviving. They continued however, to appear in catalogs into the 1920s. These pens are more commonly found in black hard rubber, although red & black mottled pens were made. Overlayed pump filling pens are extremely rare, only the "Filigree" design was offered in gold filled metal or silver, with nib up to #6. $3000-3500.

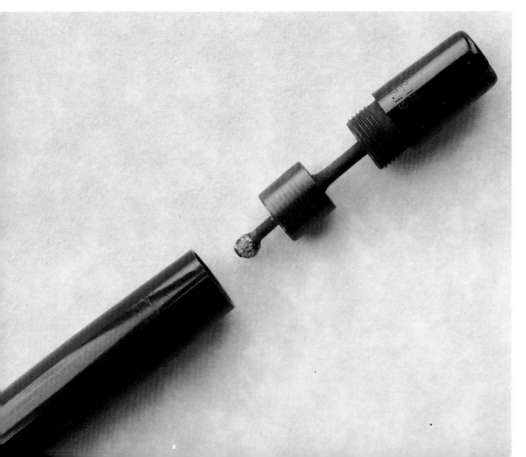

WATERMAN, ca. 1910. Close up of pump filling mechanism.

WATERMAN #212, #412, ca. 1905-1915. Sterling silver "Etched" design eyedropper filled pens. Although advertised as available only with the half-overlay, Waterman would for an additional charge modify almost any pen. The full-covered version has a place for a name engraving on both the cap and barrel, and is dated 1910. #212, $1000-1250; #412, $1500-2500.

WATERMAN, ca. 1907. Close up of a clip from an English or Canadian pen showing the 1906, rather than the 1905, U.S. patent date.

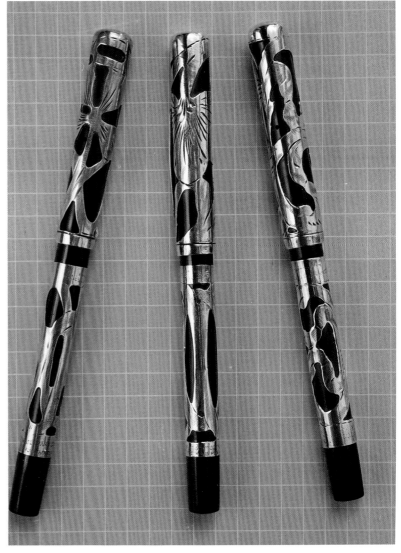

WATERMAN #412. Sterling silver "Filigree" design overlay, eyedropper filled pens. Left to right: ca. 1903-1907, 1903-1907, 1900-1903. Waterman's early "Filigree" designs vary greatly. The earliest ones are usually made of fine (999/1000) silver rather than sterling, and are made up of a series of swirling lines. The 1903 designs illustrate the Art Nouveau pattern with stylized flower. $600-850.

WATERMAN #12½, ca. 1900-1915. "Secretary" model eyedropper filled pens. Left to right: red & black mottled hard rubber, $125-175; #412½ sterling silver plain design overlay, $250-350; black chased hard rubber with two gold filled bands, $100-150 and #412½ sterling silver "Filigree" design overlay, $350-450.

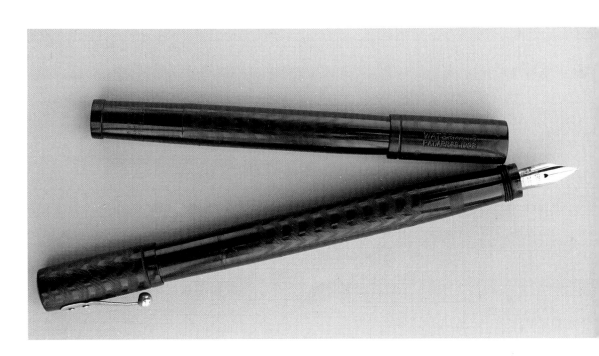

WATERMAN #312½, ca. 1905-1915. "Secretary" eyedropper filled pen with 14k gold half overlay in the "Colonial" design. $450-600.

WATERMAN #42, ca. 1907-1940. Black chased hard rubber safety pens. These pens were designed with retractable nibs, and screw-on caps so they could be safely carried in the pocket or purse. Safety pens were available with #2 through #10 nibs. They were also made in red, red & black mottled, and red Ripple hard rubber, and were available with a number of different overlay designs in silver, 14k gold, or gold filled metal. They came in baby, vest pocket, and standard lengths. $150-200.

WATERMAN #0515, ca. 1908-1915. Gold filled "Filigree" design overlay, eyedropper filled pen. This third Waterman Filigree design in the most often encountered. It was available with #2 through #10 nibs, and in silver and 14k gold. $450-550.

WATERMAN #12 SF, 1910-1915. Black hard rubber sleeve filling pen with a gold filled band. They were available with #2 through #8 nibs. $300-400.

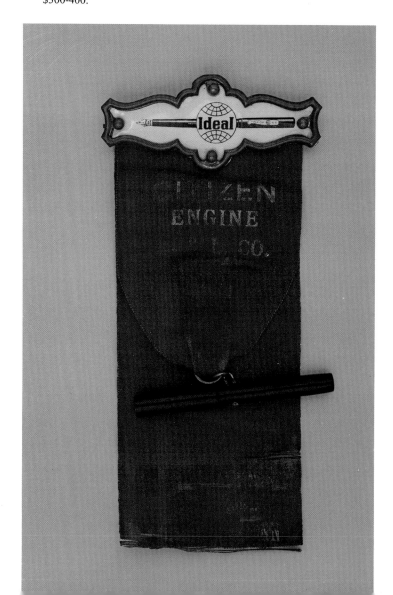

WATERMAN, ca. 1910. Ribbon with pen from a Connecticut fire department. $225-300.

WATERMAN #0518 SF, 1910-1915. Gold filled "Filigree" design overlay, sleeve filling pen. This large size overlay sleeve filling pen is very rare. $4500-6500.

WATERMAN #415 SF, 1910-1915. Sterling silver "Filigree" design overlay, sleeve filling pen. $2000-3000.

WATERMAN #0515 SF, 1910-1915. Gold filled plain design overlay, sleeve filling pen. $2000-3000.

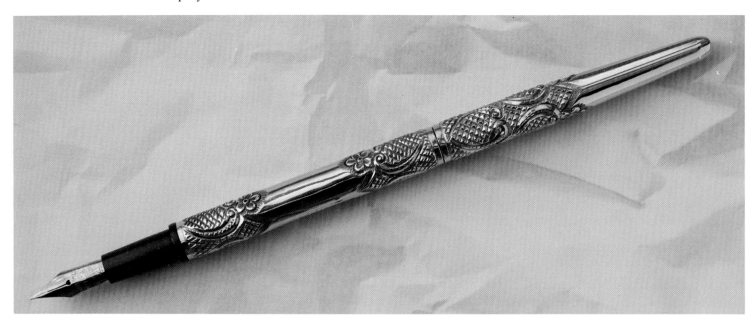

WATERMAN #0524, 1905-1920. Gold filled "Pineapple" design overlay, eyedropper filled taper cap pen. Also available in 14k gold, and sterling silver. $7500-10000.

WATERMAN #212 (?), ca. 1905-1915. Sterling silver "Line and Dot" design half overlay, eyedropper filled pen with English hallmarks. This pen may have a replaced cap. $350-550.

WATERMAN #0514, 1905-1915. Gold filled "Chased Filigree" design overlay, eyedropper filled pen. Also available in 14k gold. $1250-1750.

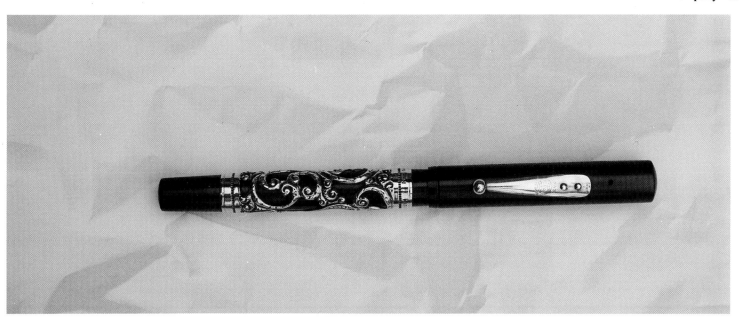

WATERMAN #314, 1905-1915. Solid 14k gold "Chased Filigree" design half overlay, eyedropper filled pen with 14k gold clip. Also available in gold filled metal. $1000-1500.

WATERMAN, ca. 1910. "Worlds smallest pen" in red hard rubber. This eyedropper filled pen is known to have been sold as a working pen, and although it has a real gold nib, it is impossible to actually use. It is also referred to as a doll's pen, and has been found as a safety pen. $5000-7500.

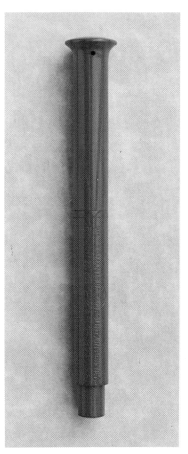

WATERMAN, 1905-1915. "Checkbook" eyedropper filled plain and sterling silver "Filigree" overlay red hard rubber pens. This pen was advertised as perfect for use in a checkbook, or small notebook. Also available in plain or silver overlayed black hard rubber. 1905, $2000-3000; 1915, $3500-5000.

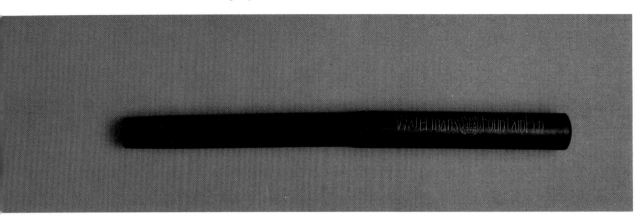

WATERMAN, ca. 1910. Painted metal, window display, dummy pen. Trays of these "pens" could be placed in a dealers window without fear of ruining good stock. $50-75.

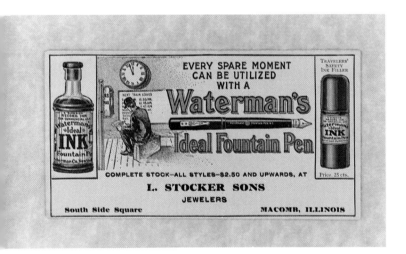

WATERMAN, ca. 1910. Advertising blotter. $20-40.

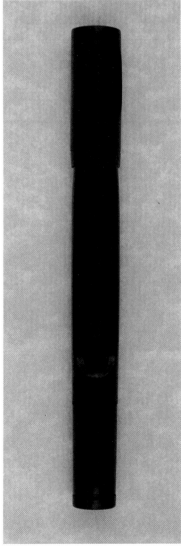

WATERMAN #412½ VP, ca. 1910-1916. Sterling silver "hammered" design overlay, eyedropper filled vest pocket pen. $950-1250.

WATERMAN, ca. 1910. Black hard rubber demonstrator safety pen. $500-650.

WATERMAN #20 S, ca. 1910. Black chased hard rubber safety pen, alongside a #42½ red hard rubber pen. $1500-2000.

WATERMAN #418, #415, ca. 1908-1915. Sterling silver "Filigree" design overlay, red hard rubber eyedropper filled pens, one with threaded section. The threaded section was offered as an aid to people whose fingers would slip towards the nib while writing. #418, $3500-5000; #415, $6500-8500.

WATERMAN #418, 1908-1915. Sterling silver "Filigree" design overlay eyedropper filled pen. $2500-3000.

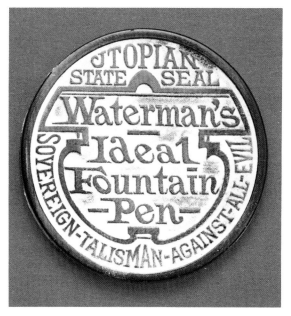

WATERMAN, ca. 1910. Black hard rubber good luck token. $75-125.

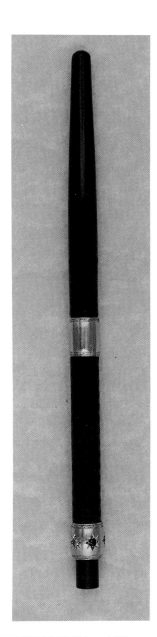

WATERMAN #24, ca. 1910. Black chased hard rubber eyedropper filled pen with unusual gold bands mounted with stones. $650-850.

WATERMAN, ca. 1910. Celluloid cigar cutter. $175-250.

WATERMAN, ca. 1910. Advertising bookmark. $50-75.

WATERMAN #414 PSF, 1913-1914. Sterling silver "Filigree" design overlay, coin filling pen with coin. Coin filling pens were supplied with the coin illustrated. It was placed in the barrel slot to depress the ink sac for filling. Coin filling pens are among the rarest Waterman's, having been produced for only one year. They were available with #2 to #6 nibs, and produced for only one year. They were available with #2 to #6 nibs, and were also made as vest pocket pens. Overlay models are especially rare. $3000-4000.

WATERMAN #0512 VP, ca. 1910-1916. Gold filled "Filigree" design overlay, vest pocket eyedropper filled pen. $200-300.

WATERMAN. Black chased hard rubber eyedropper filled pens. On the right ca. 1900, #14; on the left ca. 1914, #14POC. The pocket pen was supplied with the new style screw on cap, and flared section later found on the lever filling pens. $125-175.

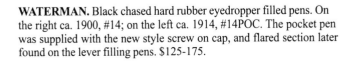

WATERMAN #442 V, ca. 1908-1929. Sterling silver "Filigree" design overlay, safety pen. Overlay safety pens were available with nibs up to #8. $350-600.

WATERMAN #472 V, ca. 1915-1929. Sterling silver "Barleycorn" design overlay, eyedropper filled pen. $350-600.

WATERMAN, ca. 1905-1915. Black hard rubber eyedropper filled stenographers pen. This pen was designed for a woman's hand, and held a generous supply of ink. $200-300.

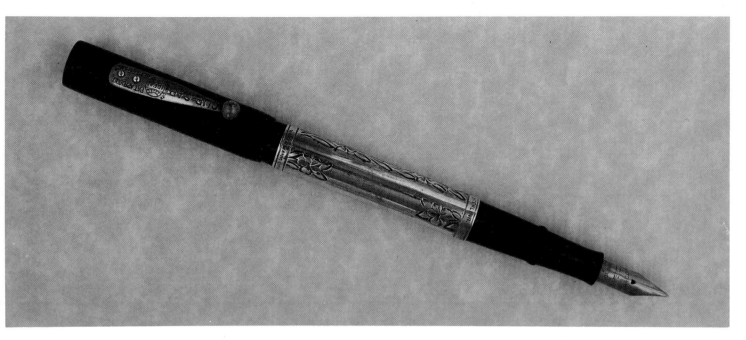

WATERMAN #214 POC, ca. 1914-1920. Sterling silver "Pansy Panel" design half overlay eyedropper filled pen. $500-750.

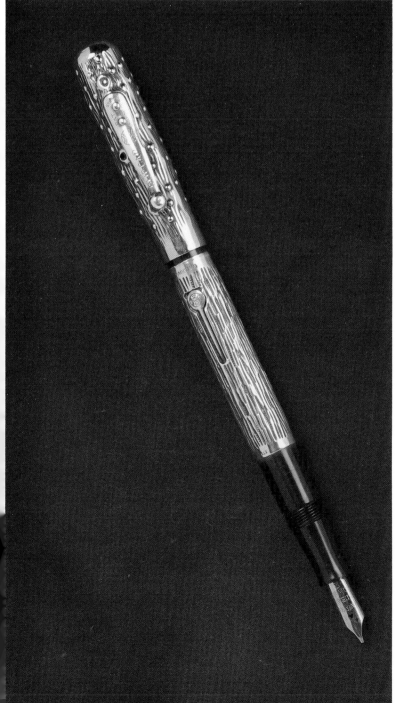

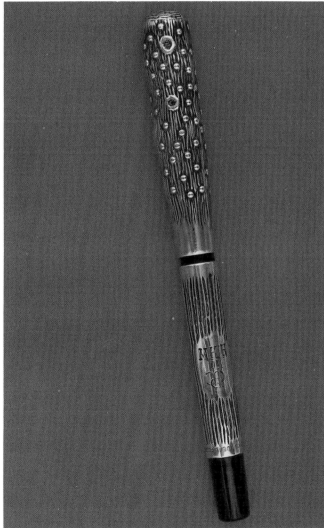

WATERMAN #452, #412, ca. 1913-1920. Sterling silver "tree trunk" design overlay, lever filling, and eyedropper filled pens. No reference has ever been found describing this design in company literature. They have been found only with the #2 nib and in sterling silver. Once thought to be unique, or a special order, there are now approximately eight lever filling and two eyedropper filled pens known to exist. #452, $5000-7000; #412, $6000-7500.

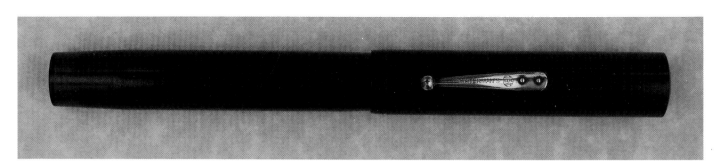

WATERMAN #78, ca. 1917-1920. Bakelite barrel eyedropper filled pocket pen. The use of Bakelite for pen barrels is associated primarily with Parker. Waterman Bakelite pens are rarely seen. $2000-2500.

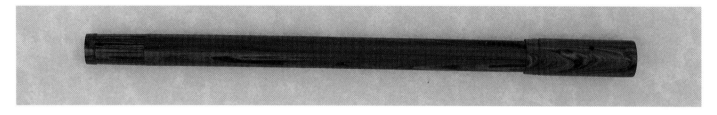

WATERMAN #41, ca. 1917. "Pitman", red & black mottled hard rubber safety pen. A large ink capacity pen for stenographers using Pitman shorthand. $200-250.

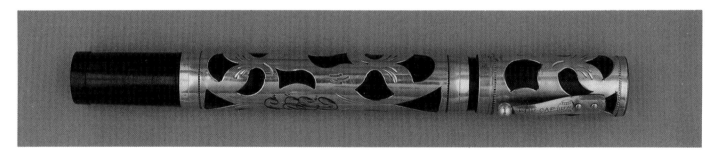

WATERMAN #0546, ca. 1908-1929. Gold filled "Filigree" design overlay, safety pen. $1250-1600.

WATERMAN, ca. 1912. Advertising blotter. $25-50.

WATERMAN #0552½, ca. 1915-1920. Gold filled "Oriental" design overlay, lever filling pen. Also available in sterling silver, and as an eyedropper POC pen. $800-1000.

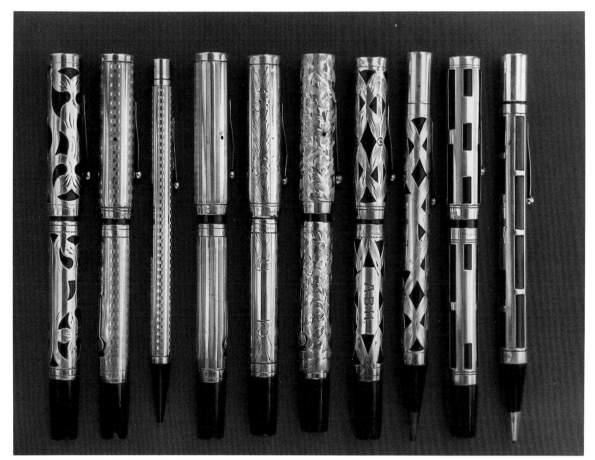

Waterman #452. Sterling silver overlay, lever filling pens and pencils. Left to right: "Filigree" design overlay, ca. 1915-1923; $225-350; "Gothic" design overlay pen and pencil, ca. 1915-1933; $225-350; "Sheraton" design overlay, ca. 1915-1930; $225-230; "Pansy Panel" design overlay, ca. 1915-1930; $275-400. "Hand Engraved Vine" design ovelay, ca. 1915-1930; $450-650. "Filigree" design overlay pen and pencil , ca. 1924-1933; $250-375; "Moderne" design pen and pencil, ca. 1928-1930; $750-1000; These designs with the exception of the " Moderne", were available in silver as shown, or gold filled, or 14k gold, and with #2 through #6 nibs. The "Filigree" design was available on red hard rubber as well, and along with the "Gothic" design was available with a #8 nib.

WATERMAN #452, 1915-1929. Sterling silver plain design overlay, lever filling pen. $300-400.

WATERMAN, ca. 1918. Ink pellets with instruction. $25-50.

WATERMAN, ca. 1915 brochure. $50-75.

WATERMAN, ca. 1911. Watch chain token commemorating the coronation of George V of Great Britain. $125-175.

WATERMAN #452, ca. 1915-1929. Sterling silver "Line and Dot" design overlay lever filling pen with English hallmarks. $300-450.

WATERMAN, ca. 1915-1929. "Duplex" bookkeeper's eyedropper filled pen in red, and black hard rubber. This unusual pen could be unscrewed at the middle to make two separate pens. $2000-2300.

WATERMAN #0352, ca. 1915-1929. Gold filled plain design half overlay lever filling pen. Not shown but also made in 14k gold, and #4 nib. $150-200.

WATERMAN #752, 1915-1929. Black hard rubber lever filling pen with 14k gold clip, lever, and hand engraved band. Solid gold trimmed pens were made as eyedropper filled, or lever filling pens, and with #2 to #10 nibs. $300-450.

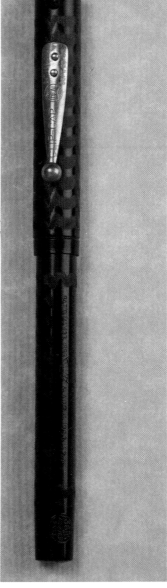

WATERMAN. Left to right: clip ca. 1905-1910, clip ca. 1911-1923, clip ca. 1924-1927, clip ca. 1928-1930.

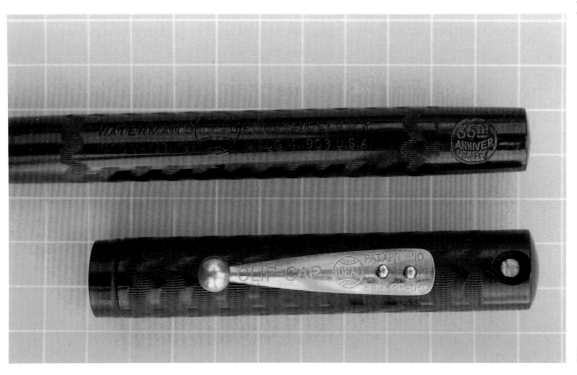

WATERMAN #13, 1919. Black chased hard rubber "Thirty-fifth Anniversary" eyedropper filled pen. The stanhope in the top of the cap shows a photo of the Pen Corner at 191 Broadway in New York City. $850-1000.

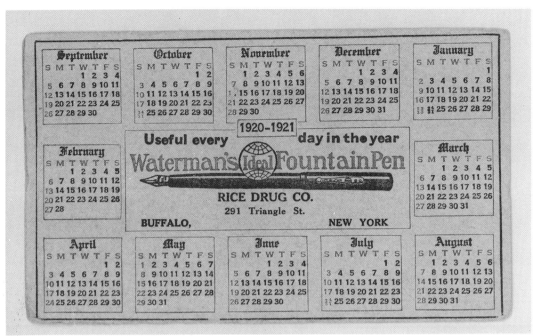

WATERMAN, 1920. Calendar blotter. $15-30.

WATERMAN #442½ V, ca. 1917-1929. Sterling silver "Hand Engraved Vine" design lady's safety pen with telescoping cap. $300-400.

WATERMAN #0552, ca. 1915-1930. Left to right: gold filled "Filigree" design, and "Pansy Panel" design overlay, lever filling pens. $250-375.

WATERMAN #452, 1915-1933. Three variations of the "Filigree" design found on pens of the 1920s.

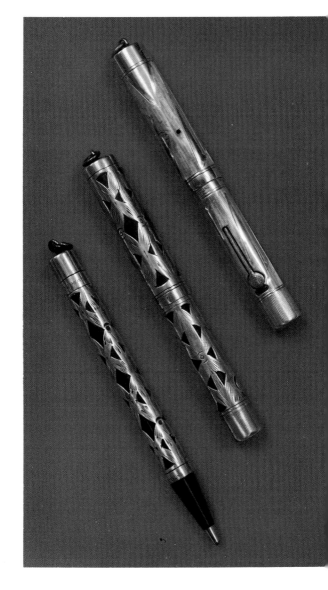

WATERMAN #452½ V, ca. 1917-1929. Sterling silver overlay lever filling lady's pens and pencil. The design of the pen on the right has only been found on this size pen and is very Art Deco in style. The lady's style of pen, was made by Waterman in almost as many varieties as their standard size pens. They were made as eyedropper filled, safety pens, and lever filling pens, with all the standard overlay designs of the 1920s. $200-300.

WATERMAN #42½ V, ca. 1908-1929. Safety pens. Left to right: sterling silver #442½ V "Scroll" design overlay, black chased hard rubber, sterling silver "Filigree", and #0542½ V gold filled "Filigree" design overlays. #42½, $175-275; #442½, $100-175; #0542½, $150-250.

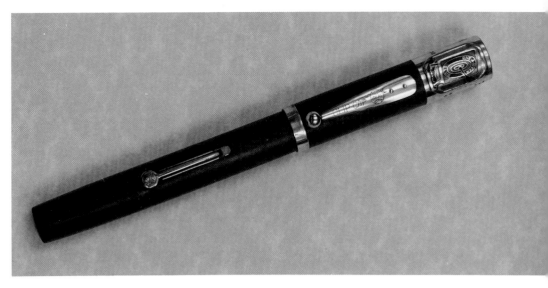

WATERMAN #55, 1915-1929. Black chased hard rubber lever filling "Emblem" pen. Waterman made a series of pens which could be purchased with the emblems of various schools or fraternal organizations. This is a special order example from the "Once-a-Week" club of the Prudential Insurance Co. $350-550.

WATERMAN #452½ V, ca. 1917-1929. Sterling silver "Hand Engraved Vine" design overlay, lever filling lady's pen and pencil set. $300-400.

WATERMAN #42, ca. 1915-1929. Gold "column" design overlay safety pen with French hallmarks. $450-600.

WATERMAN #0512½ VP, ca. 1917-1925. Gold filled lady's "Extension End", eyedropper filled pen with telescoping cap. $400-575.

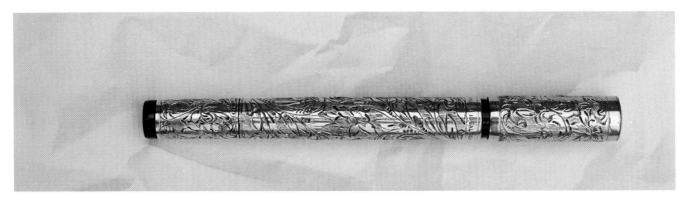

WATERMAN #0542½, ca. 1917-1929. Gold filled "Etched" design overlay safety pen. $750-1000.

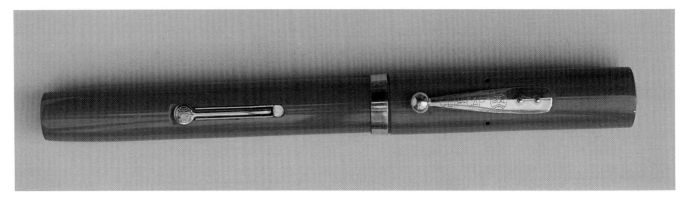

WATERMAN #56, 1915-1929. Red hard rubber lever filling pen. Available with #2 to #8 nib. $500-650.

WATERMAN, ca. 1915-1929. Solid 9k gold "Barleycorn" panel design overlay, lever filling pen with English hallmarks. $400-600.

WATERMAN #14 SF (64), ca. 1915-1920. Black chased hard rubber lever filling slip cap pen. One of the strangest pens produced by Waterman, it was a hybrid between the old eyedropper pen and the new lever filling model. $175-250.

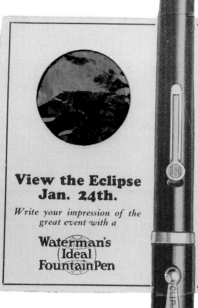

WATERMAN, ca. 1920. Advertising eclipse viewer. The dark cellophane window could be used to safely view an eclipse of the sun. $150-225.

WATERMAN #42½ baby, ca. 1917-1925. Rolled 18k gold overlay safety pen with a European design of chariots and warriors. An entire series of designs executed in Europe have been found applied to standard Waterman safety pens, known collectively as the "continental" series, they are usually done in rolled gold, and inscribed with the Waterman globe and name. $400-550.

WATERMAN #554, #554 LEC, 1915-1929. Solid 14k gold "Hand Engraved Vine" design overlay, lever filling pens. Each pen in this design was hand engraved, following a standard pattern, each pen however is slightly different because of this. Top two: $1400-2000. Bottom pen: $750-1000.

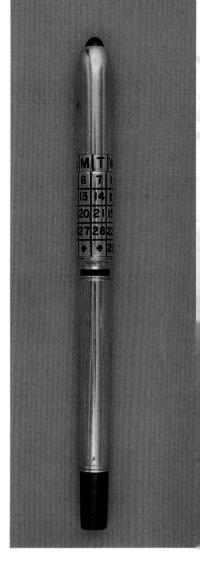

WATERMAN #552½ LEC, 1918-1929. 14k gold plain pattern overlay, lever filling pen and pencil set. LEC stood for "Lower End Covered". These pens were usually made with #2 or #4 nibs. They were available in the same designs as the standard overlay pens. $850-1000.

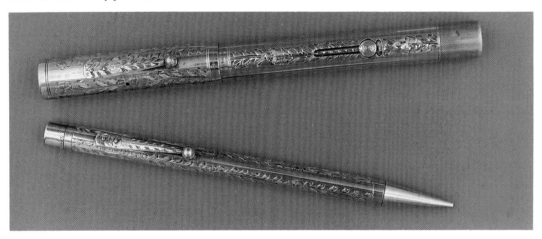

WATERMAN #554 LEC, 1918-1929. Solid 14k gold hand engraved "Pansy Panel" design overlay, lever filling pen and pencil set. When executed in 14k gold, the "Pansy Panel" design was also hand engraved, unlike the machine made pattern on the silver and gold filled pens. $1400-2000.

WATERMAN #512½, ca. 1910. Solid 9k gold overlay eyedropper filled pen with perpetual calender, and cabochon cut stone in the cap, with English hallmarks. The calender is composed of rotating rings which bring the date and the days of the week in alignment. $650-850.

WATERMAN #42, ca. 1915-1925. Rolled 18k gold "continental" design overlay safety pens. $750-1000.

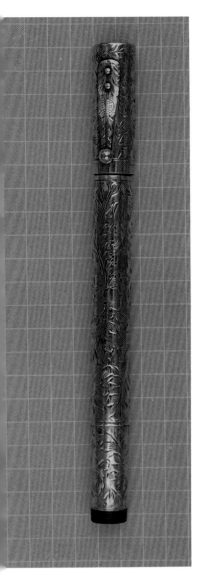

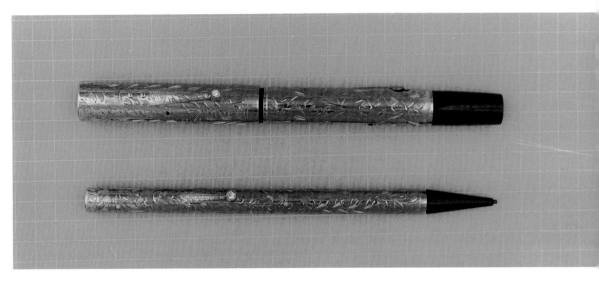

WATERMAN #554, 1915-1929. Solid 14k gold "Hand Engraved Vine" design overlay, lever filling pen and pencil set with diamonds set in the clips. In 1925 the price for this set was an incredible $120.00. $2000-2500.

WATERMAN #542½, ca. 1917-1929. Solid 14k gold "Hand Engraved Vine" design overlay safety pen. $850-1200.

WATERMAN, ca. 1920. Hard rubber lever filling pens. Left to right: #52, #54, #55, #56, #58.

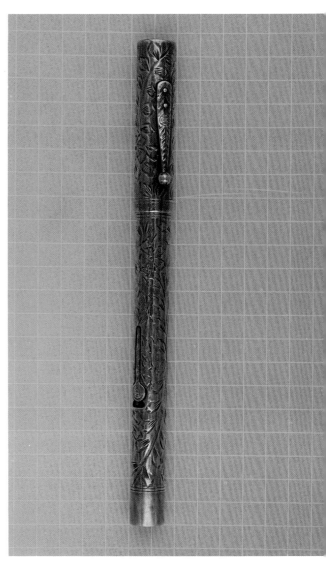

WATERMAN #75, 1923-1929. Woodgrain hard rubber eyedropper filled pen. Many people in the 1920s still preferred an eyedropper filled pen to a self-filling model. Waterman obliged them by making this style of pen through 1929. It was also available in red, red Ripple, and black hard rubber and with #2 to #10 nibs. $400-600.

WATERMAN #452½ LEC, 1918-1929. Sterling silver "Hand Engrave Vine" design overlay, lever filling pen. $350-500.

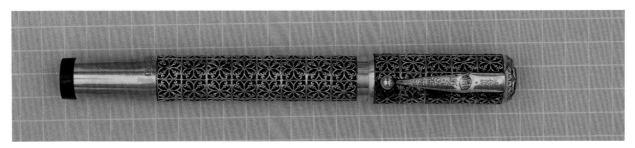

WATERMAN #42, ca. 1917-1929. Rolled 18k gold and silver "continental" design overlay safety pens. $750-1000.

WATERMAN #448, ca. 1908-1925. Sterling silver "Filigree" design overlay safety pen. $2000-3000.

WATERMAN #0556, 1915-1929. Gold filled plain, and "Gothic" design overlay, lever filling pens. $700-900.

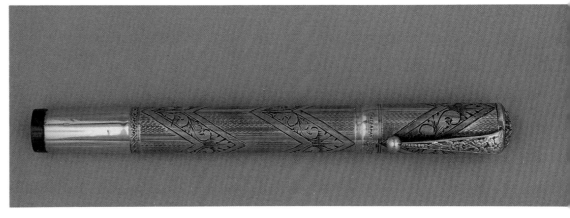

WATERMAN #42, ca. 1917-1929. Rolled 18k gold and silver "continental" design overlay safety pen. $750-1000.

WATERMAN #52, ca. 1918. Black chased hard rubber lever filling pen with military clip. $175-275.

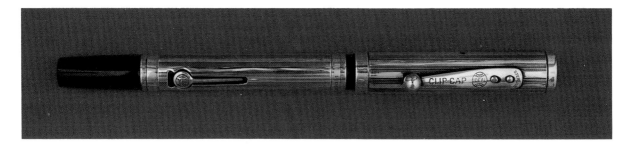

WATERMAN #452½, 1915-1929. Sterling silver "Sheraton" design overlay lever filling pen. $200-300.

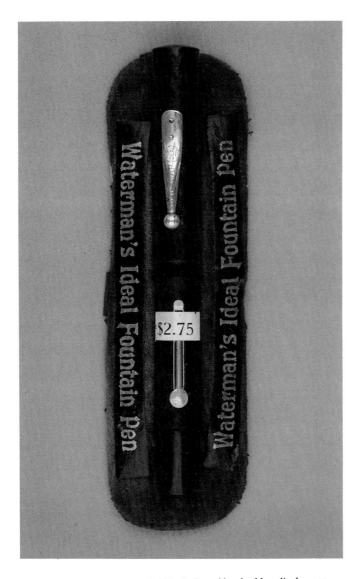

WATERMAN, ca. 1920. #52½ black chased hard rubber display pen. $75-125.

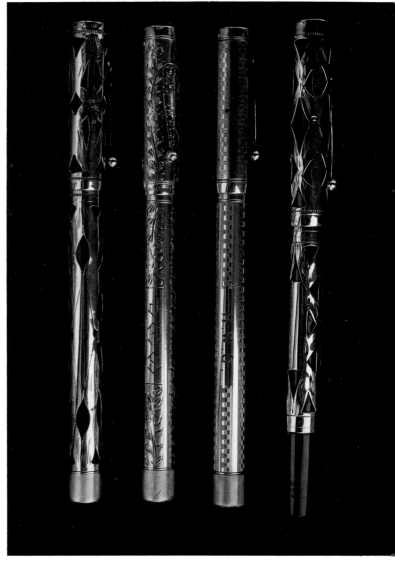

WATERMAN #552½, ca. 1915-1929. Solid 14k gold overlay lever filling pens. Left to right: LEC "Filigree" design, $600-850; LEC "Pansy Panel" design, $750-1000; LEC "Gothic" design, $600-850; and "Filigree" design, $600-800.

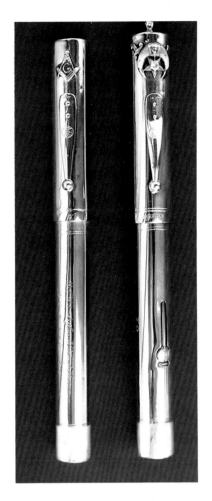

WATERMAN, ca. 1918-1929. Solid 14k gold overlay lever filling "Emblem" pens. Left to right: #555 LEC Masonic Blue Lodge, $1250-1600; #556 LEC Mystic Shrine emblem with a diamond set in the center of the star, $1500-2000.

WATERMAN, ca. 1920 brochure. $40-60.

WATERMAN #58, ca. 1915-1929. Top to bottom: woodgrain, $850-1200. black, $600-850; and red Ripple hard rubber lever filling pens, $1000-1300.

WATERMAN #554, ca. 1922. Unusual 14k gold overlay lever filling pen, with presentation inscription. All parts of this pen are covered by the overly, and there is a ring in the cap in addition to the clip. $850-1000.

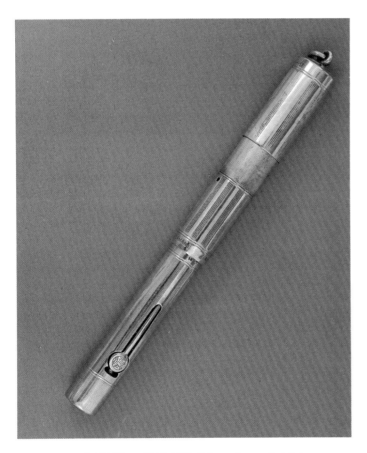

WATERMAN #552½ V, ca. 1918-1929. Telescoping cap lady's lever filling pen with 14k gold "Sheraton" design overlay. $400-600.

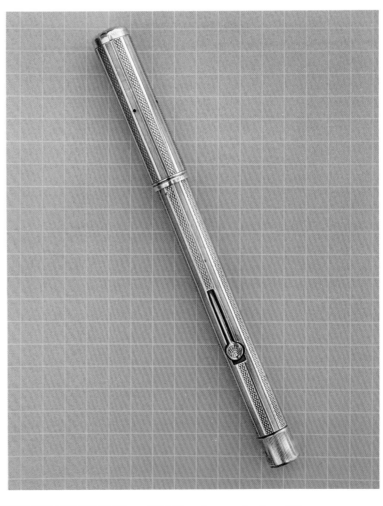

WATERMAN #452½ LEC, ca. 1925. Fine silver overlay, lever filling pen with French hallmarks. $300-400.

WATERMAN #5, ca. 1926-1930. Red Ripple hard rubber lever filling pen. This model was available with five different nib styles, and originally sold for $5.00. $175-250.

WATERMAN, ca. 1920-1929. Sterling silver "Night and Day" design overlay, lever filling pen with French hallmarks. $500-700.

WATERMAN #52, 1923-1930. Red Ripple hard rubber lever filling pen and pencil set. Red Ripple lever filling pens were available with #2 through #8 nibs. $200-250.

WATERMAN #01955, 1923-1933. Red Ripple hard rubber lever filling pen with gold filled trim. $250-300.

WATERMAN #52½ V, 1928-1930. Left to right: red Ripple hard rubber; olive Ripple hard rubber; blue green Ripple hard rubber lever filling pens. Also available but not shown, rose Ripple hard rubber. $175-400.

WATERMAN #1955, ca. 1926-1933. Red Ripple hard rubber lever filling pen and pencil set with 14k gold engraved trim. $600-850.

WATERMAN #52, ca. 1928-1930. Red Ripple hard rubber lever filling pen/pencil combination. $900-1250.

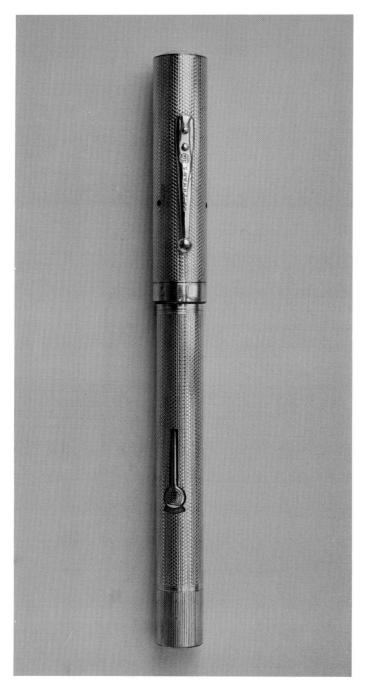

WATERMAN #0552, 1920-1929. Gold filled "Barleycorn" design overlay, lever filling pen made in Canada. $350-450.

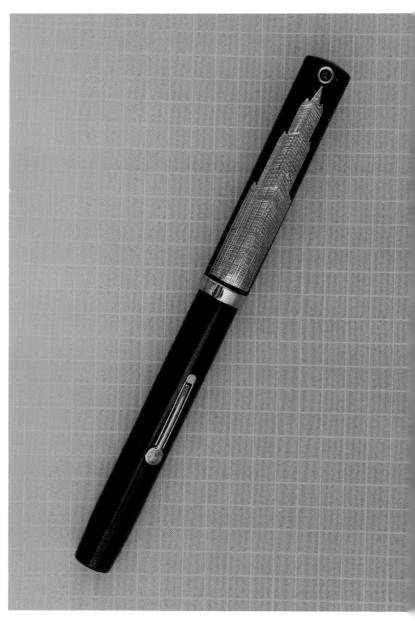

WATERMAN #7, ca. 1925. Black hard rubber lever filling pen with a gold overlay in the outline of the Woolworth Building in New York City, and a stanhope in the cap with a picture of F.W. Woolworth. This pen may have been a retirement gift for a valued employee. $2750-4000.

WATERMAN, ca. 1927. Brochure describing the #7 Ripple pen. $50-75.

WATERMAN, ca. 1928. Advertising booklet. $50-75.

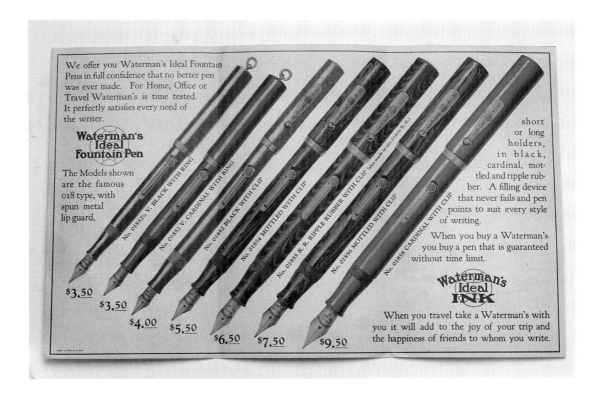

WATERMAN, ca. 1925 brochure.

WATERMAN #94, 1928-1930. Olive Ripple, $450-600; blue green Ripple, $300-450; and rose Ripple, $250-350; hard rubber lever filling pens.

WATERMAN #7, ca. 1926-1930. Red Ripple hard rubber lever filling pens illustrating all seven color bands, denoting the nib style. $250-650.

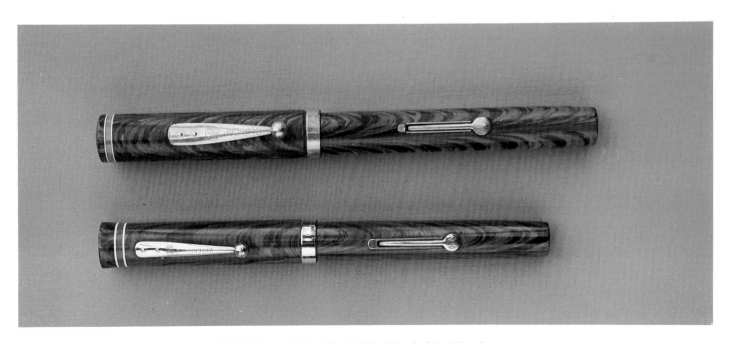

WATERMAN, ca. 1926-1930. Red Ripple hard rubber #7 on the top, and red Ripple #5 pen below, both lever filling.

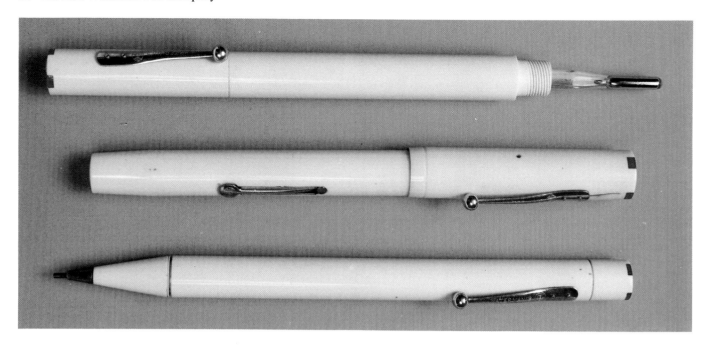

WATERMAN, ca. 1928. Doctor's pen, pencil, and thermometer case, all in white hard rubber, with red crosses in the caps. $1250-1500.

WATERMAN, ca. 1929. Sterling silver plain design overlay lever filling pen/pencil combination. Although many hard rubber Waterman combinations have been found, this is the only overlay design known. $4500-6000.

WATERMAN #7, 1930-1938. Black plastic lever filling pens. $125-225.

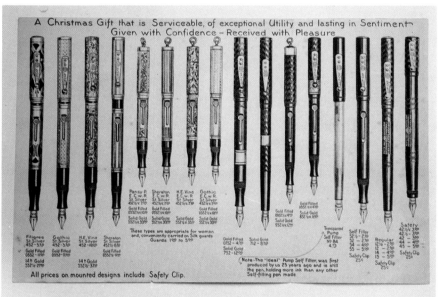

WATERMAN, ca. 1923 brochure. $50-75.

WATERMAN. Transition *Patrician* ca. 1928, on the left, compared with a standard *Patrician*, ca. 1931, both in emerald green plastic. This transitional pen differs from the standard *Patrician* in that it contains earlier elements. Riveted clip cap, globe lever, non-stepped ends (without the globe), and a solid cap band. A few examples of this pen have been found, all in emerald green. This pen should not be confused with those pens made by Waterman in the late 1930s from left over *Patrician* parts. Left, $1000-1400; right, $750-1000.

WATERMAN #0552, ca. 1923-1929. Gold filled "Gothic" design overlay, lever filling red ripple hard rubber pen. This pen is probably Canadian or English. $350-500.

WATERMAN #94, 1930-1938. Black plastic lever filling pen with sterling silver cap band, clip, and lever. Also available with solid 14k gold trim. $250-400.

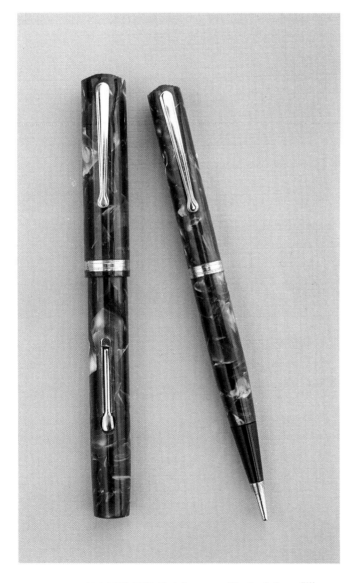

WATERMAN #94, 1930-1938. Red & gray marble plastic lever filling pen and pencil set. $175-225.

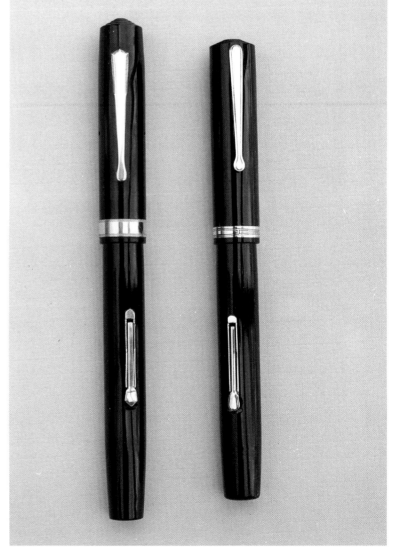

WATERMAN, 1930-1938. Left: #7 black plastic lever filling pen, $125-200; right: #5 black plastic lever filling pen, $100-175.

WATERMAN, 1929-1938. *Patrician* lever filling pens. Left to right: black hard rubber, $700-950; emerald green plastic, $750-1000; onyx (cream & red) plastic, $850-1200; moss agate (green, brown, & black) plastic pencil, $250-500; nacre (black & pearl) plastic, $750-1000; moss agate plastic, $850-1200; turquoise (blue & gold) plastic, $950-1300.

WATERMAN #7, 1932-1937. "Emerald Ray" lever filling pen. This was the only color other than black that the plastic #7 pen was made in. $275-350.

WATERMAN #92, 1931-1938. Black, red & gold, and green & gold plastic lever filling pens. $75-125.

WATERMAN #32, 1931-1938. Gray & gold, black, and silver marble plastic lever filling pens. $50-75.

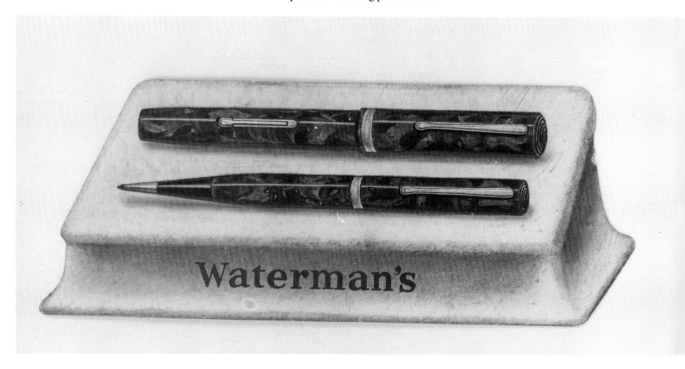

WATERMAN, ca. 1933. Die cut advertisement for #94 pen. $75-100.

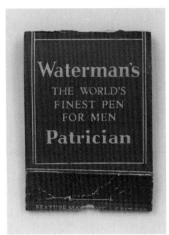

WATERMAN, ca. 1930. *Patrician* matches, each match is in the shape of a *Patrician* pen. $150-250.

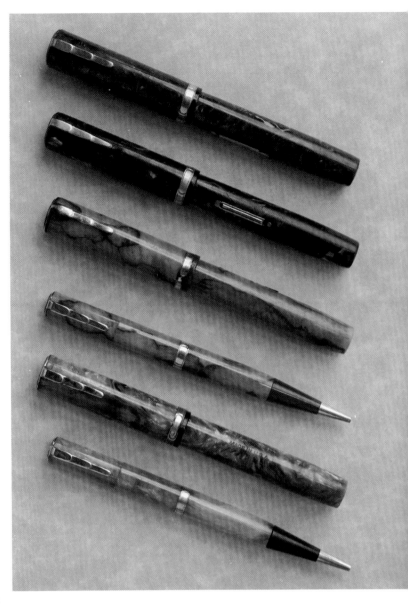

WATERMAN #94, 1930-1939. Lever filling pens and pencil in brown marble, steel quartz, moss agate, and blue & cream marble plastic. $100-275.

WATERMAN, 1930-1938. *Lady Patrician* lever filling pens and pencils. $100-250.

WATERMAN #92 V, 1933-1939. Lever filling plastic pens. This model is basically a #3 V with gold filled trim. $75-100.

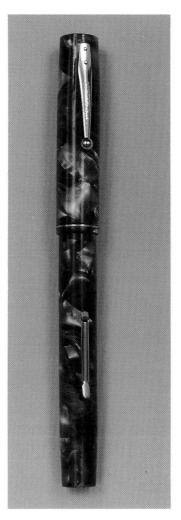

WATERMAN #3, 1933-1939. Lever filling plastic pen. $50-75.

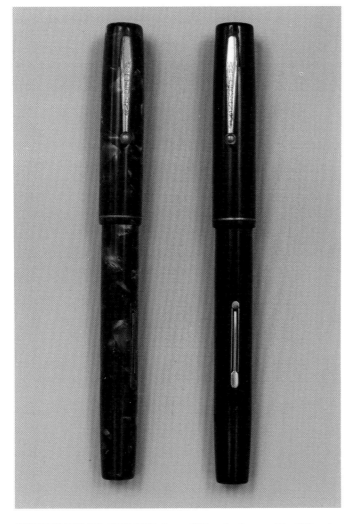

WATERMAN #32, 1933-1939. Lever filling plastic pens. The #32 and #3 were Waterman's lowest priced pens during the 1930s. $40-65.

WATERMAN #3 V, 1933-1939. Lever filling plastic pen and pencil set. $40-65.

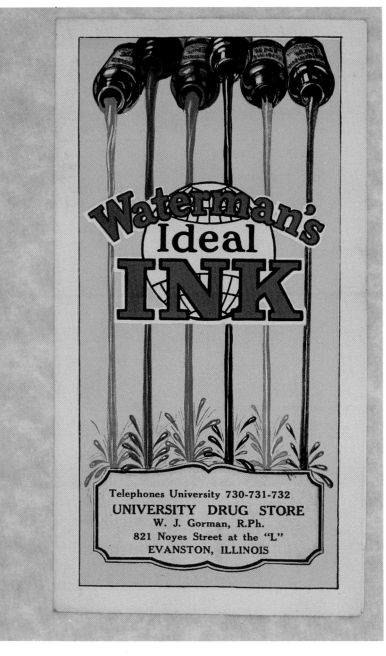

WATERMAN, ca. 1925. Ink brochure. $50-75.

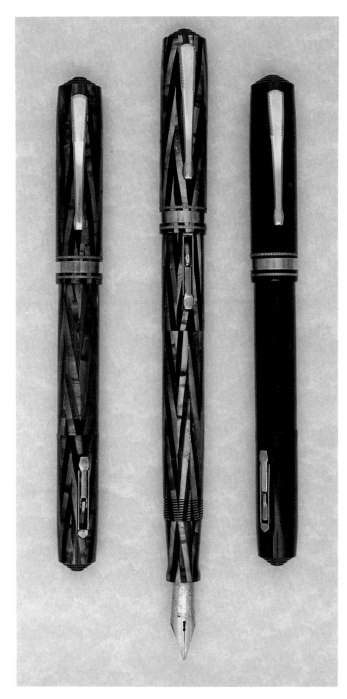

WATERMAN, 1935-1940. *Ink-Vue* Deluxe pens in copper ray, emerald ray, and jet plastic. $375-500.

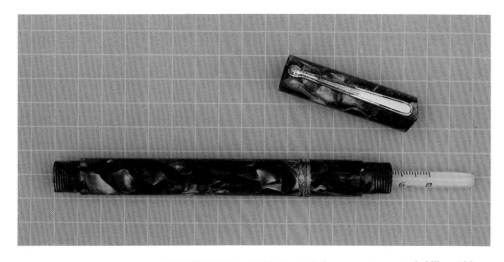

WATERMAN, ca. 1933. Doctor's thermometer case styled like a #94 pen. $200-300.

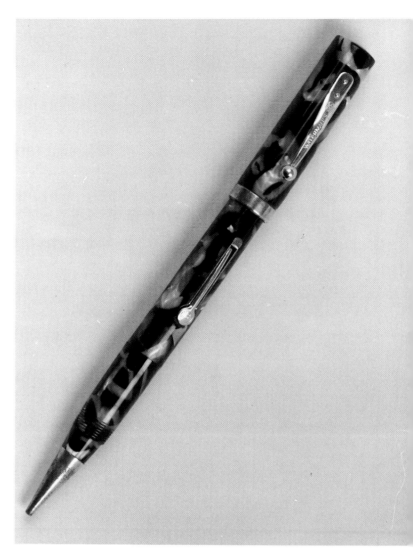

WATERMAN, ca. 1936. Christmas presentation pencil from the Waterman. $200-250.

WATERMAN, ca. 1929-1932. Black & pearl plastic lever filling pen/pencil combination. $950-1300.

WATERMAN, 1936-1940. Deluxe *Lady Patricia Ink-Vue* filling pens and pencil in black, sunset, and gray lace plastic. $60-100.

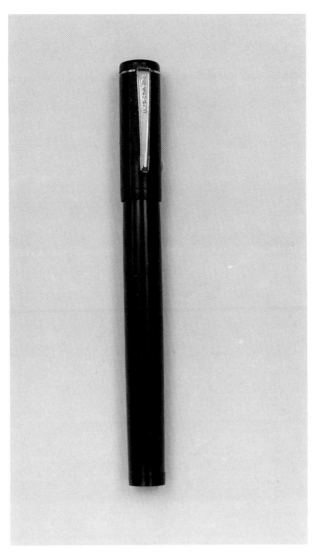

WATERMAN #42, ca. 1940. Black hard rubber safety pen. $65-85.

WATERMAN #5116, 1938-1940. *Ink-Vue* filling pen in black plastic. $100-150.

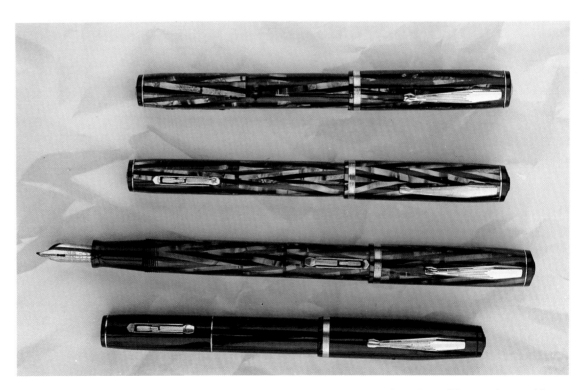

WATERMAN, 1935-1939. Standard *Ink-Vue* filling pens in emerald ray, silver ray, copper ray, and black plastic. $175-275.

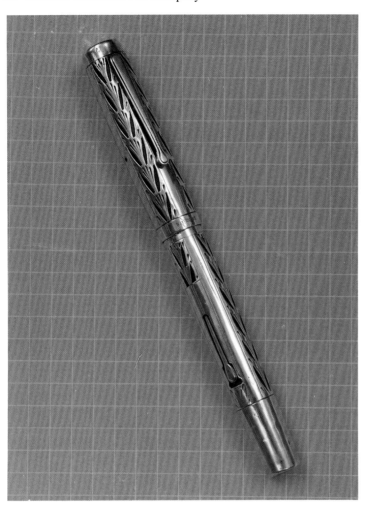

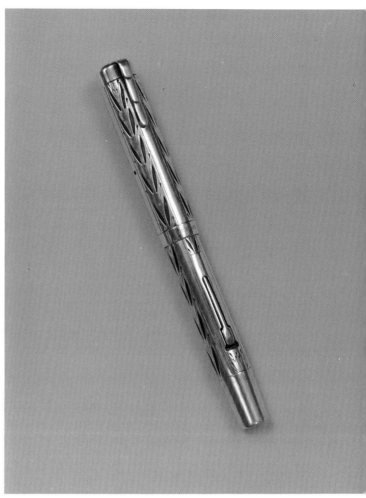

WATERMAN #494, 1936-1939. Sterling silver "Bay Leaf" design overlay, lever filling pen. $900-1250.

WATERMAN, 1936-1939. *Lady Patricia* lever filling pen in sterling silver "Bay Leaf" design overlay. $400-600.

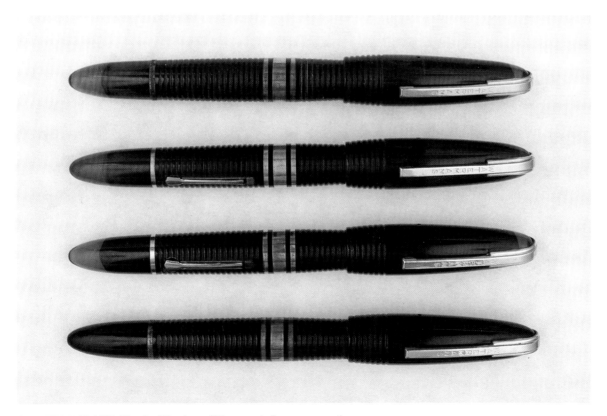

WATERMAN, 1939. *Hundred Year* lever filling pens in forest green, red, blue, and black transparent plastic. Guaranteed for 100 years, the entire Waterman line was restyled when these pens were introduced. They were modified in 1940 and other sizes were introduced. $400-650.

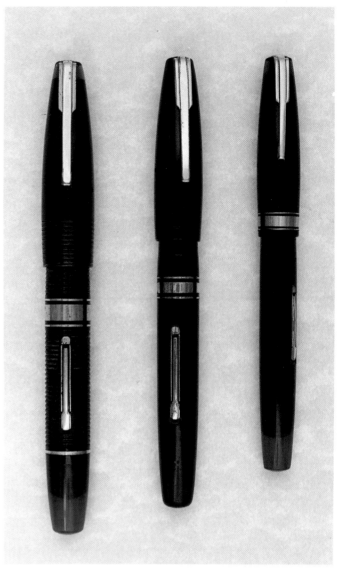

WATERMAN, 1940-1941. *Hundred Year* pens in oversize, standard size, and lady's size. Left to right: $400-600; $175-275; $125-200.

WATERMAN, 1940-1941. *Hundred Year* lever filling oversize pen and pencil set in forest green plastic. A lady's size pen was introduced in 1940 as well as a non-ribbed version, and in 1941 the band was moved from the barrel to the cap. $500-750.

WATERMAN, 1941. *Hundred Year* lever filling lady's size pen and pencil set in red plastic in the original box with guarantee. $150-250.

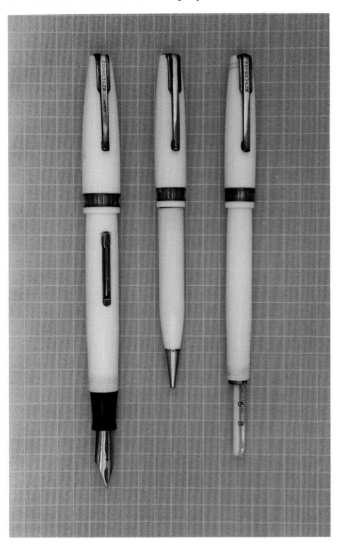

WATERMAN, ca. 1942. Doctor's *Hundred Year* type lever filling pen, pencil, and thermometer case in white plastic. $650-800.

WATERMAN, ca. 1943-1946. *Hundred Year* lever filling pen and pencil set in 14k gold. During World War II, gold and silver were not considered strategic materials. With a booming wartime economy, and a limited supply of luxury items, these pens were very popular. $750-850.

WATERMAN, 1943-1946. *Hundred Year* lever filling pen and pencil set in black plastic with gold filled caps. $100-175.

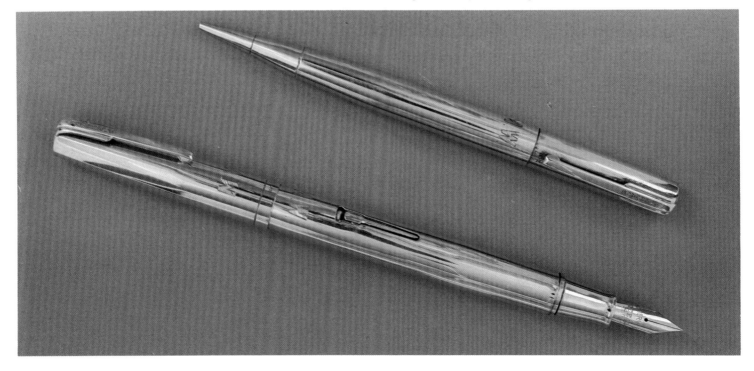

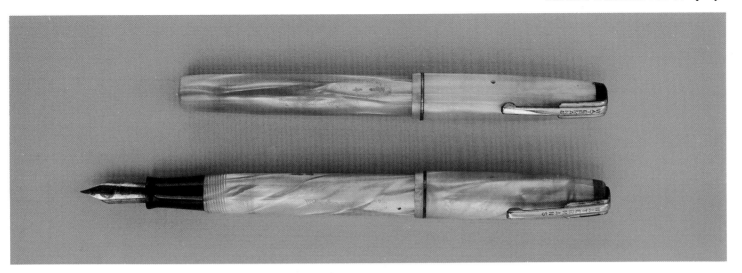

WATERMAN, ca. 1941-1948. Nurse's lever filling pen set in white marble plastic. The color band at the top of the caps indicates which pen is to be used for chart notes (black) or medication notes (red). $175-250.

WATERMAN, 1942-1946. *Commando* lever filling pen in black plastic. $65-85.

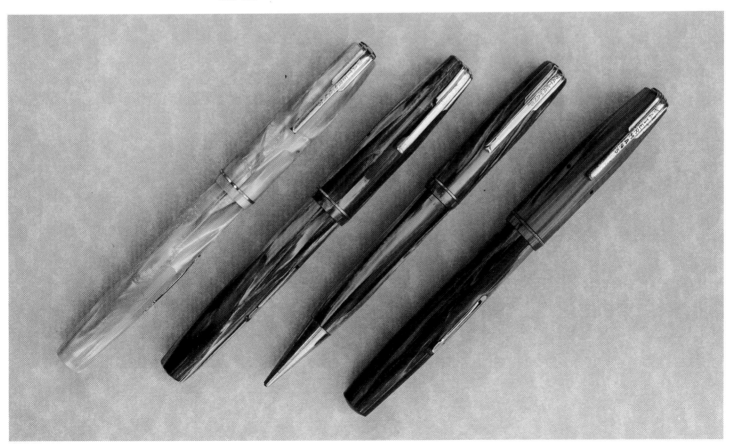

WATERMAN, ca. 1941-1946. Golden pearl, gray pearl pen, and pencil, and blue pearl pen, all lever filling. $50-75.

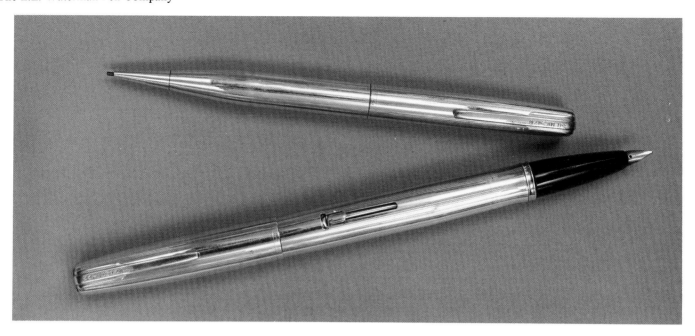

WATERMAN, ca. 1945-1953. *Taperite* lever filling pen and pencil set in 14k gold. $450-650.

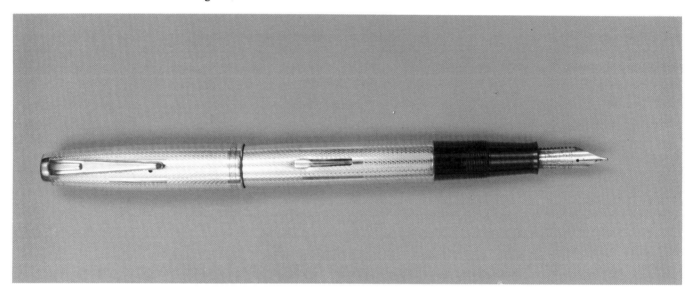

WATERMAN, ca. 1949. Gold filled overlay lever filling pen made in Italy. $200-300.

WATERMAN, 1947-1950. *Emblem* oversize lever filling pen and pencil set in black plastic. $400-500.

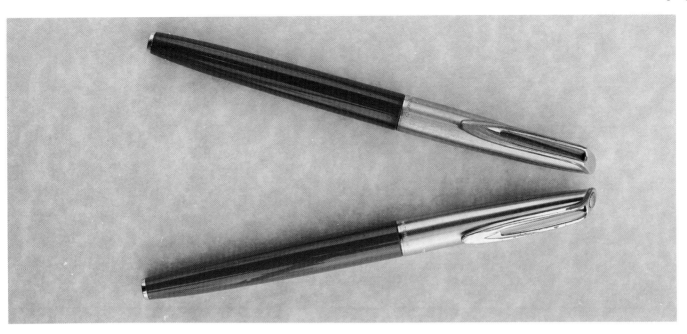

WATERMAN, 1954-1957. *C/F* cartridge filled pens. $65-85.

WATERMAN, 1958. Waterman "X" pen. Capillary attraction filling pen. This final Waterman product sold in the U.S., was made in France. It was supposed to be Waterman's answer to the Parker 61. $25-50.

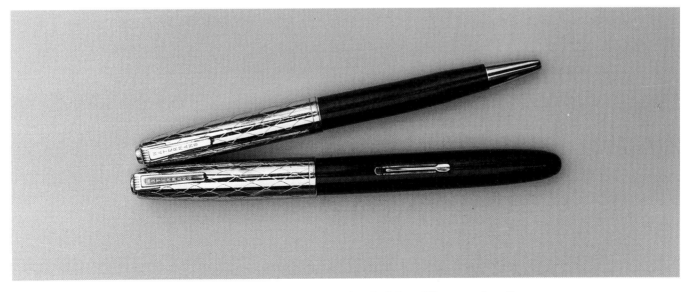

WATERMAN, ca. 1950-1955. Blue plastic lever filling pen and pencil set with chrome caps. $40-60.

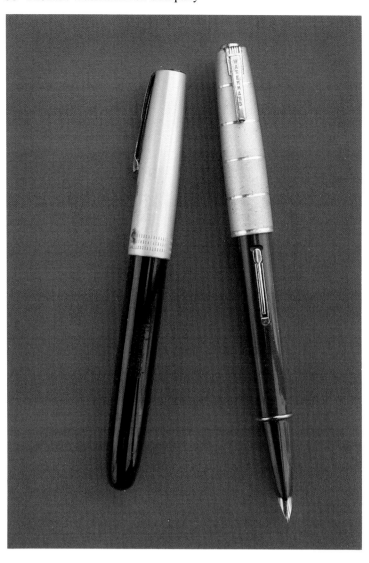

WATERMAN, ca. 1945-1953. Lady *Stateleigh Taperite* lever filling pens in black plastic with aluminum caps. $35-60.

WATERMAN, ca. 1950-1953. Black plastic lever filling pen with chrome cap. $30-60.

WATERMAN, ca. 1954. *C/F* cartridge filled demonstrator pen. $150-250.

Chapter 4

The Parker Pen Company

1888-Present

The Parker Pen company was started by George S. Parker who was born November 1, 1863 in Shullsburg, Wisconsin. He attended telegraphy school in Janesville, Wisconsin in the 1880s and eventually became a teacher there. To supplement his income he sold fountain pens to his students. Parker was also the pen repairman at the school. Like Lewis Waterman, he saw problems with the pens that he sold and discovered a way to fix the problem. With the financial backing of W.F. Palmer, an insurance salesman, he started the Parker Pen Company in 1888.

His first fountain pen patent was for a form of an over-and-under feed pen. He applied for the patent and discovered that someone else already held a patent on that idea. Not being discouraged so easily, Parker found the patent owner and bought the rights. Once he owned the rights to the competing patent, his own patent could be registered, which was done on December 10, 1889. This early Parker pen was manufactured, but sales were lackluster.

1892 is acknowledged in a 1932 Parker repair manual as the actual beginning of the Parker Pen Company. In that year, Parker designed the "Lucky Curve" pen in answer to another problem with pens. After a pen was left in a drawer or carried in the pocket (before the days of pocket clips, pens were carried in side pockets and kept horizontal) it often dropped a blob of ink onto the paper when it was turned vertically to write. Parker invented a feed that curved against the side of the barrel and channelled ink back into the reservoir. He called this the "Lucky Curve" pen. A patent for the curved feed was issued on January 9, 1894. Production was begun on this over-and-under feed, "Lucky Curve" model. Again, sales were less than spectacular.

Parker could see that the new Waterman underfeed pen was outselling his pen by leaps and bounds. He soon realized that the public was drawn to and wanted an underfeed fountain pen. The underfeed permitted the gold point to show. Pens were becoming more than a utilitarian object; they were becoming a status symbol for men. Only an educated man could read and write and a fountain pen was a sign that the owner of the pen was educated. People wanted their pens to be noticed. Parker redesigned the "Lucky Curve" in 1898 as an underfeed pen. It received public approval and with the help of advertising, Parker's sales grew steadily.

Parker made a substantial number of attractive pens. The gold, silver and gold filled overlays made between 1900 and 1915 were produced by George W. Heath & Company of Newark, New Jersey. The Heath hallmark, a capital "H" surrounded by a square, may be found on these pens.

One of the legends among pen collectors is the Parker "Snake" pen, a black hard rubber, eyedropper filler pen with a sterling silver or gold filled, green eyed snake wound around the barrel and cap. It was made for a few years beginning in 1906 and was not Parker's most expensive pen of the time. For whatever reason, a mystique surrounds this pen and makes it one of the most desirable pens made. In addition to the "Snake", Parker made some of its most beautiful pens with gold, silver, and mother-of-pearl overlays in the first 15 years of this century.

Parker made an unusual self-filler pen between 1905 and 1908. The pen had two flattened pieces sticking up from the middle of the barrel. This May 3, 1904 patented self-filler was designed by Edward Hyleman, an inventor of agricultural machines. The design compared poorly with the Conklin, which also had a piece sticking up from the middle of the barrel, and the pen was soon discontinued.

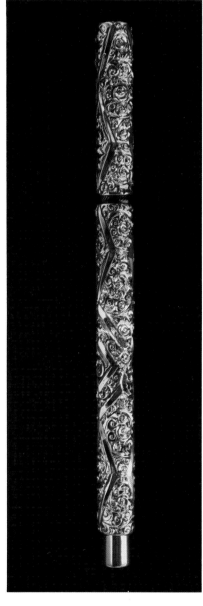

PARKER #30, ca. 1900-1915. Gold filled, diamond chased design overlay, eyedropper filled pen. $2000-3000.

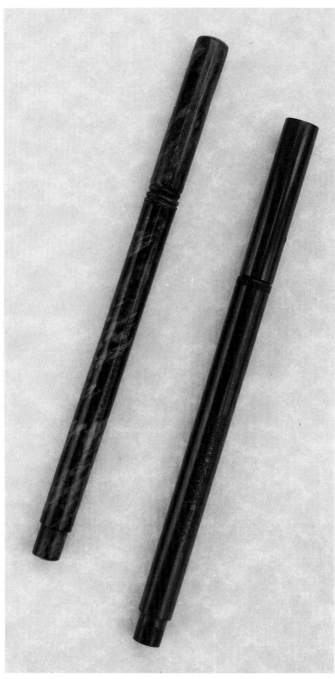

PARKER #10, ca. 1894-1905. Red and black mottled hard rubber cable chased, eyedropper filled pen. $1500-2200.

PARKER #1, ca. 1894-1915. Red & black mottled, and black hard rubber, eyedropper filled pens. This was Parker's most inexpensive early model, originally selling for $1.50. $200-275.

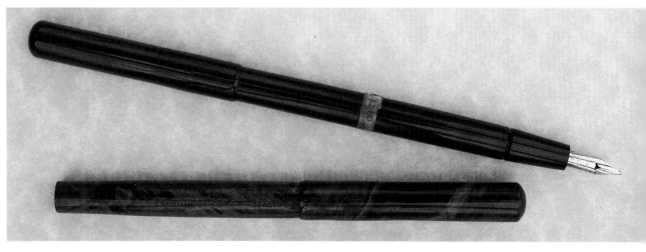

PARKER #18, ca. 1899-1918. Red & black mottled, and black chased hard rubber eyedropper filled pens. $200-250.

A rare and interesting feature to look for in the pens made during 1913 to 1916 is the Parker "Disappearing Clip". The pocket clip extended when the pen was closed and reset itself into the cap when the pen was open. In 1917, this clip itself disappeared and Parker introduced a new clip style called the "washer clip." This is the clip found on the *Duofold* pens, and it lasted until the 1933 introduction of the *Vacumatic.*

In late 1921, Parker introduced their *Duofold* pen, a pen guaranteed for 25 years, which evolved from the large "Jack Knife Safety Pen". The first "Big Red" *Duofold* made its appearance in November, 1921 and was a break from the standard, large men's pen. At that time large men's pens were made in a dignified black color, this new *Duofold* was an orange lacquer color. Parker's older management asked, "Would businessmen buy this new pen?" The answer was a resounding "Yes". They did buy it and it was an instant success. Now the symbol of an educated man, a big, expensive ($7.00), "Red" pen, could be seen from across the room.

An entire line of *Duofold* pens was started with this "Big Red". The first *Duofold* differed from later models in that it did not have a band on the lower portion of the cap. There was, however, a "Deluxe" model of 1922, available with a wide gold filled band on the cap. The nib on these early pens still said "Lucky Curve" but the barrel imprint said in large letters, "Duofold". Cracks could and often did appear at the lip of the cap so a band was put on the lower portion of the cap in 1923. As a dating aid, note that the early band was slightly raised up from the barrel. In 1926, the band was seated flush with the barrel.

Sheaffer introduced a plastic pen to the market in 1924 and Parker began to make pens from plastic in the second half of 1926. Parker's trade name for the plastic was "Permanite." With the introduction of the plastic *Duofolds*, new colors made their debut. Numerous colors were tried, but the *Duofold* line was standardized at 8 colors: orange, introduced in 1921; black, introduced in 1922; green jade, introduced in 1926; lapis blue and mandarin yellow, introduced in 1927; "moderne" black & pearl, introduced in 1928; "moderne" green & pearl, introduced in 1930; and burgundy red & black, introduced in 1930. *Duofold* pens may also be found in "sea green pearl marble", "chocolate pearl marble", and "red pearl marble". A cache of experimental colors has been found in the past few years, but these were not standard production colors. At the end of 1929, Parker streamlined the entire *Duofold* line, and ceased production of *Duofolds* by 1932. In anticipation of a new pen, Parker began to sell off the remainder of the *Duofolds*, offering a free matching pencil with every pen.

In addition to the *Duofold,* Parker made several other lines such as the *D.Q.* ("Duofold Quality"), 1926-1929, the *Moire* lady's line,1926-1931, the *True Blue, 1928-1931, the Pastel* lady's line, 1927-1932, and the *Thrift-time* pens made after the start of the Depression, 1932-1936. These *Thrift-time* pens are almost identical to the *Duofolds* in design, but are usually smaller and come in colors that never appeared in the *Duofold* line. They are beautiful pens and collector demand is approaching that of the *Duofolds*.

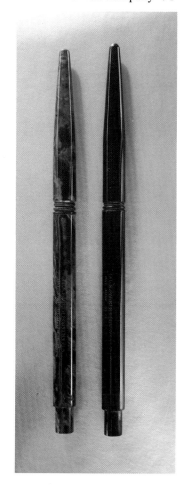

PARKER #3, ca. 1898-1910. Red & black mottled, and black hard rubber eyedropper filled taper cap pens. $250-400.

PARKER, ca. 1892-1894. Black hard rubber hexagon barrel, eyedropper filled overfeed pen. This is one of the earliest Parker pens, the imprint simply reads: "Geo. S. Parker Fountain Pen 1892". $500-650.

PARKER #6, ca. 1898-1918. Black chased hard rubber, eyedropper filled taper cap pen, with two gold filled bands. $150-300.

PARKER #11, ca. 1899-1910. Sterling silver cable chased design overlay, eyedropper filled taper cap pen. $4000-6000.

PARKER #9, ca. 1898-1918. Black chased hard rubber, eyedropper filled pens, with two gold filled bands. $150-250.

In 1933, Parker announced a wonderful, new innovation, the vacuum filler pen, soon to become the famous Parker *Vacumatic* (1933-1948). It was "a sacless pen that holds 102% more ink", said the advertisements. In actuality, the *Vacumatic* was not sacless. It had a special rubber ink sac that did not hold ink but acted as the flexible plunger mechanism. The *Vacumatic* pen was designed by industrial designer, Joseph Platt. It was made with a new laminated, striped pearl pattern of rings around the barrel and cap. The clip was also changed to the new Parker "Arrow" clip.

Several changes were made in the *Vacumatic* line during its lifetime such as new colors, new sizes, three variations in the vacuum filling system, a modified shape and different clip styles. In 1939, a small "Blue Diamond" was added to the top of the Arrow clip signifying that the pen was guaranteed for life.

The *Vacumatic* line was very successful, with many pens available to collectors today. As with any fountain pen that used soft rubber parts, the sac dried out and hardened over time. Repair of the *Vacumatic* is not for the beginning pen repairer since a special tool is needed to remove the plunger mechanism. Also, the sac is specially built with a small plastic shot in its tip. For these reasons, they should be reasonably priced when not working and offered for sale.

Parker's next pen design changed the style and look of all fountain pens to come. Until this new pen arrived, fountain pens were promoted as holding more ink than the competition's pen. To accomplish this, pen barrels were larger and different filling systems were created to hold more ink. This feature sold pens for 60 years.

In 1941, Parker showed off its new Parker *51*. The *51* was "10 years ahead of its time," according to Parker advertising. It had a hooded nib and used a new ink that dried as soon as it touched the paper. In terms of design, it was an incredibly original and fresh idea. It ushered in the period where thin pens were the "in" pens. Other pen makers tried to imitate it with almost no success.

Everyone wanted one, but Parker could not make the *51* fast enough to fill the demand. They were also involved at this time in making precision parts for the war effort and the restrictions on the use of strategic materials such as plastics and metals limited production. Parker went so far as to take out magazine advertisements apologizing for the shortage. Incredibly, a *51* pen was actually worth its weight in gold in countries outside of the United States.

At the end of World War II, Parker began to turn out over a million *51* pens a year. To capitalize on the demand for this new look in fountain pens, they produced a cheaper version of the *51* called the *41*. The *51* also marked the start of Parker's naming their fountain pens by number. Soon to follow were the Parker *21*, *61*, *45*, *75* and *180*. Parker is still in business today making a variety of writing instruments.

PARKER #15, ca. 1910-1916. Baby model pearl slab covered barrel, gold filled filigree design overlay cap, eyedropper filled pen. $1000-1250.

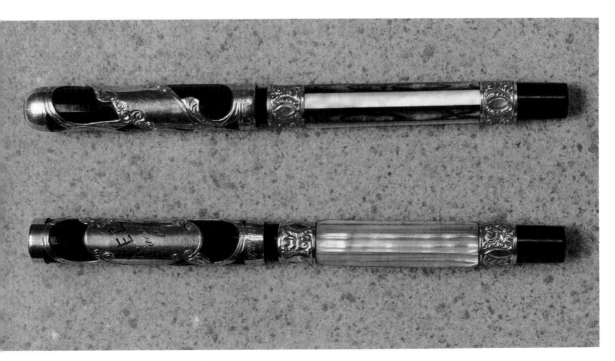

PARKER #15, Top: ca. 1905-1910, alternating pearl & abalone covered barrel pen with rounded early style gold filled filigree design overlay cap. Bottom: ca. 1910-1918, slab pearl covered barrel pen. Both pens eyedropper filled. $1750-2500.

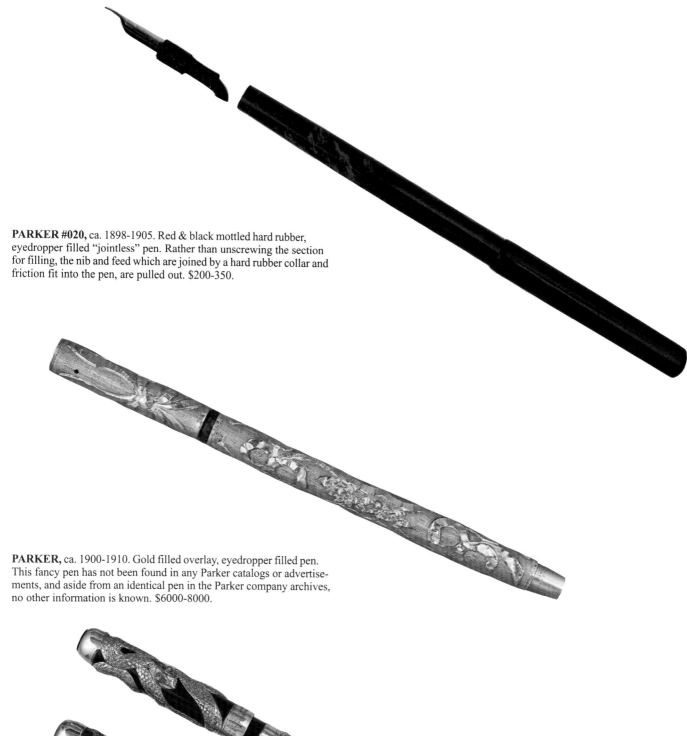

PARKER #020, ca. 1898-1905. Red & black mottled hard rubber, eyedropper filled "jointless" pen. Rather than unscrewing the section for filling, the nib and feed which are joined by a hard rubber collar and friction fit into the pen, are pulled out. $200-350.

PARKER, ca. 1900-1910. Gold filled overlay, eyedropper filled pen. This fancy pen has not been found in any Parker catalogs or advertisements, and aside from an identical pen in the Parker company archives, no other information is known. $6000-8000.

PARKER #37, #38, ca. 1905-1918. Sterling silver, and gold filled, "Snake" design overlay, eyedropper filled pen. The "Snake" is probably Parker's most famous overlay design pen. $8000-12000.

PARKER #33, ca. 1905-1918. Red, and black hard rubber, eyedropper filled pens with gold filled filigree overlays, $750-900. Parker red hard rubber pens with overlays are rare, $3500-4500. Note the cap variations.

PARKER #16, ca. 1905-1918. Gold filled filigree design overlay red, $3000-4000; and black, $750-1000; hard rubber eyedropper filled pens.

PARKER #39, ca. 1905-1915. Gold filled "Forget-Me-Not" design overlay, eyedropper filled pen, set with semi-precious stones. This pen was also available without stones as a #54. This is the only known example of this extremely rare and beautiful pen. $8000-12000.

PARKER #46, ca. 1905-1915. Slab pearl, and corrugated pearl & abalone covered barrel, eyedropper filled pens with chased design gold-filled overlay taper caps. $4500-7500.

PARKER #31, ca. 1905-1918. Sterling silver filigree design overlay, eyedropper filled pen in red hard rubber. This pen is a large version of the #14 pen. It is fitted with a #5 size nib. $4500-6000.

PARKER *Red Giant,* ca. 1902-1912. Red hard rubber, eyedropper filled pen with wide sterling silver band. This early model Giant, fitted with a #12 nib, is extremely rare in red hard rubber, with fewer than three known to have survived intact. $7500-12000.

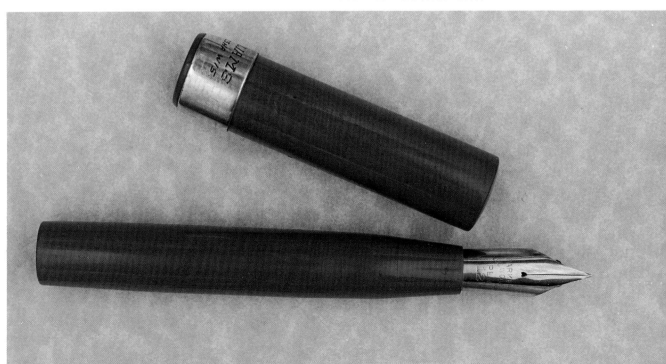

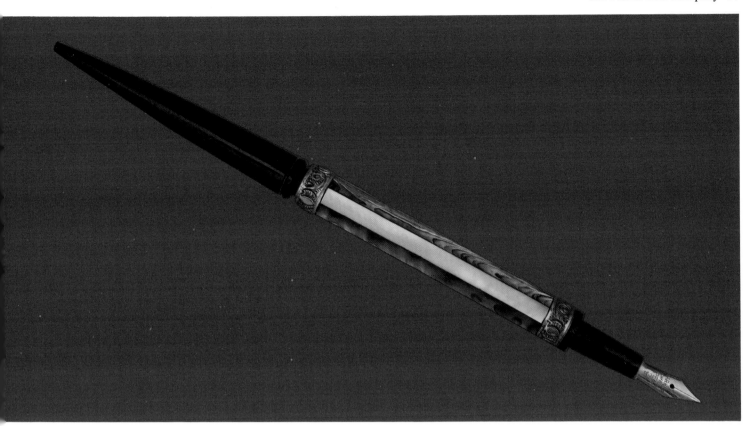

PARKER #12, ca. 1899-1915. Alternating pearl & abalone covered barrel, eyedropper filled taper cap pen. $750-1000.

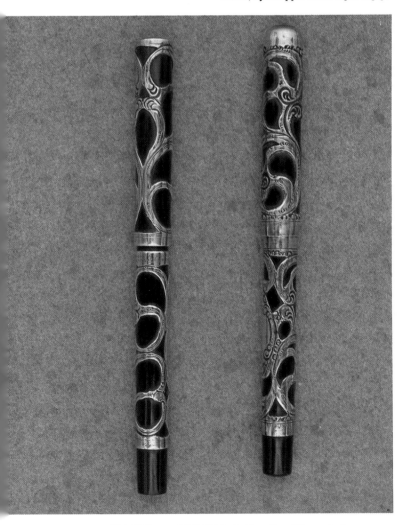

PARKER #14, Right: ca. 1898-1910, sterling silver filigree design overlay, eyedropper filled pen. Left: ca. 1910-1918 version of the same pen. $750-1000.

PARKER #34, ca. 1905-1918. Red and Black hard rubber eyedropper filled pens with sterling silver filigree overlays. Left to right: $750-1000; $3500-5000.

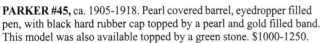
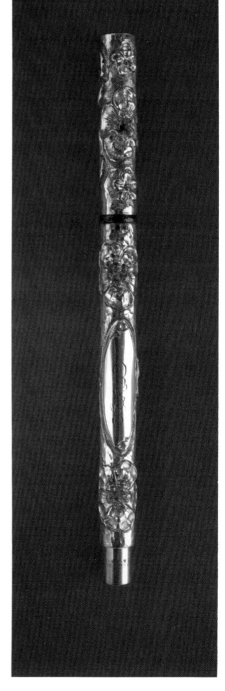

PARKER #45, ca. 1905-1918. Pearl covered barrel, eyedropper filled pen, with black hard rubber cap topped by a pearl and gold filled band. This model was also available topped by a green stone. $1000-1250.

PARKER #140, ca. 1905-1915. Sterling silver filigree design overlay, eyedropper filled pen. This model, fitted with a #4 nib, was sized between the #14, and #31. $1000-1250.

PARKER #57, ca. 1905-1915. Sterling silver "Awanyu Aztec" half overlay design, eyedropper filled pen. Available with a gold filled overlay as a #58. $15000-20000.

PARKER #35, ca. 1905-1915. Gold filled heavy floral design overlay, eyedropper filled pen. $3000-4000.

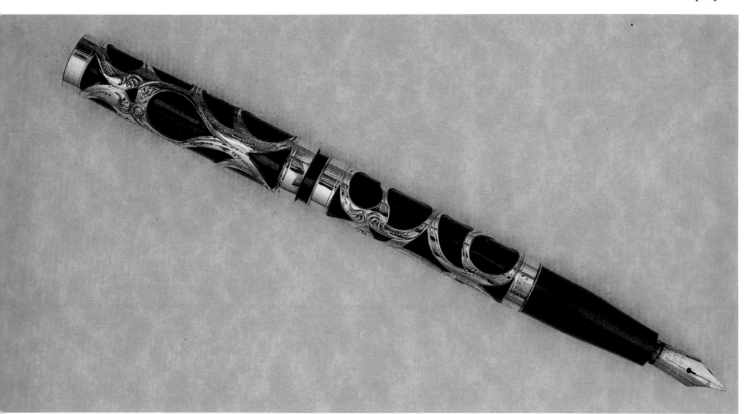

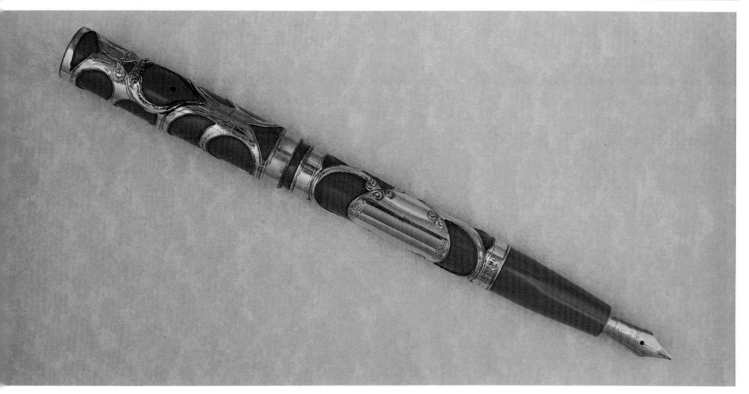

PARKER #41, ca. 1905-1918. Gold filled filigree design overlay, eyedropper filled pens in black, $2000-3500; and red hard rubber, $4000-6000. These large pens are fitted with #5 nibs.

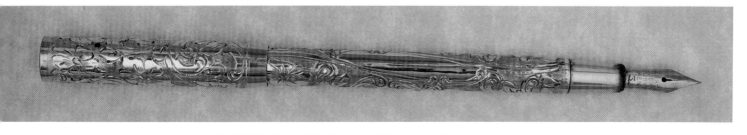

PARKER #62, ca. 1905-1915. Gold filled etched floral design overlay, eyedropper filled pen. $1500-2500.

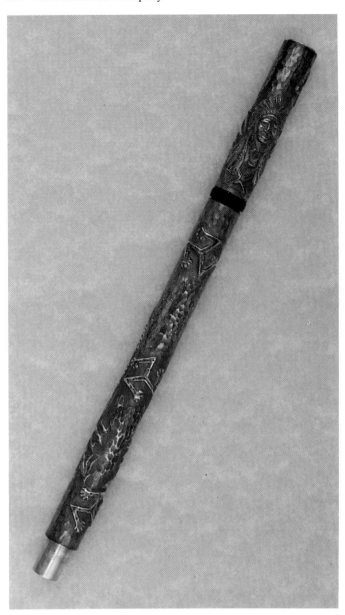

PARKER #60, ca. 1905-1915. Gold filled "Awanyu Aztec" design overlay, eyedropper filled pen. Also available in sterling as a #59. $15000-25000.

PARKER #15, ca. 1905-1918. Corrugated pearl & abalone covered barrel, eyedropper filled pen with gold filled filigree design overlay cap. $1750-2500.

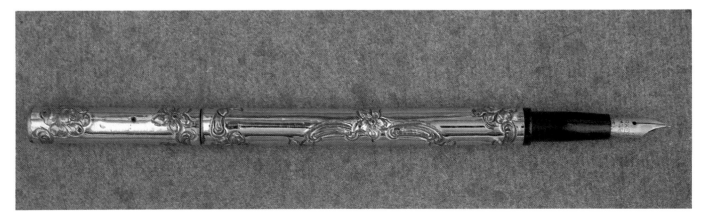

PARKER #43, ca. 1905-1915. Gold filled floral design overlay, eyedropper filled pen. Available in sterling silver as a #44. $2500-3500.

PARKER #47, ca. 1905-1915. Bulbous pearl covered barrel, eyedropper filled pens with gold filled floral design overlay caps. Two variations of cap overlay design are shown. $5500-7500.

PARKER #23, ca. 1905-1910. Black hard rubber, self-filling pen. This was Parker's first self-filling design. It was succeeded by the button filling mechanism in 1913. $500-800.

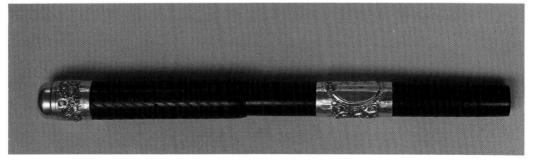

PARKER #42½, ca. 1905-1918. Black chased hard rubber, eyedropper filled pen with chased gold filled trim. One of the few standard features of Parker's numbering system was that "½" following the number indicated a chased rubber pen. $250-350.

PARKER #52, ca. 1905-1918. Sterling silver Indian "Swastika" design overlay, eyedropper filled pen. The American Indian symbol of good luck, legend has it that after it had been appropriated by Germany's Third Reich, all remaining pens on hand at the Parker factory were ceremoniously buried in the concrete of Arrow Park, the new plant built in 1940. Available in gold filled overlay as a #53. $6500-8000.

PARKER #51, ca. 1905-1918. Black hard rubber, eyedropper filled pen with gold filled name plaque. $125-200.

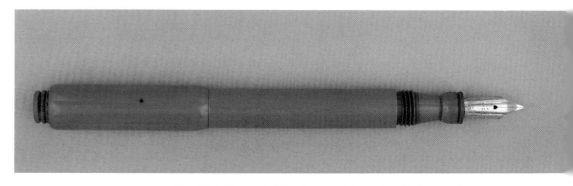

PARKER #20, 1912-1916. Short model, "Jack-Knife Safety", button filling pen in red hard rubber. $500-750.

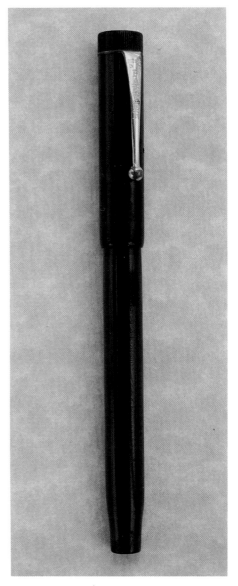

PARKER #22, ca. 1916-1925. Black hard rubber, button filling, "Jack-Knife Safety" pen. The closest Parker came to a standard numbering system was the "20" series used on the hard rubber "Jack-Knife Safety" cap pens of the 1920s. The pens were assigned numbers according to size from 22 to 28, reflecting the nib size. They were available with a variety of gold filled bands, in plain or chased hard rubber, clip cap, and lady's models, and in three lengths; baby, short, and standard. $100-175.

PARKER, ca. 1905-1910. Ultra Giant eyedropper filled pen in black hard rubber, with red hard rubber baby pen insert. Larger than the Giant, this pen was probably used as a salesman's sample. Although a working pen, fitted with a #12 nib, it is too large to actually use. $5000-7500.

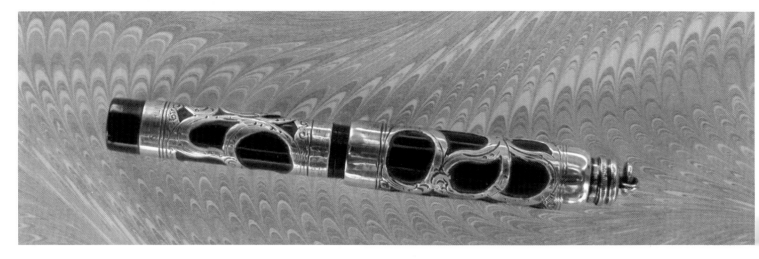

PARKER #14, ca. 1912-1916. Baby model, "Jack-Knife Safety",
eyedropper filled pen with sterling silver filigree design overlay.
$400-600.

PARKER #31, ca. 1913-1916. Sterling silver filigree design overlay,
button filling pen. Beginning around 1913, many of Parker's eyedropper filled models became available as button filling pens. Some overlay
designs, including the "Snake" pattern have been found as button filling
pens. $2000-3500.

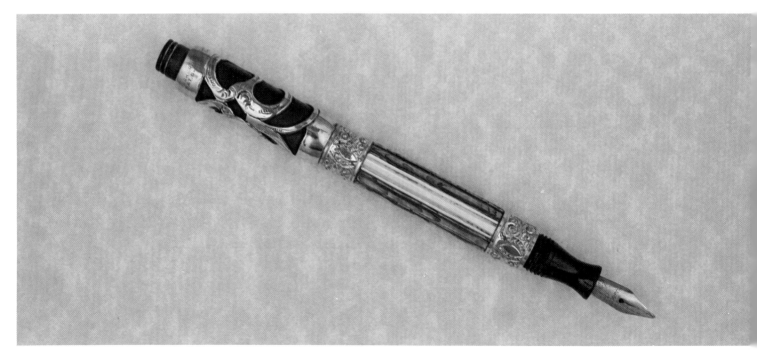

PARKER #15, ca. 1912-1916. Short model, "Jack-Knife Safety", eyedropper filled
pen with alternating slab pearl & abalone covered barrel, and gold filled filigree
design overlay cap. $750-1000.

PARKER #45, ca. 1912-1916. Short model, "Jack-Knife Safety", pearl slab covered barrel, eyedropper filled pen with a green stone mounted in the top of the cap. $700-900.

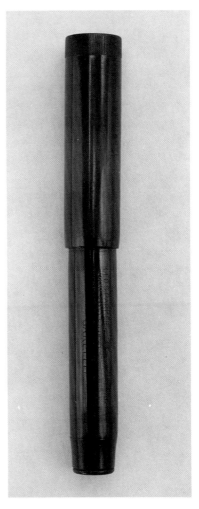

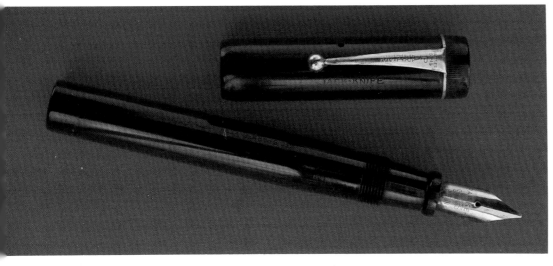

PARKER #28, ca. 1913-1921. Black hard rubber, "Jack-Knife Safety", eyedropper filled pen. Other than the Giant, the largest standard pen made by Parker. $400-600.

PARKER #25, ca. 1916-1925. "Jack-Knife Safety" button filling pen with Bakelite barrel and hard rubber cap. Pens with the transparent Bakelite barrel are more often found as eyedropper filled models.
$400-600.

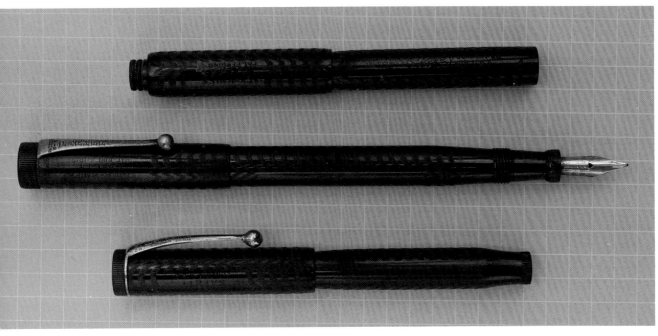

PARKER #20½, Top: ca. 1912-1916, black chased hard rubber, eyedropper filled pen. Center: ca. 1916-1925, "Jack-Knife Safety", button filling pen. Bottom: ca. 1916-1925, short model "Jack-Knife Safety", button filling pen. $100-150.

PARKER #23, ca. 1916-1925. Red & black mottled hard rubber, "Jack-Knife Safety" eyedropper filled pen with washer clip. $300-450.

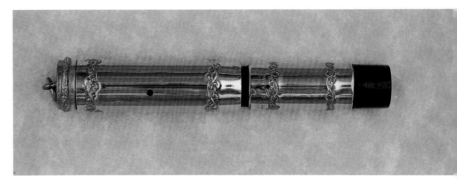

PARKER #49, ca. 1917-1921. Baby model gold filled overlay, eyedropper filled "Jack-Knife Safety" pen. $350-500.

PARKER #20½, ca. 1912. Black chased hard rubber, eyedropper filled pen with "planchet" type "Jack-Knife Safety" cap. $300-500.

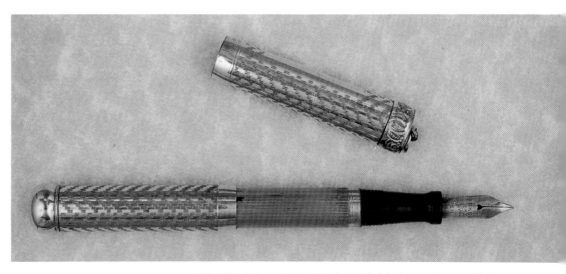

PARKER #70, ca. 1910-1918. Gold filled design eyedropper filled telescoping pen. $350-500.

PARKER *Black Giant,* ca. 1916-1921. Short model, eyedropper filled, "Jack-Knife Safety" pen. $600-1000.

PARKER *Black Giant,* ca. 1916-1921. Eyedropper filled, "Jack-Knife Safety" pen with washer clip. $600-1000.

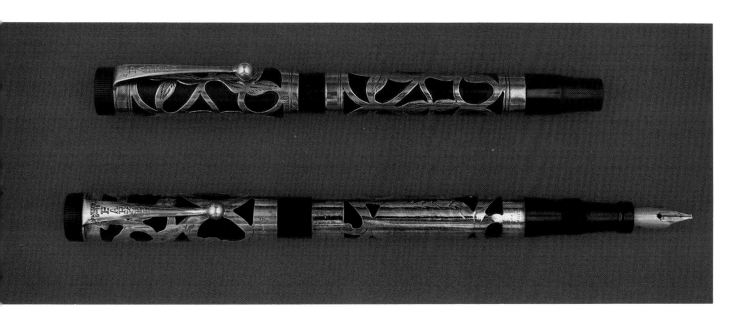

PARKER #14, ca. 1916-1925. Sterling silver filigree design, "Jack-Knife Safety", button filling pens. $450-650.

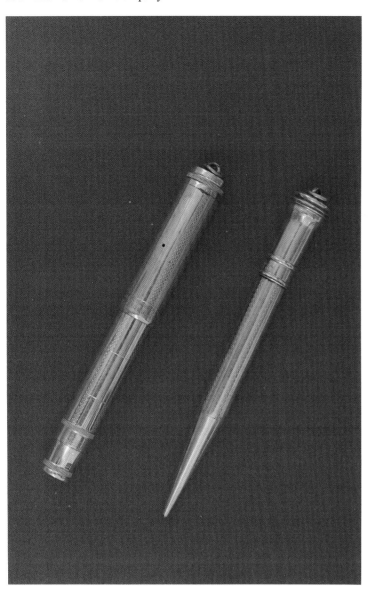

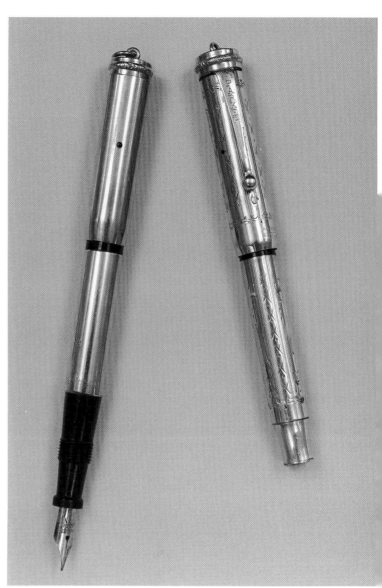

PARKER, ca. 1919-1925. Gold filled "Jack-Knife Safety" button filling lady's pens and pencil. Left, $150-275; right, $175-300.

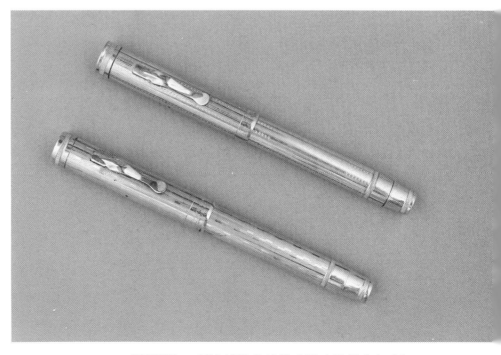

PARKER, ca. 1919-1925. Gold filled, "Jack-Knife Safety", button filling pens. $150-275.

PARKER #16, ca. 1912-1916. Baby model, gold filled filigree design overlay, "Jack-Knife Safety" eyedropper filled pen. $250-375.

PARKER #16, ca. 1917-1925. Gold filled filigree design overlay, "Jack-Knife Safety", button filling pens, illustrating two different filigree patterns. Left, $150-225; right, $150-225.

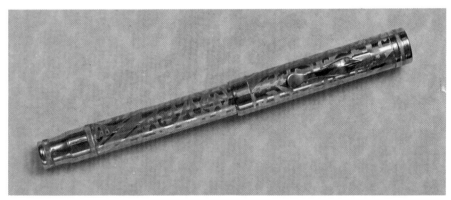

PARKER, ca. 1919-1925. Gold filled and sterling silver "Brocade" design, button filling pens. Top, $175-275; bottom, $275-400.

PARKER #20, ca. 1916-1925. Baby model, red & black mottled hard rubber, eyedropper filled, "Jack-Knife Safety" pen, with gold filled cap band. $250-350.

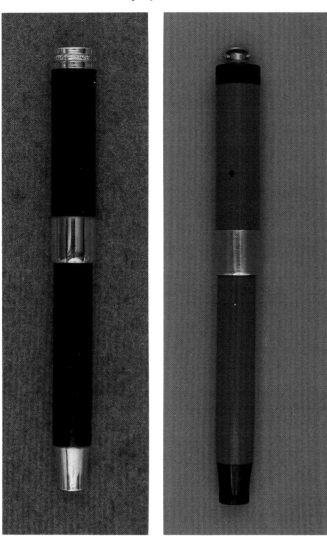

PARKER #83, ca. 1919-1923. Black chased hard rubber, "Jack-Knife Safety", button filling pen, with gold filled trim. Left, $175-300.

PARKER, 1922-1926. Lady *Duofold* button filling pen in red hard rubber. The wide gold filled band was standard on all Lady *Duofolds* of this period. $100-175.

PARKER #25, ca. 1916-1925. Black hard rubber, "Jack-Knife Safety", button filling pen. $100-175.

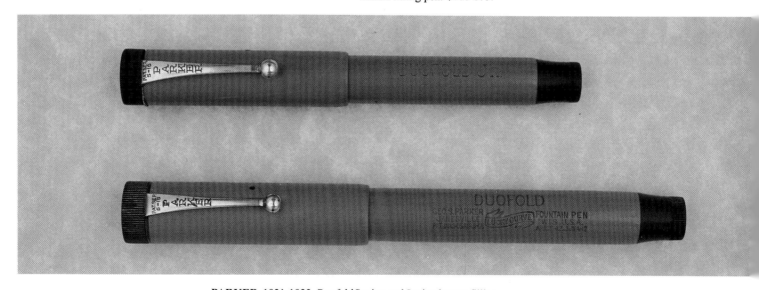

PARKER, 1921-1922. *Duofold* Senior, and Junior, button filling, red hard rubber pens. Top, $275-400; bottom, $400-650.

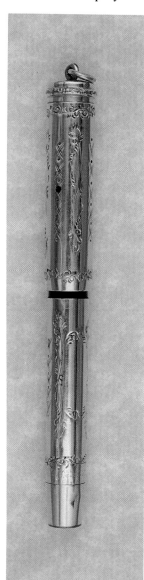

PARKER #24½, ca. 1916-1925. Black chased hard rubber, "Jack-Knife Safety", button filling pen with gold filled band. $125-175.

PARKER, ca. 1917-1925. Gold filled, "Jack-Knife Safety", button filling, and eyedropper filled lady's pens. Left, $200-300; right, $200-300.

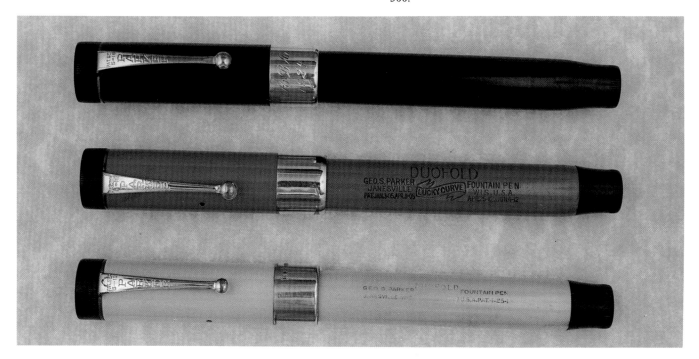

PARKER. *Duofold Deluxe* Senior button filling pens with wide gold filled bands. Top to bottom: ca. 1924 black hard rubber pen, $350-500; ca. 1923 red hard rubber pen, $450-650; ca. 1927 mandarin yellow Permanite pen, $650-850.

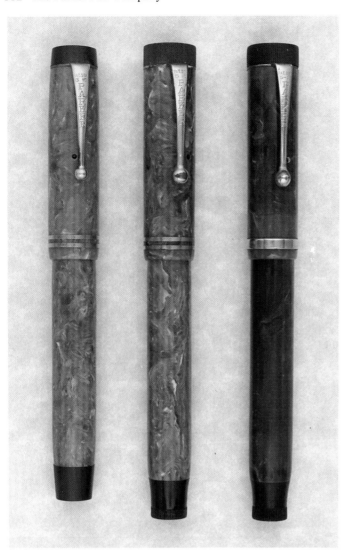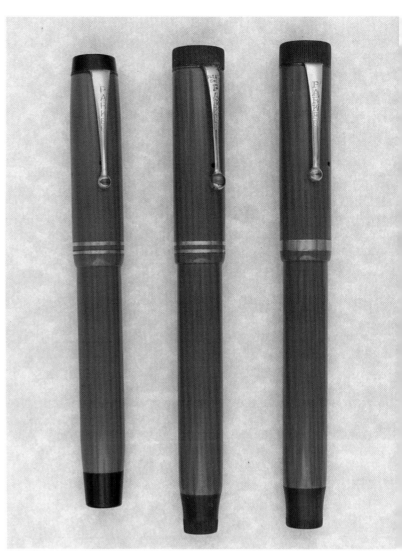

PARKER. *Duofold* Senior button filling pens in jade green, and red Permanite. Right to left: 1926-1928; 1928-1929; 1929-1933. Left to right: $200-250, $200-250, $225-275, $200-250, $200-250, $200-250.

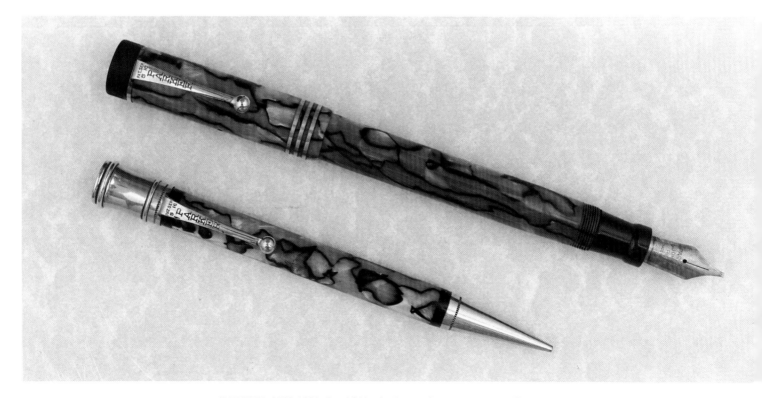

PARKER, 1928-1929. *Duofold* Senior button filling pen and pencil set in moderne black & pearl Permanite. $275-350.

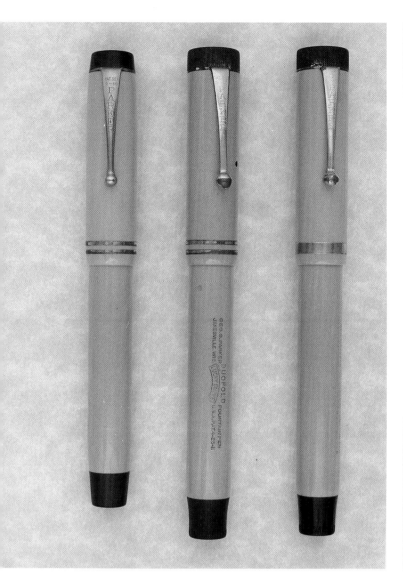
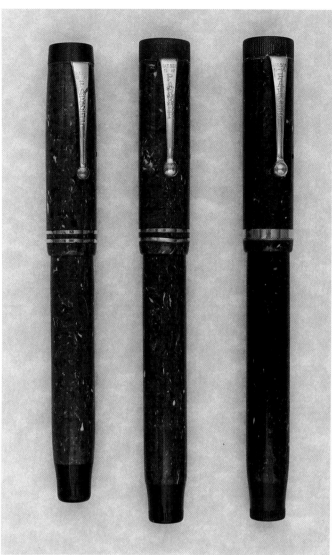

PARKER. *Duofold* Senior button filling pens in mandarin yellow, and lapis blue Permanite. Right to Left: 1927-1928; 1928-1929; 1929-1933. Left to right: $500-600, $600-700, $650-750, $250-350, $300-400, $350-500.

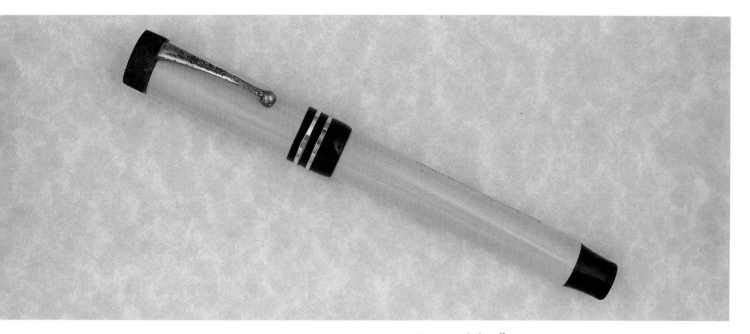

PARKER, ca. 1928. *Duofold* Senior button filling, mandarin yellow Permanite experimental pen. The yellow *Duofold* was not a popular pen and the Parker model shop tried many band and color variations on the pen. This illustration shows only one of those tried. $1250-1400.

PARKER, ca. 1929 *Duofold* advertisement.

PARKER, ca. 1923. Die-cut advertisement illustrating the button filling mechanism. $150-225.

PARKER, 1928-1929. *Duofold* Senior desk base and lamp in green anodized metal. The base is shown with two *Duofold* Senior mandarin yellow pens. When originally sold, it was fitted with two moderne black & pearl pens. Originally selling for $100.00, this was one of the most expensive desk bases offered by Parker. $550-750.

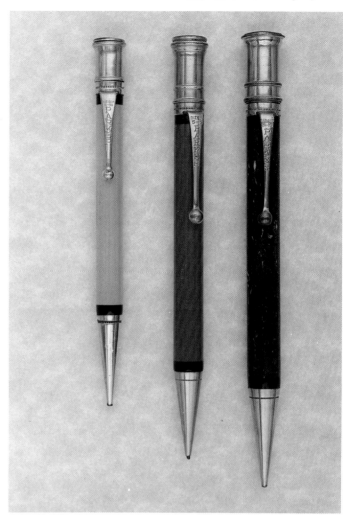

PARKER. *Duofold* Senior streamlined button filling pens. Right to Left: sea green pearl Permanite pen, 1921-1933; moderne green & pearl Permanite pen, 1930-1933; burgundy Permanite pen, 1930-1933; moderne black & pearl Permanite pen, 1929-1933. $275-400.

PARKER, ca. 1938. *Duofold* pencils. Right to left: lapis blue *Duofold* Senior pencil, $75-125; red *Duofold* oversize Junior pencil, $75-125; mandarin yellow Junior pencil, $100-150.

PARKER, 1927-1929. *Duofold* Senior and Junior button filling pens in black Permanite. Top, $175-225; bottom, $100-150.

PARKER, 1926-1932. Pastel and moire pattern *Petite* button filling Permanite pens and pencils, available as either ring cap or clip cap models. The colors were described as: Naples blue, mauve; coral, magenta, and gray beige which was changed to apple green in 1928. $175-300.

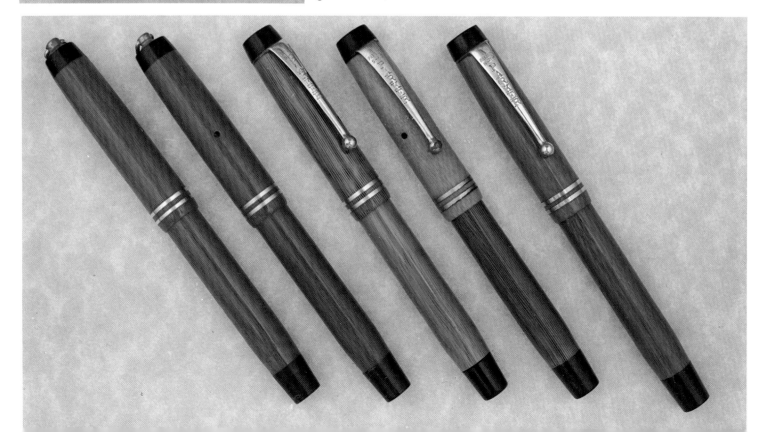

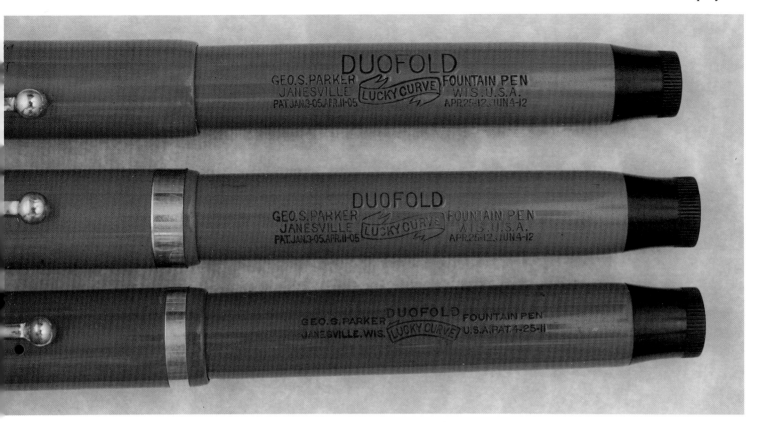

PARKER. *Duofold* barrel imprints, top to bottom: 1921-1922 large imprint; 1923 large imprint; 1926-1928 standard imprint.

PARKER, 1928-1929. *Duofold* Senior desk base with Waltham 8 day clock. Essentially the same as the lamp base on page 114, but with the lamp replaced by the clock. $550-750.

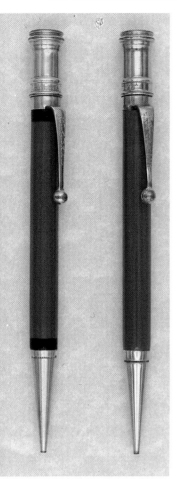
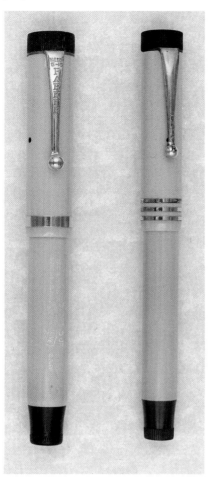

PARKER, 1927-1929. *Duofold* pencils. Prior to 1927, the barrel color of the pencils extended the length of the barrel. Beginning in 1927, two black bands were added to the ends of the barrels. $50-75.

PARKER, ca. 1928. *Duofold* Junior pen compared with a *Duofold* Juniorette pen, both in mandarin yellow Permanite. $150-250.

PARKER, 1926-1930. *Petite* pastel lady's button filling pen and pencil set in beige gray Permanite. $100-150.

PARKER, 1930-1933. Vest pocket *Duofold,* button filling pen in mandarin yellow Permanite. Best pocket pens and pencils were available in the standard *Duofold* colors, either as clip, or more commonly as ring cap models. $200-300.

PARKER, 1930-1933. Vest pocket *Duofold* pen and pencil sets in burgundy, and green Permanite. Left; $225-325, right; $225-325.

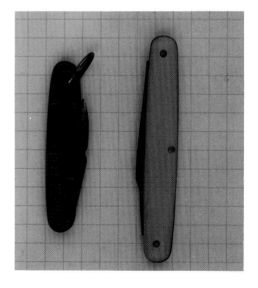

PARKER. Pocket knifes were available as companion pieces for the *Duofold* and *Vacumatic* pens. The yellow *Duofold* knife is ca. 1930, and the *Vacumatic* knife is ca. 1940. $50-75.

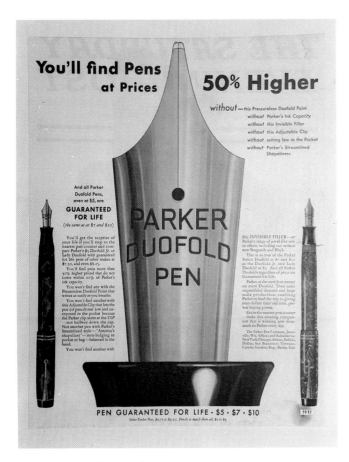

PARKER, ca. 1931 advertisement.

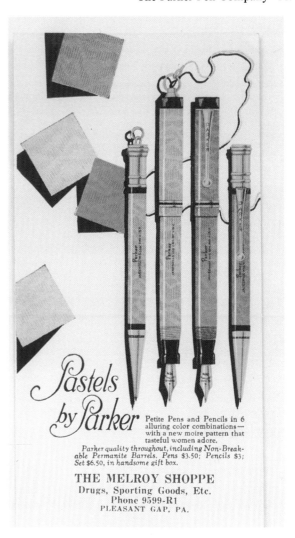

PARKER, ca. 1927. Advertising blotter. $25-50.

PARKER #7x, ca. 1924-1926. Black lined hard rubber, button filling
pen. Although similar in size and appearance to a standard black
Duofold, this pen was offered as a lowered priced alternative. It was
supplied with a 7x *Duofold* size nib, and did not come with the *Duofold*
guarantee. $150-200.

PARKER, ca. 1930. Experimental green Permanite *Duofold* Junior pen with fluted ends, and unusual band. $350-600.

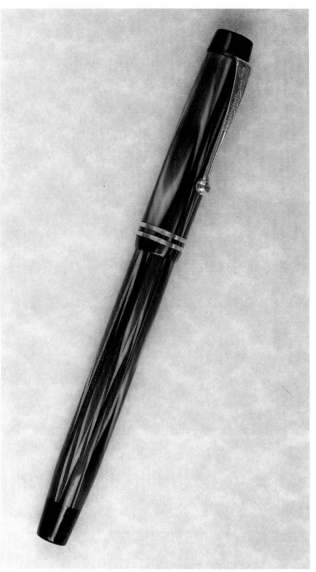

PARKER, 1929-1933. *True Blue,* Permanite button filling pen. This pen, along with the black lined hard rubber *D.Q.* (*Duofold* quality) pen, were advertised as low cost student models. $125-175.

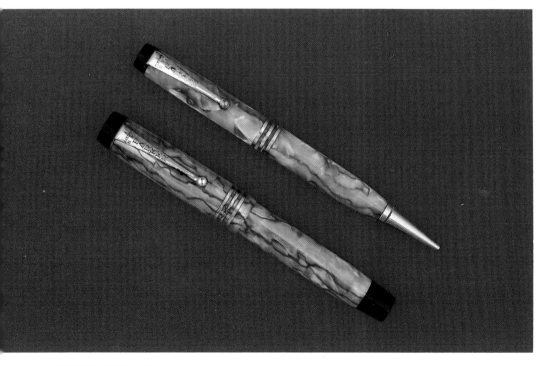

PARKER, 1930-1933. *Duofold* Junior streamlined, button filling pen and pencil set in moderne green & pearl Permanite. $200-300.

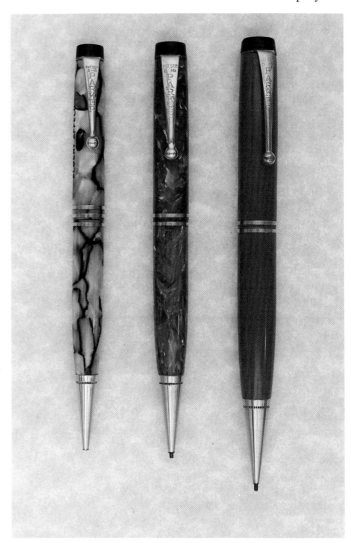

PARKER, ca. 1923-1925. *Duofold* Junior button filling pen in black chased hard rubber. *Duofold* pens from this period are sometimes found in chased or lined black hard rubber. $125-175.

PARKER, ca. 1930. *Duofold* streamlined pencils. Right to left: red Permanite *Duofold* Senior; jade green Permanite oversize *Duofold* Junior moderne black & pearl Permanite *Duofold* Junior. $65-125.

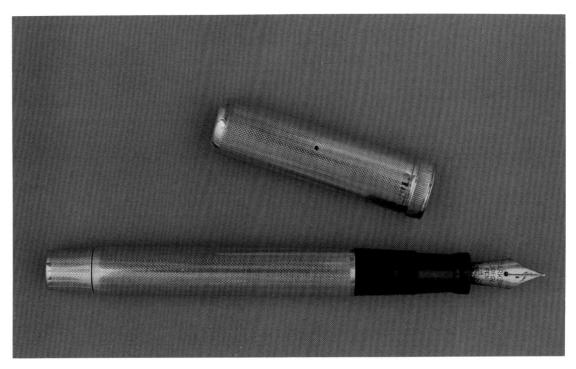

PARKER, ca. 1930-1933. *Duofold* streamlined, button filling pen in 9k gold, with English hallmarks. $750-900.

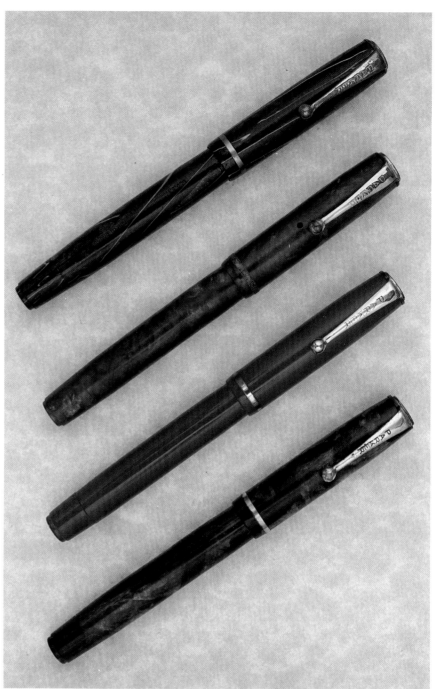

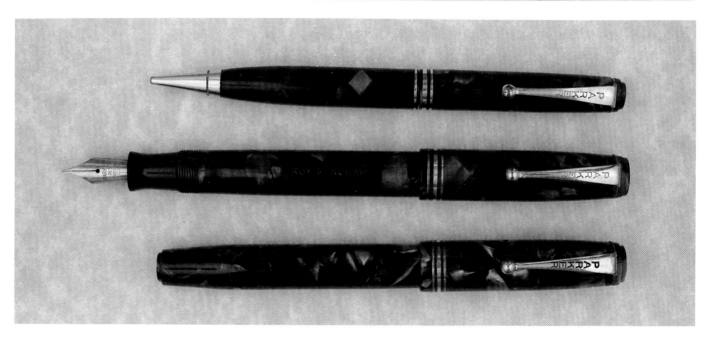

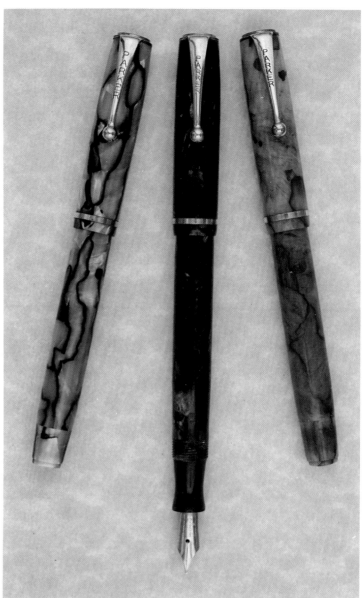

PARKER, ca. 1932-1936. Depression era *Thrift Time,* button filling pens and pencils. During the height of the depression, Parker introduced a budget priced series of pens. Not heavily promoted, they were made in plastic colors and patterns which were not used in other pens by Parker. There are over 20 colors known, and four style variations. Top left; $75-125, top right; $200-350, bottom; $300-450, opposite page; top: $200-350, bottom: $175-250.

PARKER, ca. 1930-1933. *True Blue* button filling pen made for the Zaner Bloser Company in Columbus, Ohio. $250-400.

PARKER, ca. 1932-1936. Black Permanite button filling pen/pencil combination. Very rare, it is also found in brown & gold marble Permanite. $950-1250.

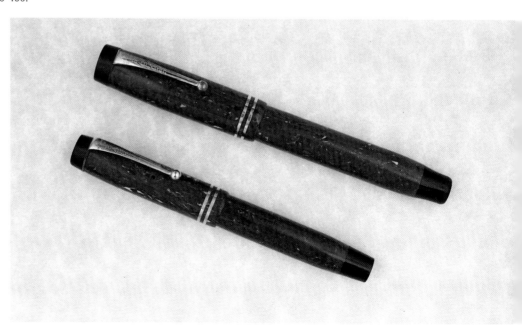

PARKER, 1930-1933. *Duofold* Senior streamlined and Junior button filling pens in lapis blue Permanite. $200-300.

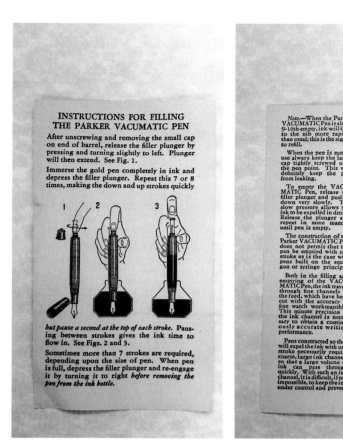

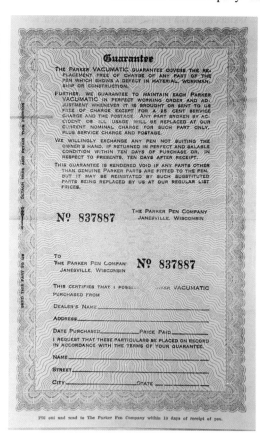

PARKER, ca. 1935. *Vacumatic* filling instructions and guarantee.

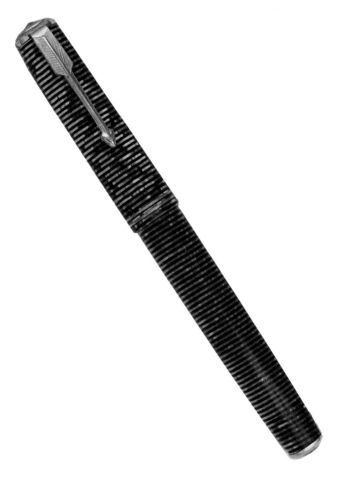

PARKER, 1932-1933. *Vacuum-Filler* pen in silver pearl laminated plastic. $125-175.

PARKER, ca. 1932 *Thrift Time* advertisement.

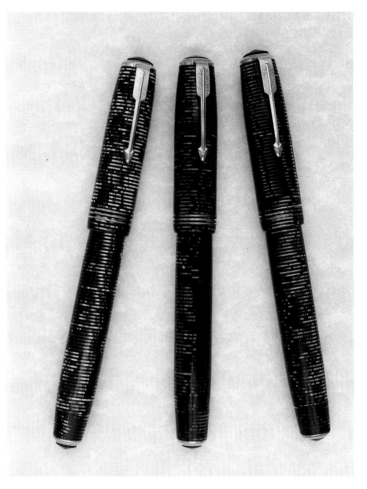

PARKER, 1933-1936. *Vacumatic* Oversize pens in golden pearl, burgundy pearl, silver pearl laminated plastic. Not shown are emerald pearl laminated, and jet plastic. $250-450.

PARKER, 1932-1933. *Vacuum-Filler* demonstrator pen. Prior to 1933, the new *Vacuumatic* pen was known as the *Vacuum-Filler.* $225-300.

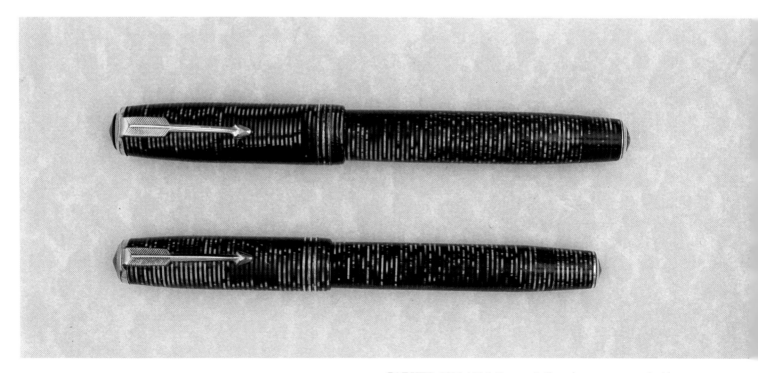

PARKER, 1933-1936. *Vacumatic* Oversize pen compared with a standard *Vacumatic*.

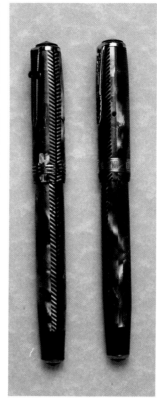

PARKER, ca. 1934-1938. *Royal Challenger* button filling pens. Pens shown in silver, burgundy, and gold herringbone plastic. The *Royal Challenger* is readily recognized by it's unique "sword" style clip, and later stepped clip. Left to right: $175-225, $175-225, $175-225.

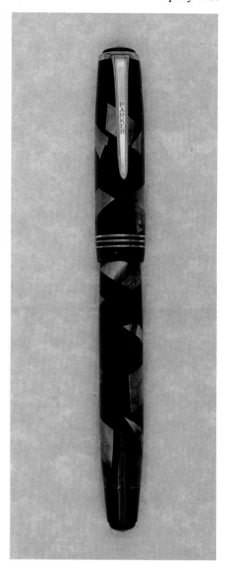

PARKER, ca. 1934-1938. *Challenger* gray pearl marble button filling pen. $150-200.

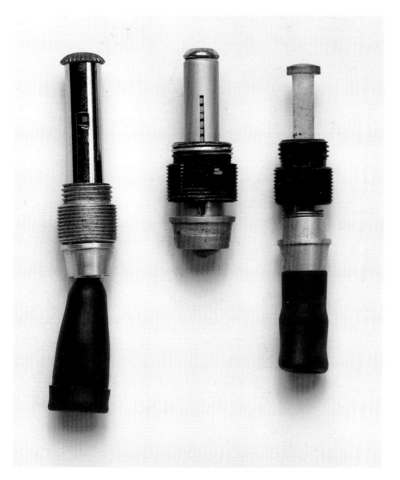

PARKER. *Vacumatic* filling units. Left to right: 1933-1936 lock button unit; 1939-1940 "Speedline" unit; 1941-1948, plastic disposable *51* type unit.

PARKER, ca. 1933-1948. *Vacumatic* fitting block. The tool used by Parker repairmen to service the *Vacumatic* pen. $200-250.

PARKER, 1933-1936. *Vacumatic* standard pen and pencil sets in burgundy pearl, and silver pearl laminated plastic. Standard size pens were available in the same colors as the Oversize pens. Left, $125-200; right, $125-175.

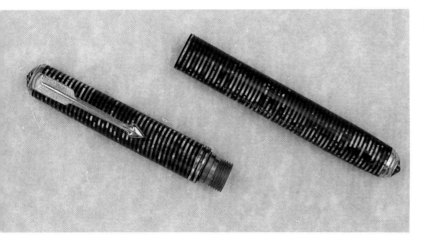

PARKER, ca. 1935. *Vacumatic* thermometer case.

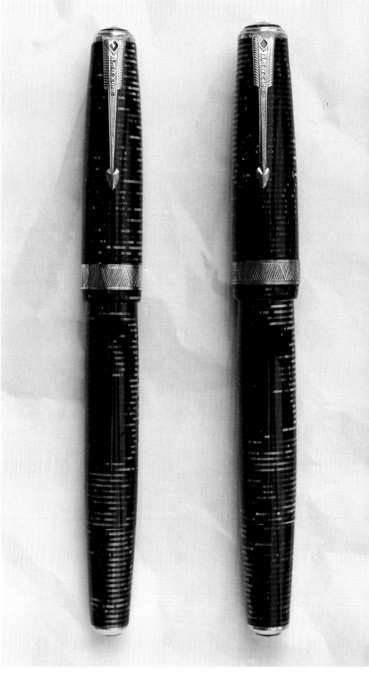

PARKER, 1939-1943. *Vacumatic* slender Maxima in emerald pearl laminate, compared with a silver gray pearl laminated Maxima pen. $250-375.

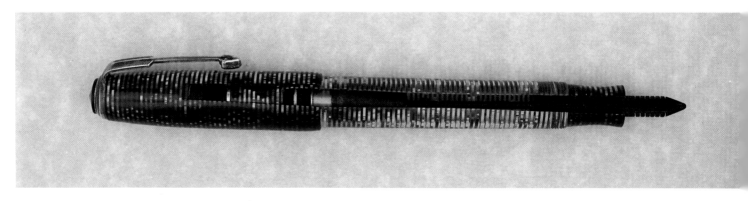

PARKER, ca. 1934. *Vacumatic,* cut-out demonstrator pen. $200-250.

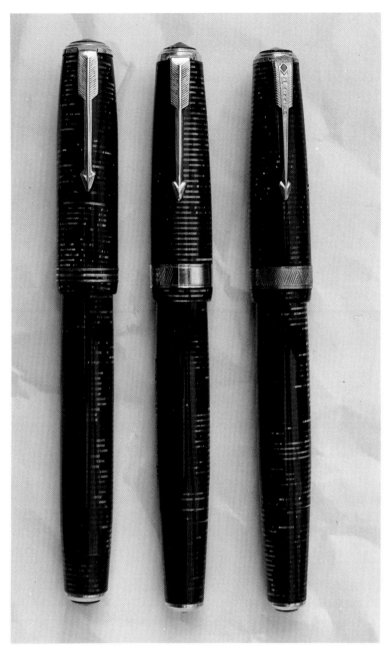

PARKER. Left to right: 1934-1936, *Vacumatic* Oversize pen; 1937-1938, Senior Maxima *Vacumatic* pen, 1939-1943 *Vacumatic* Maxima pen.

PARKER, 1939-1943. *Vacumatic* Maxima pens in golden pearl, emerald pearl, azure blue pearl laminated plastic. Not shown, silver gray pearl laminated, and jet plastic. $275-450.

PARKER, 1937. *Vacumatic* Senior Maxima "Speedline" pens with "Parker Vacumatic" inscribed on the cap bands. $400-550.

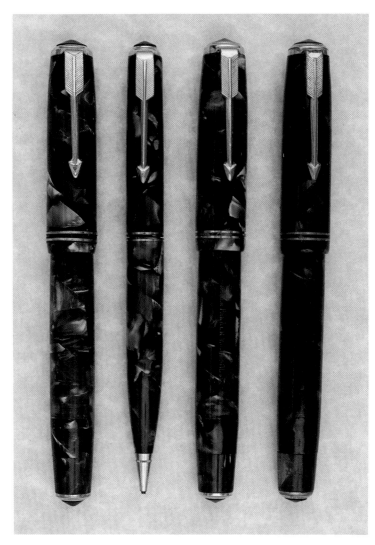

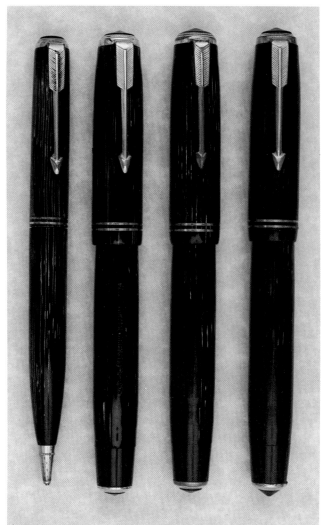

PARKER, 1934-1937. *Vacumatic* Junior pens and pencil in burgundy marble, emerald marble, and gray marble plastic. $75-150.

PARKER, 1937-1938. *Vacumatic* Junior pens and pencil in burgundy, gold, and green shadow wave pattern plastic. Also available in gray and black plastic. $100-175.

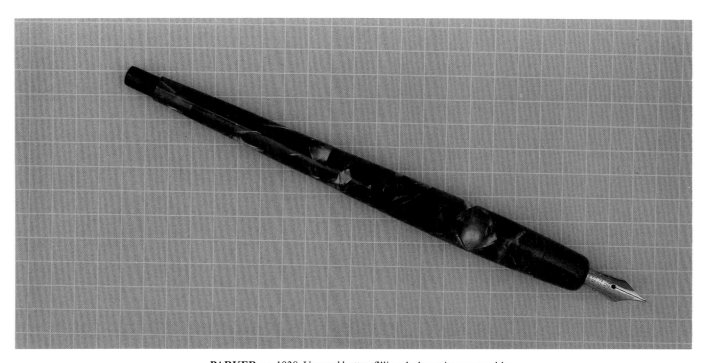

PARKER, ca. 1938. Unusual button filling desk pen in gray marble plastic with Parker *Duofold* nib. The small button at the end of the taper is attached to a rod running the length of the taper. When pressed, it pushes in the button filling mechanism in the pen barrel. $100-150.

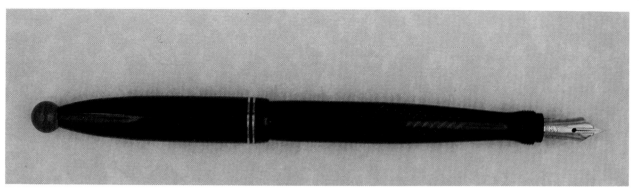

PARKER, ca. 1942. *Vacumatic* pen in black plastic, with red telephone dialer on the end of the cap. $100-150.

PARKER, ca. 1943. *Vacumatic* "loaner" pen. $75-125.

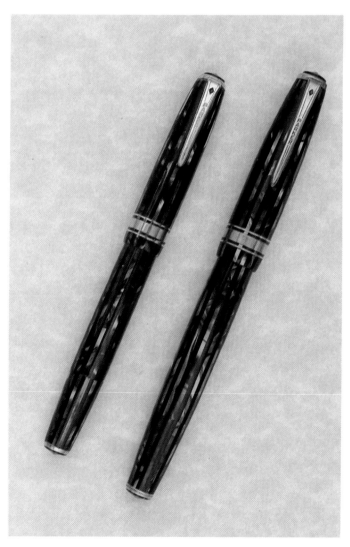

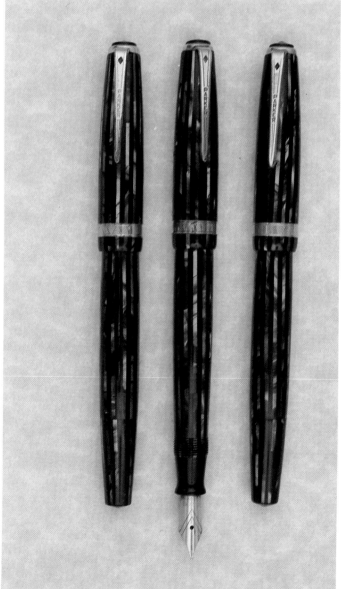

PARKER, 1940-1945. *Duofold,* vacumatic filling pens. During World War II, Parker re-introduced the *Duofold* name on a moderately priced line of pens and pencils, featuring either vacumatic filling, or button filling models. The pens were offered in blue, green, and red vertically striped laminated plastics. Above left; $65-95, above right; $100-150, right; $100-150.

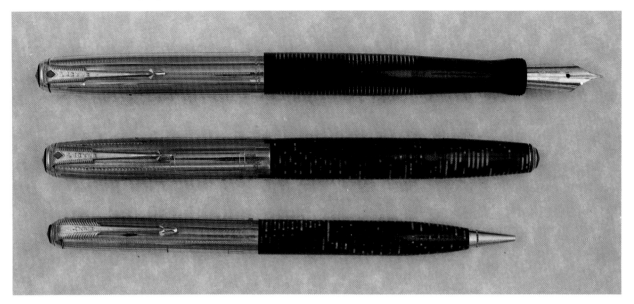

PARKER, 1940-1941. *Imperial Vacumatic* pens and pencil with gold filled caps. A transitional model, leading to the introduction of the *51*, this pen was marketed to compete with the "Crest" model sold by Sheaffer. It was available in both standard and Debutante (lady's) size, and in golden pearl laminate and black plastic. Models were also advertised in all gold filled and solid 14k gold. $400-500.

PARKER, ca. 1943. Top to bottom: Debutante *Vacumatic* pen; standard *Vacumatic* pen; *Vacumatic* Major pen. Top to bottom: $35-50; $50-75; $65-95.

PARKER, 1941-1948. *Vacumatic* standard pens in golden pearl, and silver gray pearl laminated plastic. $65-95.

PARKER *51*, 1941. Vacumatic filling pen with plain steel cap, gold filled band and aluminum end jewels. This is the first model of what is probably the world's most recognizable pen. In it's own way it created as great a revolution in the pen industry as did the ballpoint pen four years later. Copied by all the other major pen manufacturers, it outlived and outsold them all. $125-175.

PARKER *51*, 1941-1948. Top to bottom: mustard barrel, silver cap; cordovan brown barrel, lustraloy cap; black barrel, silver cap; dove gray barrel, silver cap; blue barrel, lustraloy cap. Top to bottom: $100-150; $50-75; $75-125; $75-125; $50-75.

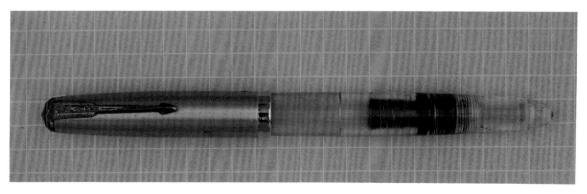

PARKER *51*, 1942-1948. Clear lucite demonstrator pen. $175-275.

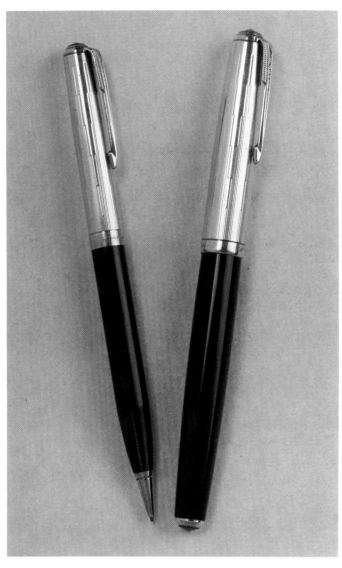

PARKER *51*, ca. 1944. Vacumatic filling pen and pencil set with 14k pink and yellow gold caps in the unusual "icicle" or "Empire State" pattern. $1000-1500.

PARKER *51*, 1942-1945. Vacumatic filling pen in mustard color plastic barrel with plain sterling silver cap. $100-150.

PARKER *51*, 1941-1948. 51 cap varieties, Left to Right: stainless steel with gold filled band; plain gold filled; gold filled "Custom" design; gold filled "Insignia" design; sterling silver "Insignia" design; sterling silver plain design; 14k gold "Heirloom" design.

PARKER, ca. 1943 *51* advertisement.

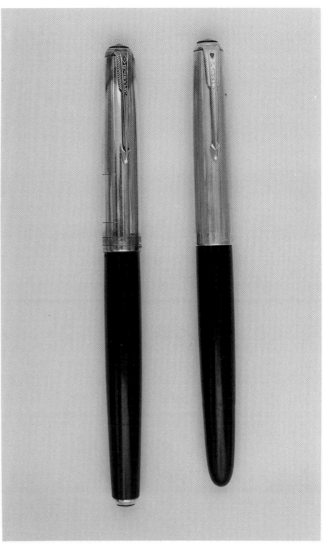

PARKER *51*, 1942-1948. Parker 51s were offered with or without barrel jewels up to 1947. This illustration shows identical pens with, and without the jewels.

PARKER *51*, 1942-1948. 51 cap varieties, Left to Right: 14k gold pink and yellow gold "icicle" design,; 14k gold scallop design; sterling silver plain design; gold filled "Custom" design; sterling silver hammered design; lustraloy metal with gold filled clip.

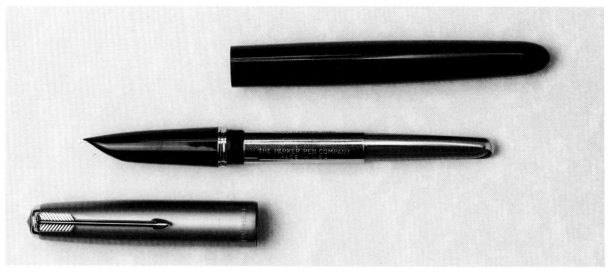

PARKER *51*, 1948-1978. Aerometric filling pen with lustraloy cap. In 1948 the famous arrow clip was modified and the Blue Diamond removed. The following year the new style aerometric filling 51s were introduced. New colors were available and with some modifications through the years, including a cartridge filling model, it was sold well into the 1970s.

PARKER *VS*, 1947-1949. Button filling, plastic barrel, lustraloy cap pen. This exposed nib pen, with clear lucite feed was produced as a moderately priced alternative to the *51*. It was also available with gray or rust colored barrel. $65-85.

PARKER *41*, 1950-1951. Aerometric filling pens with chrome caps. These pens were intended to be a mid-priced line positioned between the *51* and *21*. They were short lived and were soon replaced by the Super *21* series of pens. $65-85.

PARKER *51*, 1949-1960. Gold filled "Signet" model, aerometric filling pen and pencil set. $150-250.

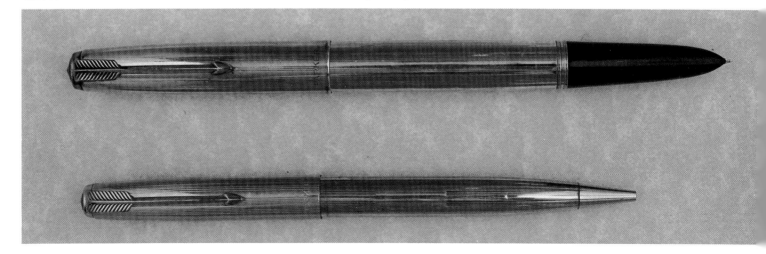

PARKER *41*, 1950-1951. The 41 was made in many colors. This illustrates the colors available.

PARKER, ca. 1948. Lucky 51 token. $25-50.

PARKER *51*, 1959-1962. "Flighter" model pen and pencil set in brushed stainless steel. $150-250.

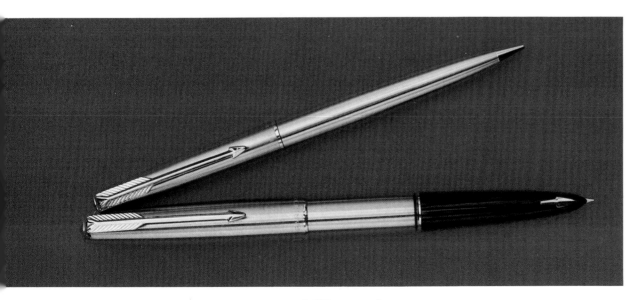

PARKER *51*, 1950-1960. "Flighter" model, aerometric filling, pen and pencil set in brushed stainless steel, with gold filled trim. Beginning with this pen, Parker produced a "Flighter" version of their successive models. $150-250.

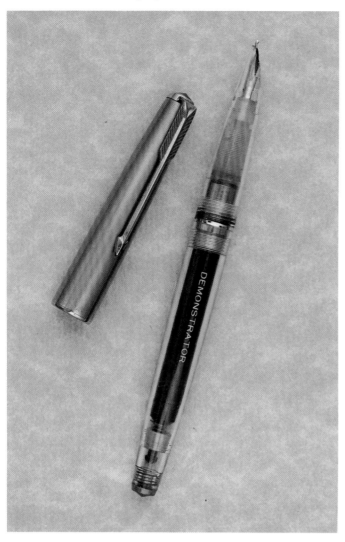

PARKER, *61*, 1957-1962. Capillary attraction filling demonstrator pen. $175-250.

PARKER *61*, 1956. First Edition model, capillary attraction filling pen with gold filled cap, and First Edition crest. The 61 was available with black, red, gray, or turquoise plastic barrels. Also available in stainless steel, gold filled, and 14k gold, and with a variety of caps, the most attractive of which are the two tone rainbow caps in sterling silver or gold filled metal. $100-150.

PARKER *21*, 1948-1965. Aeromatic filling pens, including demonstrator model. The *21* was Parker's low priced line of pens. $35-60.

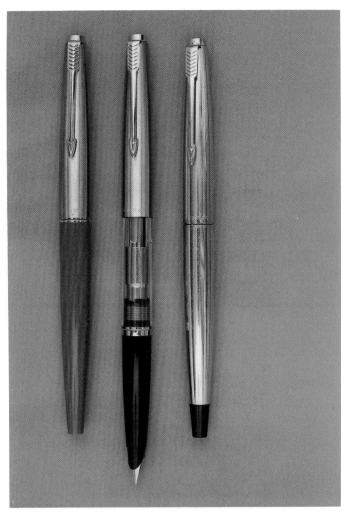

PARKER, 1954. Jotter ballpoint pen, with nylon plastic barrel. This was Parker's first entry into the ballpoint market. This well designed first model will accept the ballpoint cartridge used today by Parker. $40-70.

PARKER *45*, 1960-1980. Aerometric, or cartridge filling pens. The *45* featured a removable octanium, or 14k gold nib, and was available in many versions including a series in colored anodized aluminum.

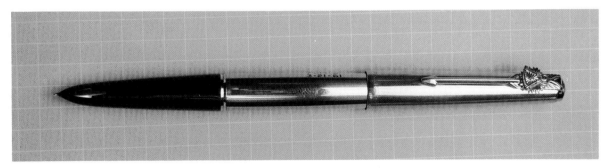

PARKER *61*, 1957-1962. 1959-1962. "Signet" model, capillary attraction filling, gold filled pen with Masonic Blue Lodge emblem on the clip. $100-150.

PARKER *61*, 1957-1962. Capillary attraction filling pen with gold filled cap. $75-100.

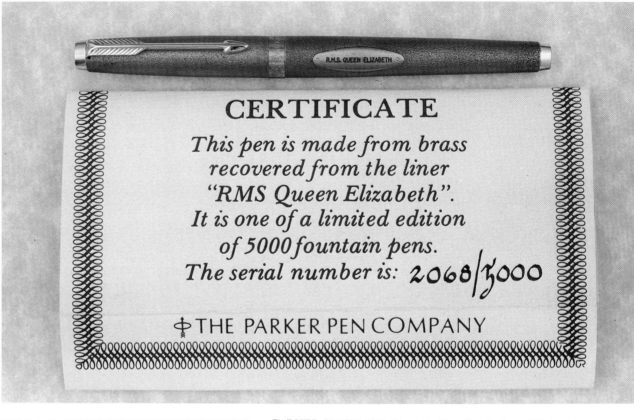

PARKER *75,* 1977-1978. Limited edition "RMS Queen Elizabeth" pen made from brass of the famous ship. $750-1000.

PARKER. "Flighter" *45* on the left, 1965-1980; and "Flighter" *75* on the right, 1970-1979. Left to right: $40-60; $75-125.

PARKER, 1963. Parker advertisement.

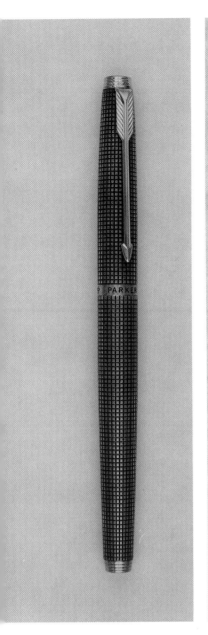

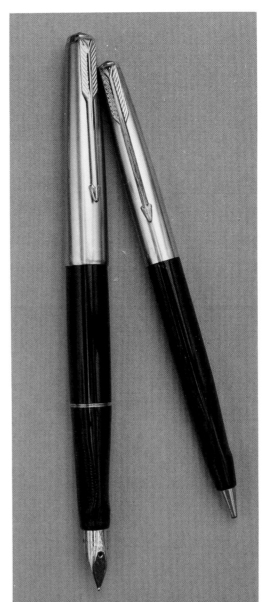

PARKER *75*, 1964-1980. Sterling silver checked design, aerometric, or cartridge filling pen. Available in a variety of metals over the years including vermeil, gold filled, and 14k gold, and as a series of limited edition pens. $100-150.

PARKER *75*, 1965. Limited edition "Spanish Treasure" pen. Made from silver recovered from a Spanish galleon, "Spanish Treasure Fleet 1715" is engraved on the cap band, the barrel tassie is impressed with the seal of Philip V of Spain, and the mint mark of Mexico City in the cap. $850-1250.

PARKER *VP*, 1962-1964. Pen and pencil set with brushed steel caps. The *VP*, or *Very Personal* pen, introduced the adjustable and removable nib of the more popular *75* series. The very unusual filling system of this pen consisted of an aerometric filling unit attached to a narrow glass neck. To fill the pen, the entire unit was removed from the pen, and the neck held in the ink while squeezing the pressure bar. Unfortunately, this made the filling unit prone to breakage, and working pens are hard to find. The pens were available with gray, blue, or rust plastic barrels, and with gold filled caps. $100-175.

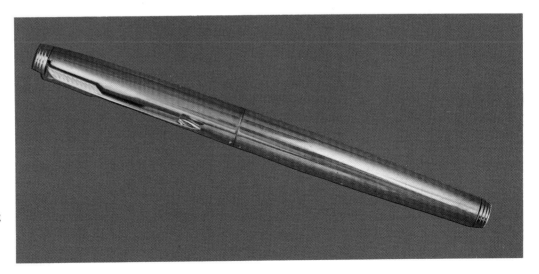

PARKER *75*, ca. 1964. Sterling silver, aerometric or cartridge filling pen. This example is unusual in that there is no design in the silver. $450-600.

PARKER *105,* 1981. Limited edition pen commemorating the marriage of the Prince of Wales. Aerometric, or cartridge filling, gold plated pen. $850-1250.

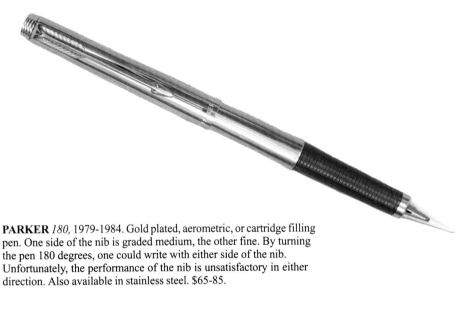

PARKER *180,* 1979-1984. Gold plated, aerometric, or cartridge filling pen. One side of the nib is graded medium, the other fine. By turning the pen 180 degrees, one could write with either side of the nib. Unfortunately, the performance of the nib is unsatisfactory in either direction. Also available in stainless steel. $65-85.

PARKER *75,* 1976. Limited edition "Bicentennial" pen in pewter with a small piece of wood from Independence Hall in the cap tassie. $400-650.

PARKER *75,* 1977-1983. Vermeil pen made in France. $200-300.

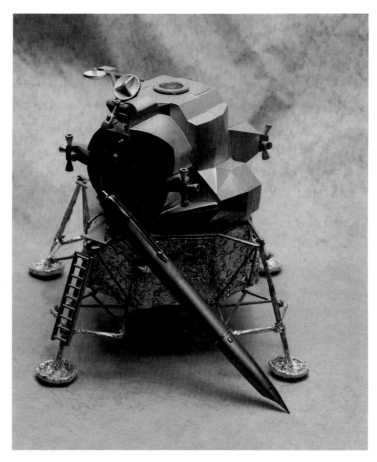

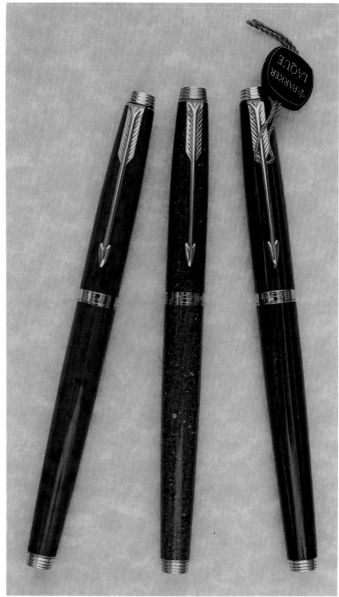

PARKER *T-1,* 1970-1971. Integral nib, aerometric or cartridge filling pen made entirely of titanium with gold filled trim. It was created in honor of our landing a man on the moon. Titanium was used in the lunar lander, and the rocket that took it to the moon. It was expensive and extremely difficult to work with. The pen was produced for only one year, was too expensive to make, and did not sell well. Parker lost money on every pen made. $400-600.

PARKER *75,* 1970-1980. "Ambassador" model, lined sterling silver pen with chrome trim. $175-250.

PARKER *75,* 1977-1983. Lacquer pens made in France. $175-250.

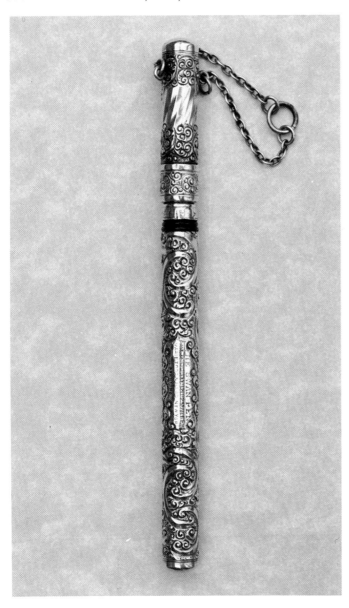

MABIE, TODD, & BARD, ca. 1900-1905. Swan sterling silver chased design, chatelaine eyedropper filling pen with bayonet cap. $1000-1500.

MABIE, TODD, & BARD, ca. 1900-1908. Swan sterling silver chased and floral hammered design overlay, eyedropper filled pen. The design on this pen is essentially the same as the L.E. Waterman "Puritan" design. $3000-5000.

MABIE, TODD, & BARD, ca. 1900-1908. Swan sterling silver fancy chased design overlay, eyedropper filled pen with bayonet cap. $1000-1500.

Chapter 5

The Swan Pen: Mabie, Todd, & Co.

1843-1939

The Mabie Todd Company was the successor to the Mabie, Todd & Bard Company which was the offspring of the Bard Bros. Bard was started in 1843, in New York City, making gold pen points and pen point holders. The company, with new management, was reformed as the Mabie, Todd & Bard Company in 1873. By 1880, they were producing stylographic pens at 17 Maiden Lane, under their own name and were producing pen points for other pen companies. About 1884, they opened an office in England. About 1908, the name "Bard" was removed from the company name, although many of the pens still carried that name. Mabie Todd made very high quality eyedropper pens.

Mabie Todd's *Swan* is often thought of as an English-made pen, as their advertising called the *Swan* "the pen of the British Empire". Most of their pens made before 1920, however, were manufactured in New York. Mr. Mabie sold his interest in the company to an Englishman named Watts in 1908. The ownership remained mostly American until 1919, when it was sold to a group in Great Britain.

The top of the Mabie Todd line was the *Swan* pen and in the late teens, the matching pencil was called the *Fyne Poynt* pencil. The sterling silver pencils made by Mabie Todd were of incredibly high quality and exhibited a sturdiness that only came from the use of a heavier silver rather than thinner silver over a brass liner. The company's silver and gold work around the turn of the century was comparable to the metal work of Tiffany. The Mabie Todd hallmark, often found as a small "M" on top of a "T" with the "CO" under the eaves of the "T", is a mark of quality.

The pens of Mabie Todd made with gold and silver overlays, were as much a form of men's jewelry as they were writing instruments. The earliest model fountain pens had unusual features built into the feed. The feed in some models had a twisted silver wire extending into the pen while other models had a sliding device built into the feed that could be used to adjust the ink flow. Another feature on the early models was a hard rubber blade on the rear of the feed that scraped the inside of the pen barrel as the section was screwed on. On some *Swan* pens there is a gold needle-like piece on top of the nib. This was *Swan's* "Gold Top Feed" (in addition to the bottom feed) which was supposed to guarantee ink flow to the nib, regardless of writing pressure. This feature first appears on some 1880s pens and continued, on some models, into the early 1920s.

Another interesting Swan feature appeared on a pen made about 1913. It had clear portholes in the side of the barrel so that the ink level could be seen. Lever filler models were made about 1918, but just before the introduction of the lever filler, they made an ink pellet model in which the rear end of the pen unscrewed and an ink pellet was inserted. The pen was then filled with water and wrote with ink. It was designed for the traveler. Swan's contribution to the "lifetime" models was the *Eternal* which was introduced about 1924. It was made in hard rubber and several years later, plastic models were available in a wide array of colors. A slightly less expensive pen in the Mabie Todd line was the *Swallow* pen and one step down from that was the *Blackbird* pen.

The United States division of Mabie Todd Co. ceased production about 1938. English-made *Swan* pens were manufactured into the 1950s. The company was sold to Biro Pen Mfg. Company in the 1940s and later sold to Bic (French) in 1957. The name of the company became Biro-Bic Ltd. Mabie Todd was never connected with the Edward Todd Pen Company.

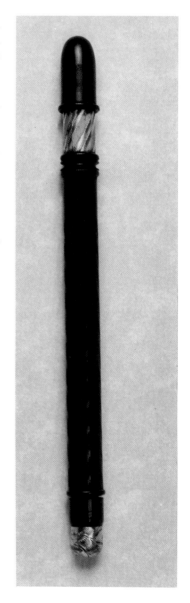

MABIE, TODD, & BARD, ca. 1890-1895. Black chased hard rubber stylographic pen. $100-150.

A mystery remains as to the connection of Mabie Todd to the Hutcheon Brothers, another pen and pencil maker active in New York City from just before the turn of the century to the early 1920s. A comparison of the pens of both makers show incredible similarities such as the same "ladder" feed, the same pocket clip (patented January 19, 1915) and the same turned area on the collar (on pre-1919 models). A "magazine pencil" (patented June 7, 1910) was made by both Hutcheon Bros. and Mabie Todd. A side by side comparison of the sterling silver models shows almost no difference. They share the same high quality. Also Hutcheon's thin lead pencil was called the *Fine Pointe* pencil.

MABIE, TODD, & BARD, 1878 advertising calendar. $100-175.

MABIE, TODD, & BARD, ca. 1895-1905. Sterling silver pen holder, with black hard rubber pen. $250-350.

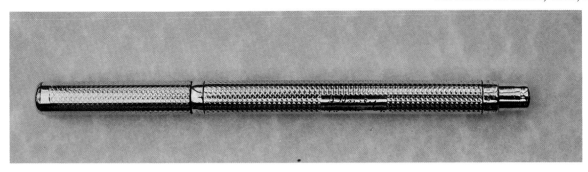

MABIE, TODD, & BARD, ca. 1900-1908. Swan gold filled barleycorn design overlay, eyedropper filled pen. $400-650.

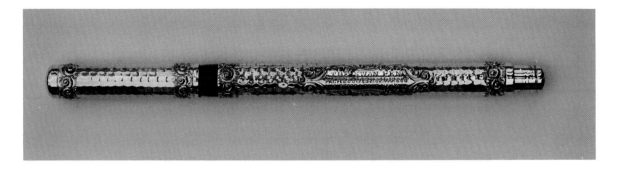

MABIE, TODD, & BARD, ca. 1900-1908. Swan gold filled hand hammered design overlay, eyedropper filled pen. $500-750.

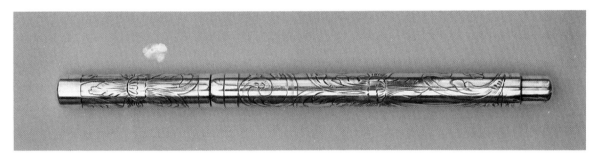

MABIE, TODD, & BARD, ca. 1900-1908. Swan sterling silver etched floral design overlay, eyedropper filled pen. $3000-4000.

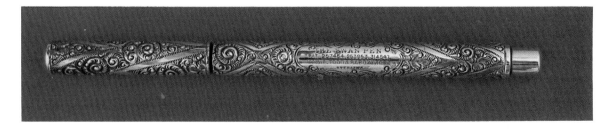

MABIE, TODD, & BARD, ca. 1900-1908. Swan sterling silver "V" design overlay, eyedropper filled pen. $1000-1500.

MABIE, TODD, & BARD, ca. 1900-1908. Swan gold filled cable chased design overlay, eyedropper filled pen. $750-1000.

MABIE, TODD, & BARD, ca. 1900-1908. Swan gold filled floral chased design overlay, eyedropper filled pen. The clip on this pen is a later addition. $750-1000.

MABIE, TODD, & BARD, ca. 1900-1908. Swan gold filled chased design overlay, eyedropper filled pen. $650-850.

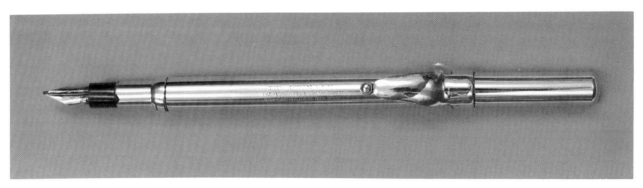

MABIE, TODD, & BARD, ca. 1900-1908. Swan gold overlay, eyedropper filled pen with spade clip. $450-650.

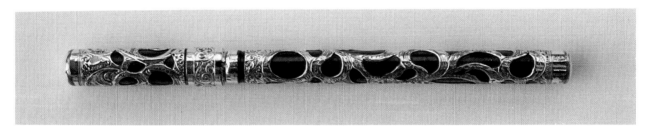

MABIE, TODD, & BARD, ca. 1905-1908. Swan gold filled filigree design overlay, eyedropper filled pen with bayonet cap. $450-650.

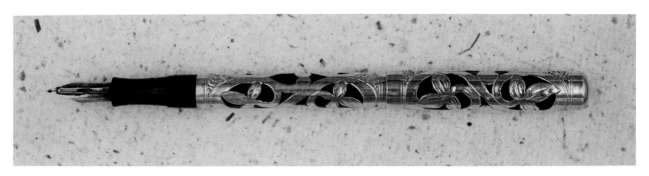

MABIE, TODD, ca. 1912-1918. Swan gold filled filigree design overlay, "Safety Sealed" eyedropper filled, over under-feed pen. $400-600.

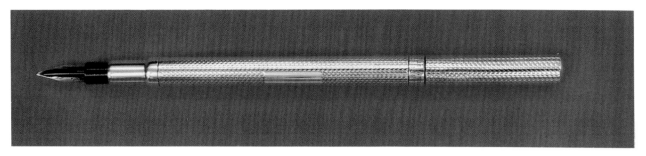

MABIE, TODD, & BARD, ca. 1900-1908. Swan sterling silver barleycorn design overlay, eyedropper filled pen. $350-500.

MABIE, TODD, & BARD, ca. 1905-1908. Swan black hard rubber eyedropper filled pen with spade clip. $75-150.

MABIE, TODD, ca. 1910-1915. Sterling silver etched design "Magazine" pencil. The design on this pencil depicts silkworm at work. $300-375.

MABIE, TODD, ca. 1908-1912. Swan #3603 black hard rubber eyedropper filled pen. $50-75.

MABIE, TODD, ca. 1908-1912. Swan gold filled chased twist design overlay, eyedropper filled pen. $750-950.

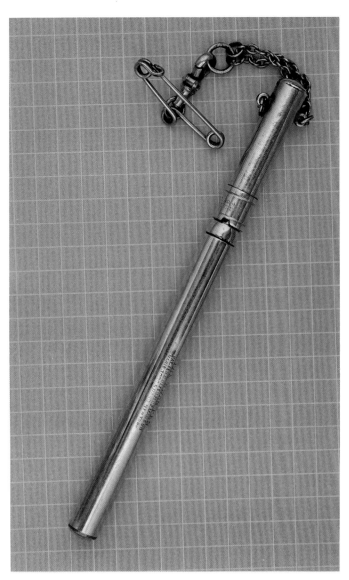

MABIE, TODD, & BARD, ca. 1900-1908. Swan gold filled overlay, bayonet cap eyedropper filled pen. $300-400.

MABIE, TODD, ca. 1908-1912. Swan black chased hard rubber chatelaine eyedropper filled pen with bayonet cap. $100-150.

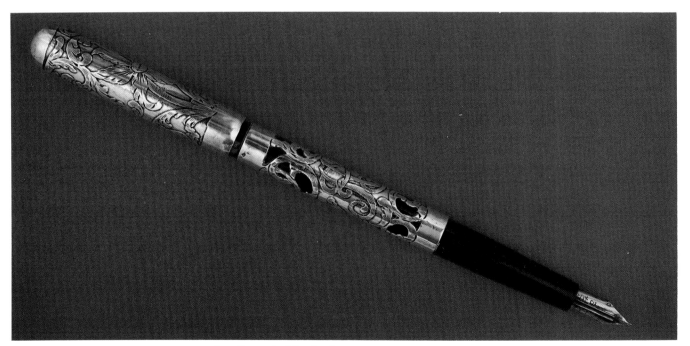

MABIE, TODD, ca. 1912-1918. Swan sterling silver etched floral and filigree design overlay red & black mottled hard rubber eyedropper filled pen. $1500-2500.

MABIE, TODD, & BARD, ca. 1900-1908. Swan sterling silver hand engraved design overlay, eyedropper filled pen. $750-1000.

MABIE, TODD, ca. 1910. Advertising reverse glass sign. $600-850.

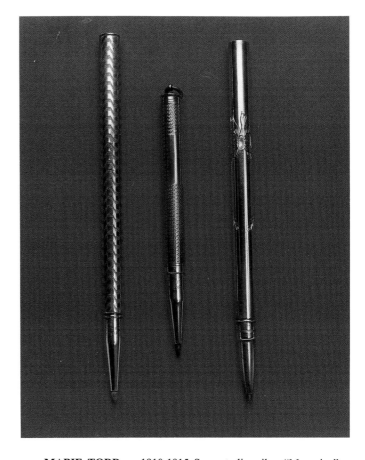

MABIE, TODD, ca. 1910-1915. Swan sterling silver "Magazine" pencils. $50-100.

MABIE, TODD, ca. 1910-1915. Swan gold filled filigree design overlay, eyedropper filled pens. Top to bottom: $300-450; $350-500.

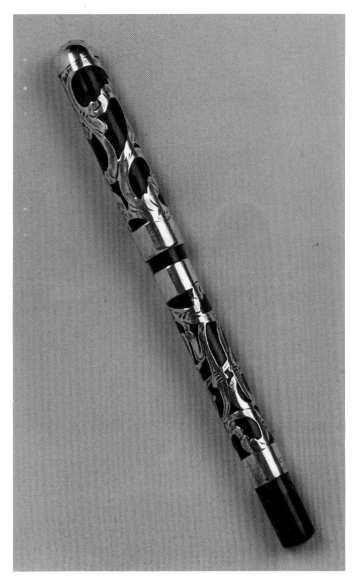

MABIE, TODD, ca. 1912-1918. Swan sterling silver filigree design overlay, red & black hard rubber eyedropper filled pen. $1400-1800.

MABIE, TODD, ca. 1919-1923. Swan #5 black chased hard rubber, lever filling pen. $70-90.

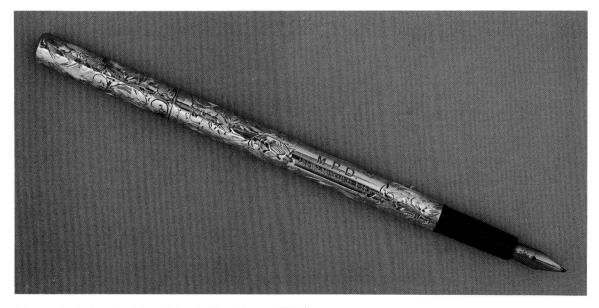

MABIE, TODD, ca. 1914. Swan 14k gold "Hand Engraved" design overlay, eyedropper filled pen. $2500-3000.

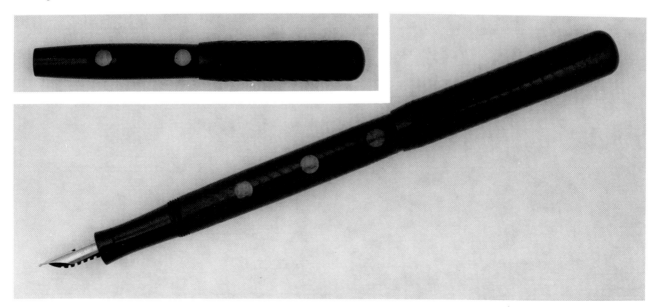

MABIE, TODD, ca. 1916-1923. Swan black chased hard rubber, "Safety Sealed" eyedropper filled vest pocket pen. $50-75.

MABIE, TODD, ca. 1915-1923. Swan black chased hard rubber, "Safety Sealed", eyedropper filled pen. $40-60.

MABIE, TODD, ca. 1908-1915. Anodized metal pen pocket, with black hard rubber pen. $35-50.

MABIE, TODD, ca. 1912-1914. Swan black hard rubber "Posting" pens with ink viewing portholes. The small transparent windows in the pen barrel allowed the writer to see how much ink was left in the pen. $75-125.

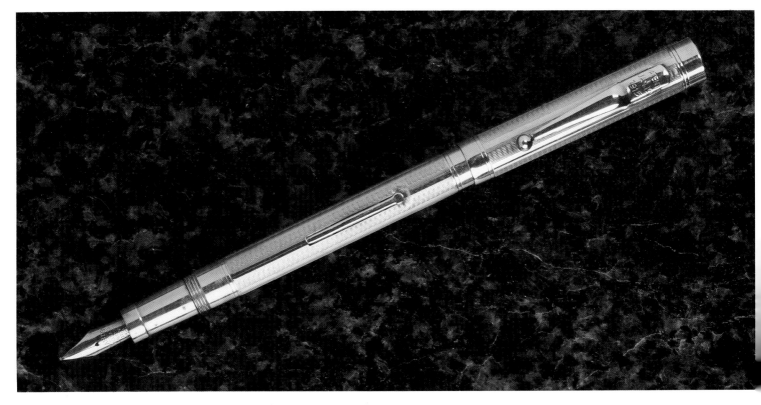

MABIE, TODD, ca. 1920-1929. Swan sterling silver overlay, lever filling pen. $250-400.

MABIE, TODD, ca. 1917-1919. Swan sterling silver etched design half overlay, black chased hard rubber eyedropper filled pen. $350-600.

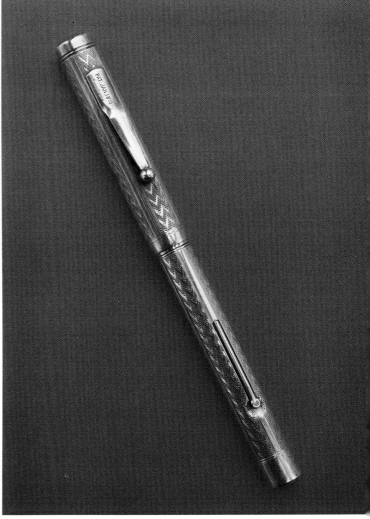

MABIE, TODD, ca. 1920-1929. Swan sterling silver "wave" design overlay, lever filling pen. $250-400.

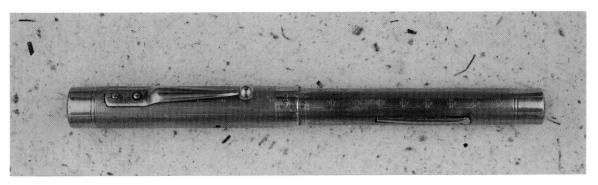

MABIE, TODD, ca. 1920-1929. Swan "Rosette" pattern 9k gold overlay, lever filling pen. $500-650.

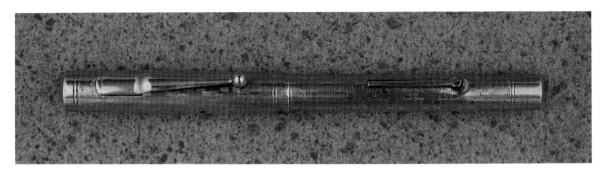

MABIE, TODD, ca. 1920-1929. Swan 14k gold "Block Engine Turned" design overlay, lever filling pen. $500-650.

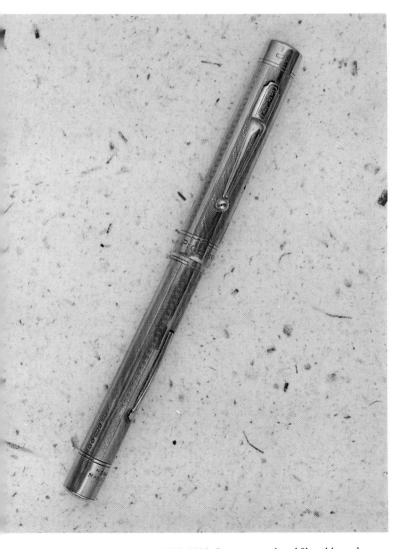

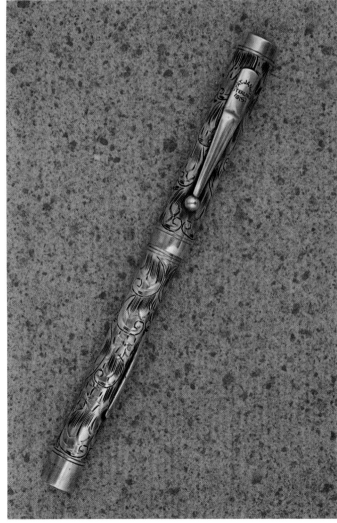

MABIE, TODD, ca. 1920-1929. Swan rose colored 9k gold overlay, lever filling pen. $500-650.

MABIE, TODD, ca. 1920-1929. Swan sterling silver "Hand Engraved" design overlay, lever filling pen. $475-550.

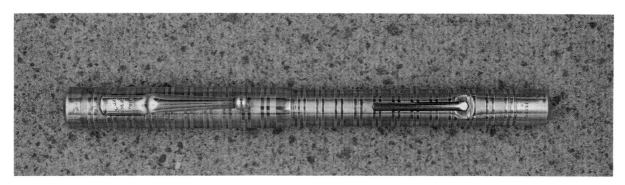

MABIE, TODD, ca. 1920-1929. Swan 14k gold "Ring" design overlay, lever filling pen. $500-650.

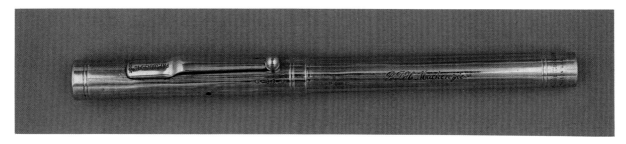

MABIE, TODD, ca. 1920-1925. Swan 15k gold lined design overlay, eyedropper filled pen. $400-500.

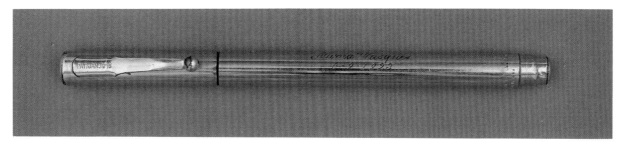

MABIE, TODD, ca. 1920-1925. Swan gold filled plain design overlay, eyedropper filled pen. $125-175.

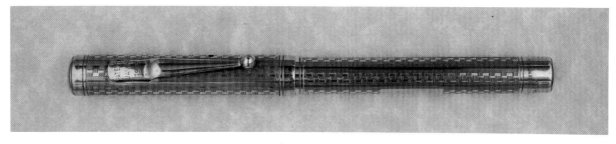

MABIE, TODD, ca. 1920-1929. Swan gold filled "link Engine Turned" design overlay, lever filling pen. $150-250.

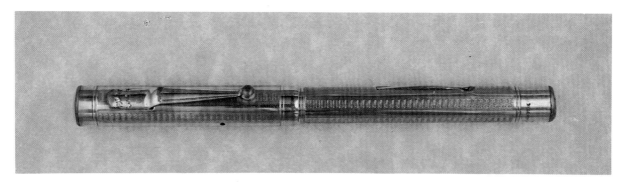

MABIE, TODD, ca. 1920-1929. Swan gold filled overlay, lever filling pen. $150-250.

 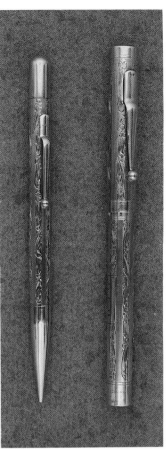 

MABIE, TODD, ca. 1920-1929. Swan gold filled, and black hard rubber, lever filling lady's pens. $50-75.

MABIE, TODD, ca. 1920-1929. Swan 14k gold "Lined & Engraved" overlay, design lever filling pen and pencil set. $600-750.

MABIE, TODD, ca. 1920-1929. Swan 14k gold "Hand Engraved" design overlay, lever filling pen and pencil set. $600-750.

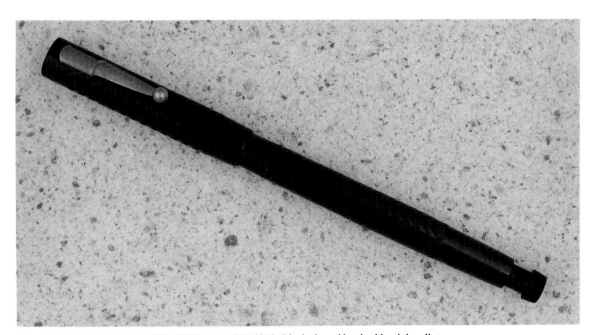

MABIE, TODD, ca. 1917-1919. Black chased hard rubber ink pellet filled pen. The knob at the bottom of the barrel unscrews to reveal a compartment for the ink pellet. The section of the pen is then opened and filled with water to make ink. Ink pellet pens were popular during World War I, and many companies made ink pellets so soldiers would not have to carry bottles of ink for their pens. $175-250.

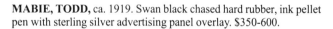

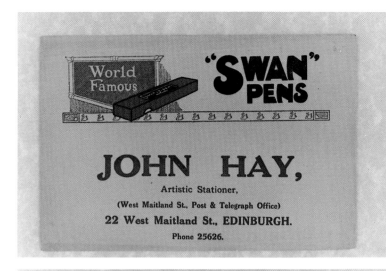

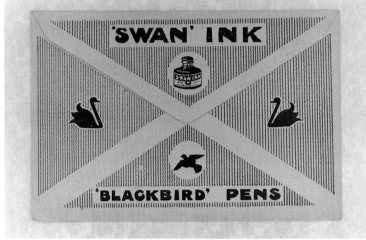

SWAN, ca. 1918 Advertising envelope.

MABIE, TODD, ca. 1919. Swan black chased hard rubber, ink pellet
pen with sterling silver advertising panel overlay. $350-600.

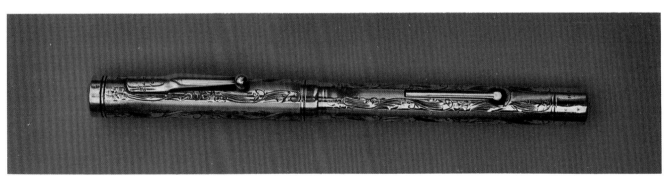

MABIE, TODD, ca. 1920-1928. Swan 14k gold, and sterling silver
"Lined & Engraved" design overlay, lever filling pens. Top to bottom:
$450-600; $450-600.

MABIE, TODD, ca. 1919-1923. Swan #5SF black chased hard rubber, lever filling pen with wide gold filled band. $100-150.

MABIE, TODD, ca. 1920-1926. Swan #142/34 black hard rubber eyedropper filled pen with gold filled bands. $100-150.

MABIE, TODD, ca. 1920-1926. Swan #144/31 black hard rubber eyedropper filled pen with gold filled bands. $100-150.

MABIE, TODD, ca. 1919-1923. Swan black chased hard rubber lever filling pen. $100-150.

MABIE, TODD, ca. 1919-1923. Swan black hard rubber lever filling lady's pen. $50-65.

MABIE, TODD, ca. 1922-1925. Swan #42 red & black mottled hard rubber lever filling pen. $75-100.

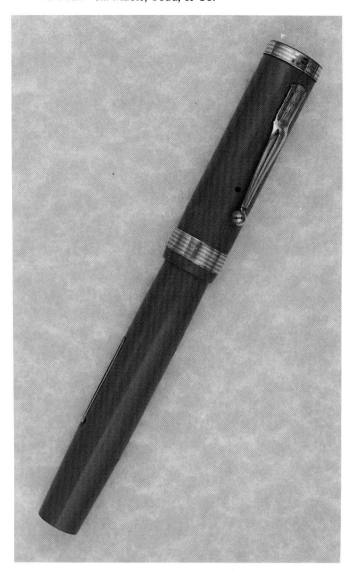

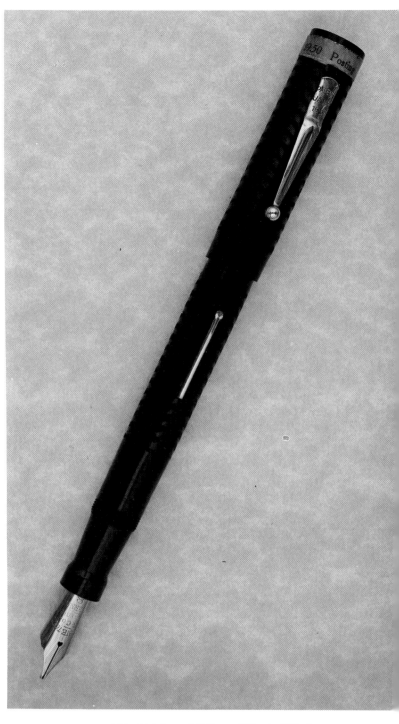

MABIE, TODD, ca. 1924-1929. Swan #48 ETN *Eternal* red hard rubber lever filling pen. $500-600.

MABIE, TODD, ca. 1924-1929. Swan #46 ETN *Eternal* red & black mottled hard rubber lever filling pen. $350-500.

MABIE, TODD, ca. 1923-1924. Swan #48 *Eternal* "Posting" black chased hard rubber lever filling pen. $400-500.

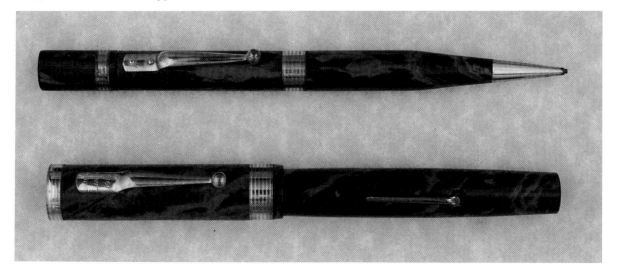

MABIE, TODD, ca. 1924-1929. Swan #46 ETN *Eternal* short model red & black mottled hard rubber lever filling pen. $200-300.

MABIE, TODD, ca. 1924-1929. Swan #44 ETN *Eternal* red hard rubber lever filling pen. $200-300.

MABIE, TODD, ca. 1927-1930. Swan salmon moire plastic lever filling lady's pen and pencil set. $75-125.

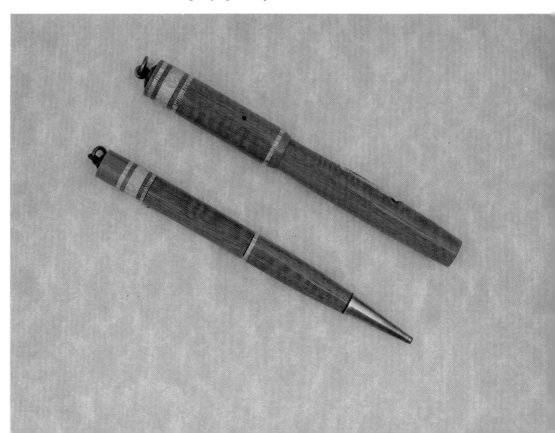

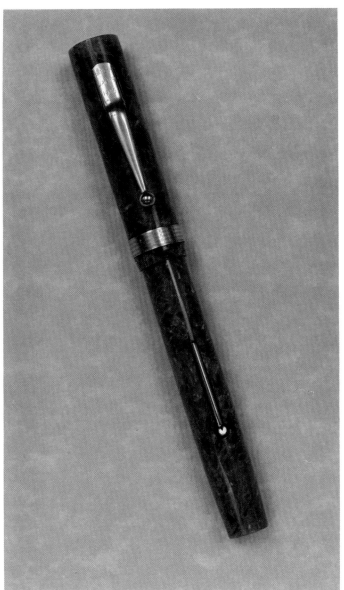

MABIE, TODD, ca. 1925-1932. Swan black hard rubber, lever filling pen with woodgrain hard rubber cap insert. $75-125.

MABIE, TODD, ca. 1927-1929. Swan #44 ETN *Eternal* green marble plastic lever filling pen. $100-150.

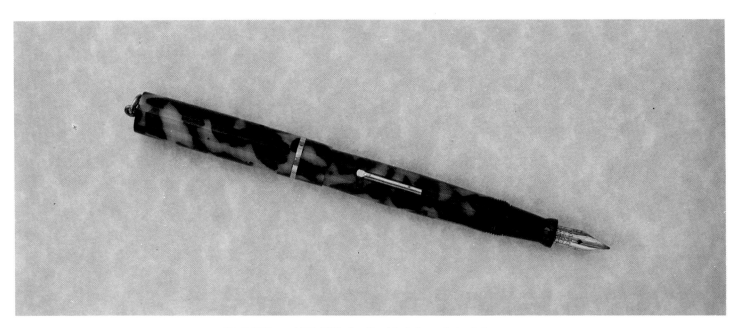

MABIE, TODD, ca. 1928-1930. *Swallow* black & pearl plastic lever filling lady's pen. $40-65.

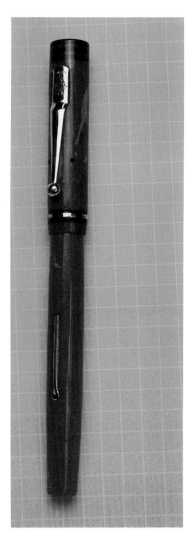
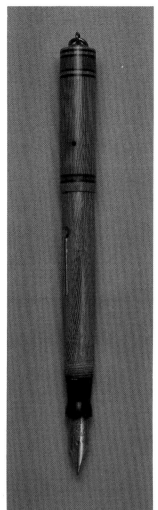

MABIE, TODD, ca. 1926-1930. Swan salmon marble plastic lever filling pen and pencil. $200-350.

MABIE, TODD, ca. 1926-1930. Swan mauve moire plastic lever filling lady's pen. $100-150.

MABIE, TODD, ca. 1926-1930. Swan red marble plastic lever filling pen. $65-95.

MABIE, TODD, ca. 1929-1932. Swan #54 ETN *Eternal* green marble plastic lever filling pen. $65-100.

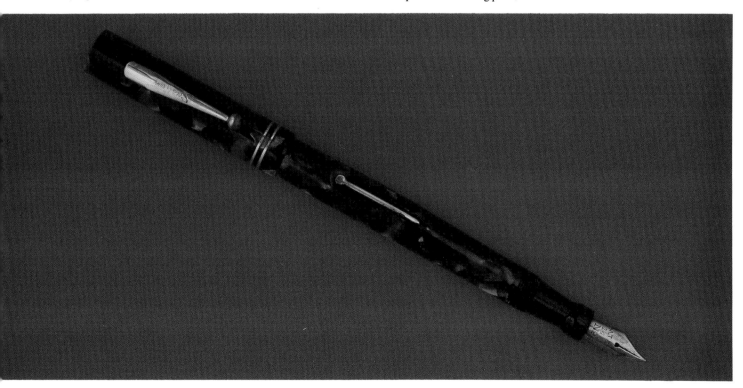

MABIE, TODD, ca. 1929-1932. *Swallow* gray pearl marble lever filling pen. $45-65.

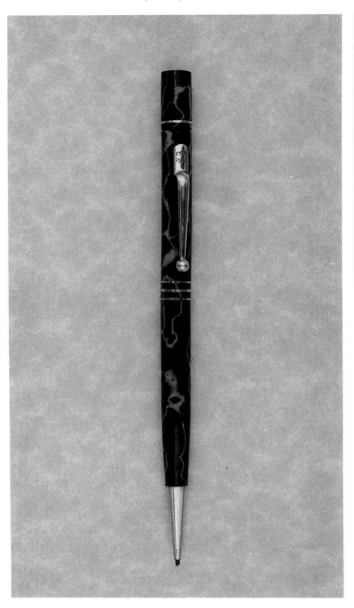

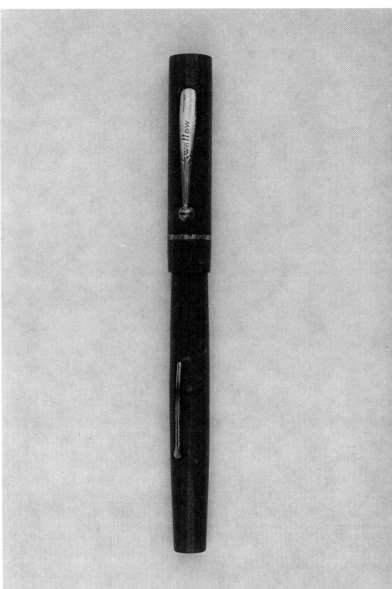

MABIE, TODD, ca. 1929-1932 Swan *Fyne Poynt* pencil in green and black marble plastic. $35-60.

MABIE, TODD, ca. 1929-1932. *Swallow* red marble plastic lever filling pen. $75-125.

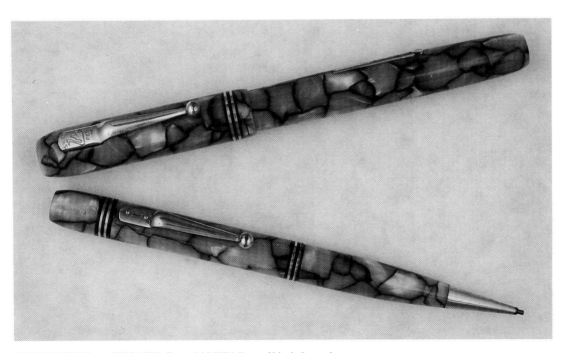

MABIE, TODD, ca. 1932-1935. Swan #44 ETN *Eternal* black & pearl plastic lever filling pen and pencil set. $100-150.

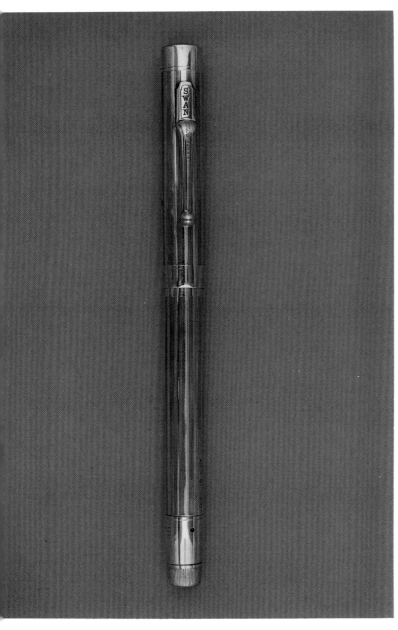

MABIE, TODD, ca. 1933-1936. Swan 9k gold lined design leverless twist filling pen. $300-500.

MABIE, TODD, ca. 1929-1932. Swan #46 ETN *Eternal* black & pearl plastic lever filling pen. $150-225.

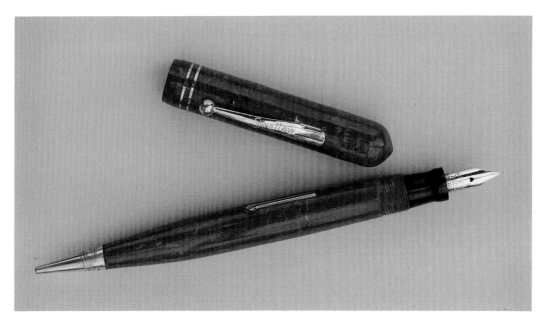

MABIE, TODD, ca. 1932-1936. *Swallow* red marble plastic lever filling pen/pencil combination. $250-300.

MABIE, TODD, ca. 1933-1938. Swan green marble plastic *Capacity* leverless twist filling pen. $40-65.

SWAN #2060, ca. 1947-1953. Leverless twist filling black plastic pen. $50-75.

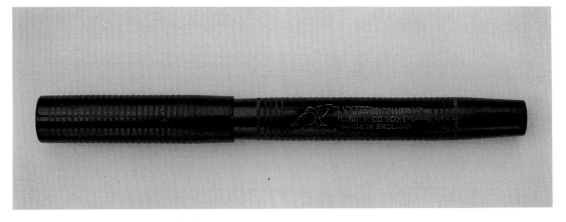

MABIE, TODD, ca. 1935-1940. *Blackbird* black hard rubber lever filling pen. The *Blackbird* and *Swallow* were Mabie, Todd's lower priced lines. $25-40.

Chapter 6

The Sheaffer Pen Company

1913-Present

Walter A. Sheaffer was born on July 27, 1867 in Bloomfield, Iowa. He was trained as a jeweler and later worked in his father's jewelry store. After gaining experience there, he opened his own jewelry store in Fort Madison, Iowa in 1906. The store sold and repaired fountain pens. Sheaffer designed the lever filling mechanism in 1907 and patented it in 1908. Several years passed while he sought partners and advice about starting his own fountain pen company. Things that he had to consider were that: 1) there were several large established fountain pen companies, Waterman, Parker, etc.; 2) Walter Sheaffer was over 40 years old, with a wife and children to support; and 3) he had an established, profitable jewelry business. Starting up a new fountain pen company on the theory that the public would prefer to buy a lever filling Sheaffer pen in place of a Waterman or Parker was hopeful thinking indeed.

Sheaffer took the risk and by 1912, started production. The Sheaffer Pen Company was incorporated in Fort Madison, Iowa, by Walter A. Sheaffer (51% owner), Ben Coulson & George Kraker (40% owners), and James Brewster, a banker (9% owner) on January 1, 1913. Coulson and Kraker were former Conklin Pen salesmen and were the first sales force of the company.

The lever filler was clean, simple and instantly popular. It startled the existing pen manufacturers since it became popular almost overnight. Several pen manufacturers stole the lever idea and called it their own, but Sheaffer fought to protect his patent rights and was rather successful. Other manufacturers redesigned the lever system and obtained patents that allowed them to produce versions of the lever filler pen.

Sheaffer Pen was not a one idea company. They were working constantly to be the largest pen manufacturer. Sheaffer created another first for the pen industry in 1920 when the *Lifetime* model was introduced. This pen was guaranteed for the life of the original owner and would be repaired or replaced, no matter what type of damage, for free. Stories are told of Sheaffer receiving a handful of *Lifetime* pen parts with a letter saying "My dog chewed it to pieces, can you fix it?" or "...a wagon ran over it". Sheaffer promptly sent a replacement at no cost.

As an aside, you may have noticed that many "lifetime guaranteed" pens, from whatever maker, have the owner's name stamped on the side of the pen. Since the policy was to replace or repair the pen for free, merchants often had to take a pen out of stock to replace a badly broken pen. This gave them one less pen to sell until they received a replacement from the manufacturer. Someone came up with the idea to "personalize" each pen by stamping the name of the owner on the side of the pen at no additional cost. Merchants embraced this idea since, when the person returned a broken pen, the merchant would then mail it to the manufacturer for repair rather than replace it from their selling stock.

Identification of the *Lifetime* models was originally made by the *Lifetime* size, a larger pen with a #8 nib. Needing a more obvious way of identifying their *Lifetime* models, Sheaffer, in 1921, began to make pens with the "Lifetime" nib and thereafter, in 1923, by the "Lifetime" white dot somewhere on the pen. The large men's *Lifetime* sold for $8.75, a new high price for writing instruments at that time. A Sheaffer *Lifetime* in one's pocket became a status symbol, very much like the large, present-day Montblanc pen. The advertisements of the day showed bankers and important businessmen using Sheaffers.

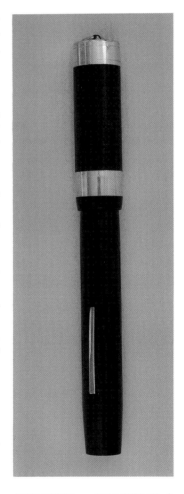

SHEAFFER, ca. 1914-1922. Black hard rubber, lever filling lady's pen, with two gold filled bands. $40-80.

SHEAFFER, ca. 1917-1924.
Sterling silver overlay, lever filling
pen. $300-400.

In 1924, Sheaffer again stunned the pen market with the introduction of the first plastic (called "Radite") pen in a stunning jade green color. A 1927 advertisement noted, "Always it is an infallible writing instrument, made of brilliant, staunch Radite, capable of making three clear carbon copies. An aristocratic pocket decoration!". Other companies did not introduce a plastic pen until the second half of 1926 or later. These large green *Lifetime* pens competed admirably with the Parker "Big Red" and the Waterman *Ripple.*

Sheaffer streamlined its pen line in 1930, calling the new streamlined version the *Balance* pen. The price of its *Lifetime* pen was raised to $9.50. A two tone nib with the area from the point to the air hole being platinum plated, called the "Feathertouch" point, was introduced in 1932.

In 1934, Sheaffer, while still making the lever filler, began making a pump filler in response to the Parker *Vacumatic* which had been introduced in 1933. Sheaffer's pump used a long, thin metal rod attached to several washers to create suction to pull the ink into the barrel. There was no sac in these models. The system may have worked well when the pen was new, but over time, as the rubber washers hardened and the packing deteriorated, the pen would leak or not fill at all. Today they are difficult to repair and are avoided by many collectors. Many collectors believe that Sheaffer expected this problem as their higher priced pens were mostly made as lever fillers.

Another type of pump filler pen was introduced in 1949, the *Touchdown* pen. It had a thick metal tube that slid into the barrel and contained a thin ink sac. When the tube end of the pen was pushed in, the air pressure compressed the sac. Again in response to another pen maker's innovative product (Parker's introduction of the Parker *51*) Sheaffer introduced the "Triumph" nib which was used from 1942 to 1962 alongside its regular nib style. The "Triumph" was a rather stiff writing nib designed as a small cylinder of gold that rose up into a point. It competed quite well with the *51* pen.

Another popular innovation, the "Snorkel" pen (1952-1963), introduced in 1952, had a slotted tube that retracted and extended when you twisted the rear of the barrel. The tube went through the center of the feed under the nib. Advertisements claimed that the nib never needed wiping after filling the pen, as only the snorkel entered the ink. The "Snorkel" pen used the pump filler system with the sac. It was a good system, fitting in with the thinner pen style of the day but, the "Snorkel" could not hold much ink in its skinny ink sac. The "Snorkel" was used on the large *PFM* (Pen For Men) line into the early 1960s.

Sheaffer introduced a ballpoint, called the *Stratowriter*, in 1947. If a ballpoint pen worked well, it could write longer than a fountain pen and there was no need to keep an inkwell handy. The popularity of the ballpoint marked the demise of the fountain pen as the first choice of writing instrument. The first ballpoints did not work well and fountain pens continued to sell well into the 1960s.

Sheaffer pens are somewhat easy to date by their shape, but knowledge of the clip styles on the earlier models can sharpen the dating ability to within a few years of when the pen was actively on the market. The earliest pens had a flat top cap and a relatively straight clip with a ball on the end. The clip was attached to the top of the cap. This style was used from the inception of the company through 1926.

In 1927, the pen still had a flat top cap, but the clip was lowered so that the pen stuck up higher in one's pocket. This allowed the *Lifetime* dot to show when worn in an outside pocket. The clip was given a humpback shape so that it would not damage the top of a pocket. The flat top with the lowered clip was made through 1929. When the cap was streamlined in 1930, the clip remained the same and was attached at the same general area on the cap.

1930 was a year of change for Sheaffer. The image of the wealthy banker was eroded by the stock market crash as banks failed and the loss of jobs reverberated throughout the nation. There was still a market for expensive pens, but more people were buying less expensive pens if they had to buy a pen at all. Some cheap non-Sheaffer pens were available for only 25 cents. The advertising changed to show that the Sheaffer *Lifetime* was a great value as it was guaranteed for life and was the only pen that one would ever have to buy.

In 1934, Sheaffer introduced its mother-of-pearl inlaid pen and its red veined gray marble pen of 1933, with a new clip, the flattened ball style. The flattened ball was very much like the clip style on the 1930 streamlined cap except that the ball was flattened on top.

The clip was again modified in 1937 to raise the clip further off the cap and to give it a more rounded look. This style lasted until 1945. Also new that year was the pattern called the "2 Tone". The "2 Tone" was a two-toned, striped pearl plastic available in several colors.

During this clip style period, the Second World War broke out. Sheaffer advertised a new clip in 1941 that allowed the pen to sit lower in the pocket. This was the "War Clip" and it wrapped over the top of the pen and coexisted with the 1937 "civilian" style. Perhaps it was designed to offer less of a target for enemy snipers, but more likely it was designed to sit lower in the pocket, allowing the pocket flap to be buttoned.

The clip changed again to a more streamlined style in 1945. The flattened ball clip of 1937 was further flattened on its sides so that it was only curved on the bottom. Most "Snorkel" pens have this clip as it lasted into the 1960s.

A snub clip style pen was offered in 1947 through 1951. It was called the "Tuckaway" and was advertised as being specially designed for women.

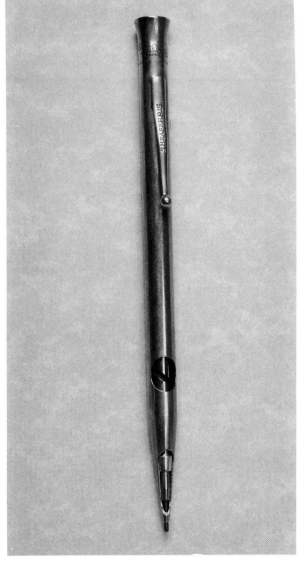

SHEAFFER, ca. 1914-1922. Black chased hard rubber, lever filling pen wit #3 self-filling nib. Red chased hard rubber pens are known, and are extremely rare. $40-60.

SHEAFFER, ca. 1915-1925. Nickel plated demonstrator pencil. Demonstrator pens and pencils were used by salesmen to show the mechanism. $50-75.

SHEAFFER, ca. 1914-1922. Black chased hard rubber, lever filling pen with #4 nib and 15k gold band. $125-200.

SHEAFFER, Ca. 1913 barrel imprint.

SHEAFFER, ca. 1914 barrel imprint.

SHEAFFER, ca. 1914-1919. Black lined rubber, lever filling pen with #8 self-filling nib. This large pen was the predecessor to the *Lifetime* pens introduced in 1920. $150-250.

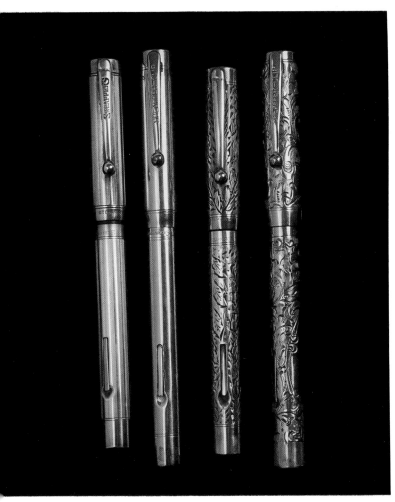

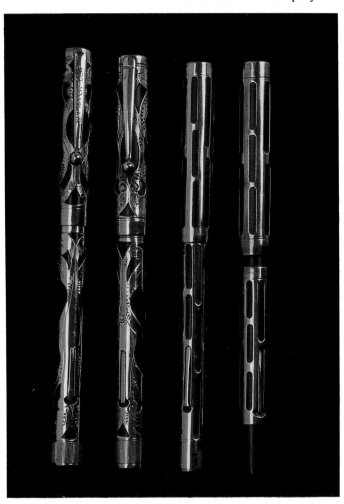

SHEAFFER, ca. 1917-1924. Lever filling, overlay pens. Left to right: sterling silver lined design; gold filled plain design; sterling silver hand engraved design; gold filled hand engraved design. Left to right: $300-500; $450-650.

SHEAFFER, ca. 1917-1924. Lever filling, overlay pens. Left to right: gold filled, and sterling silver filigree designs; gold filled, and sterling silver "Straight" designs. $350-500.

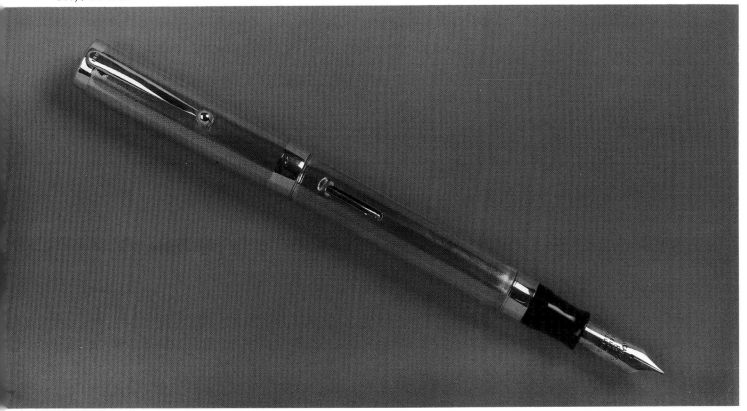

SHEAFFER, ca. 1922-1924. Solid 14k gold overlay, lever filling pen with #8 nib. This was the largest solid gold pen produced by Sheaffer, and is extremely rare. $2500-3000.

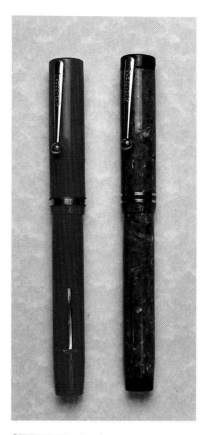

SHEAFFER. Casein plastic "Secretary", lever filling pen ca. 1924; jade green Radite plastic lever filling 7-30 pen, ca. 1925.

KRAKER, ca. 1915-1917. Hard rubber lever filling pens. Kraker, a former partner of Sheaffer's went into business for himself, and copied most of Sheaffer's pens. He was put out of business after Sheaffer successfully sued for patent infringement. $200-300.

SHEAFFER, ca. 1920. Black chased hard rubber, lever filling "porthole" demonstrator pen. $125-175.

SHEAFFER, ca. 1922. Hard rubber Skrip ink bottles. $20-35.

SHEAFFER, ca. 1922. Early desk pen holders in hard rubber. $25-40.

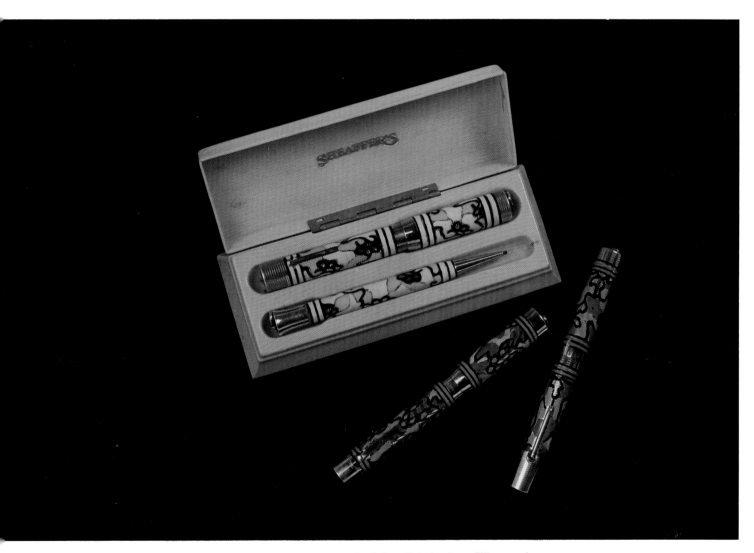

SHEAFFER, ca. 1922. "Mosiac Oriental" design, lever filling pens in hand enamelled, and lacquered gold filled metal. The original cost of a pen and pencil set was $15.00. $300-450.

SHEAFFER, 1924-1929. *Lifetime*, jade green Radite, lever filling pen. The first company to introduce a plastic pen, it created a revolution in the industry, forcing the other pen makers to introduce their own plastic pens, and spelling the end of hard rubber pens. $200-275.

SHEAFFER, ca. 1928. Green jade Radite lever filling "porthole" demonstrator pen. $225-300.

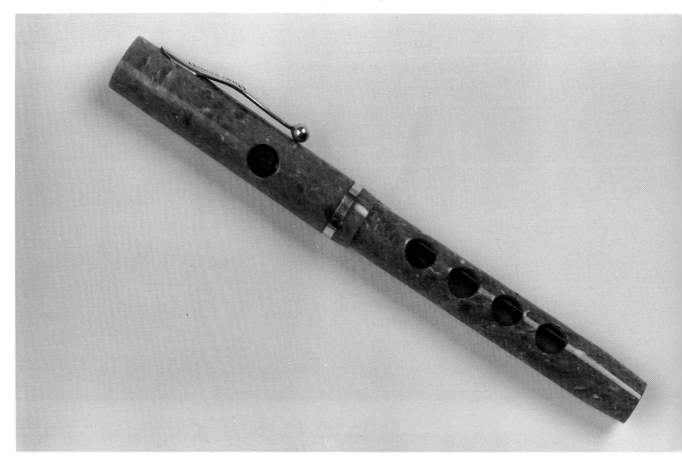

SHEAFFER, 1923-1929. Red hard rubber, and jade green Radite, lever filling lady's pens. $75-125.

SHEAFFER, 1924-1929. Jade green Radite, lever filling 7-30 pen. The same as the *Lifetime* model, this pen without the guarantee, was priced at $7.30, rather than $8.75, and the nib was not marked *Lifetime*. Sheaffer's numbering system, when it was used, indicated the price of the pen, as it does here. $150-250.

SHEAFFER, ca. 1922-1924. Red casein plastic "loaner" pen. Sheaffer produced casein plastic pens prior to the introduction of Radite (Pyroxylin) plastic. After the pens had been sold it was found that the casein would expand and contract depending on the temperature. In warm weather this caused the sections to fall out. As a consequence, Sheaffer abandoned the sale of these pens, and utilized the remaining stock as loaner pens, to be given out while a customer's pen was being repaired. A few were also sold as a "Secretary" model for office use. $225-275.

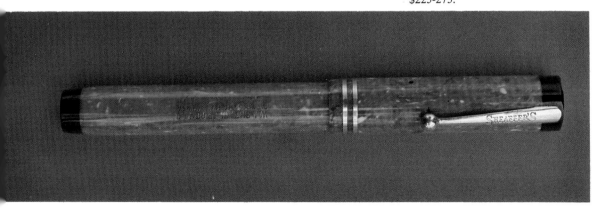

SHEAFFER, 1924-1929. *Lifetime,* lever filling pens. Left to right: black Radite; jade green Radite; black & pearl Radite; jade green Radite. These smaller *Lifetime* pens were available in the same colors as the full size pens. Most of Sheaffer's pens of the 1920s to 1960s were available in both *Lifetime* and non-*Lifetime* versions. The only difference being the absence of the White Dot and the *Lifetime* guarantee. The White Dot in effect symbolized a service contract on the pen for the life of the owner. $75-100.

SHEAFFER, 1927. *Lifetime,* black Radite lever filling pen and pencil set. The clip style on Sheaffer pens was modified after 1926, lowering it on the cap, and giving it a graceful curve. $135-200.

SHEAFFER #46, ca. 1923-1929. Red hard rubber, lever filling, pen and pencil set. Also called the "Student" model, it was available in black hard rubber as well. $100-150.

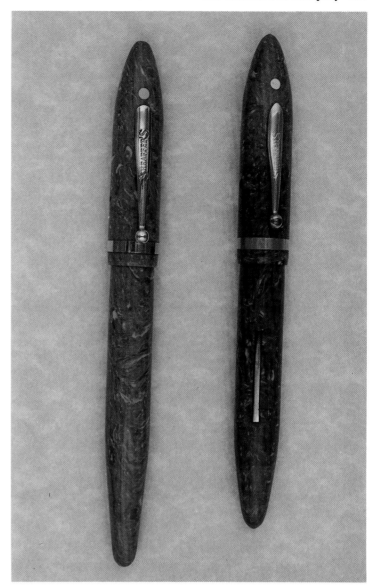

SHEAFFER, 1924-1929. *Lifetime,* black Radite lever filling pens. The split cap band first appeared on Sheaffer pens in 1928. $100-150.

SHEAFFER, ca. 1930-1933. *Lifetime,* jade green Radite, lever filling *Balance* pens. In 1930 Sheaffer introduced its streamlined models. They were initially available in the same colors as the old style *Lifetime* pens, and the same variety of sizes. Through the years, the sizes and colors available changed. $175-275.

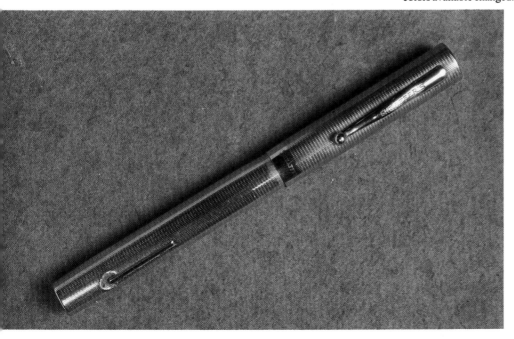

SHEAFFER, ca. 1917-1924. Gold filled overlay, lever filling pen. $150-250.

SHEAFFER, ca. 1932 advertisement.

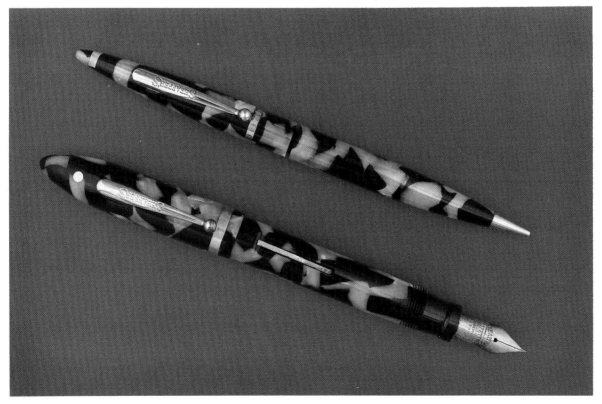

SHEAFFER, ca. 1929-1933. *Lifetime* lever filling "telephone dialer" pens. The long ends of these pens were used for dialing telephones. $225-275.

SHEAFFER, ca. 1930-1933. *Lifetime,* black & pearl Radite, lever filling *Balance* pen and pencil set. Most of the early plastic used in pens was not very stable, and consequently is often found discolored. This set illustrates very good original color. $175-250.

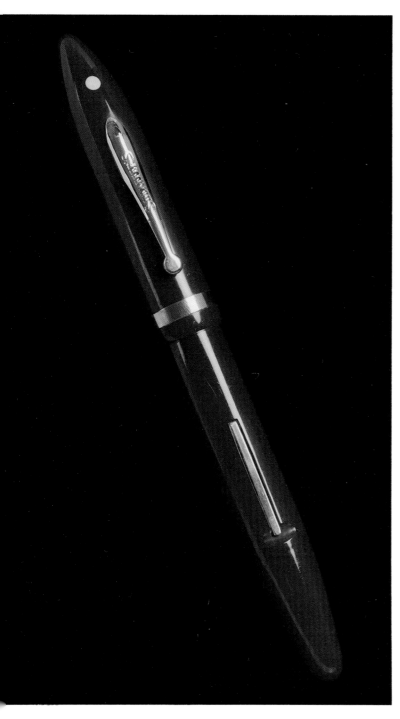

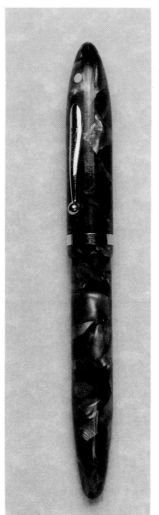

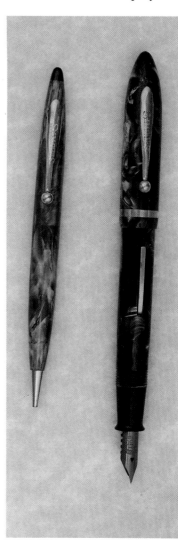

SHEAFFER, ca. 1932-1935. *Lifetime,* lever filling *Balance* pens and pencil set in red veined gray marble Radite. $100-175.

SHEAFFER, ca. 1935. *Lifetime,* lever filling *Balance* pen in red casein plastic. Probably an experimental model, this is the only known example of this type of pen. $1500-3000.

SHEAFFER, ca. 1931-1934. *Lifetime,* lever filling, full size *Balance* pens in green and black Radite. This color was introduced in 1931. The wide band is 14k gold.

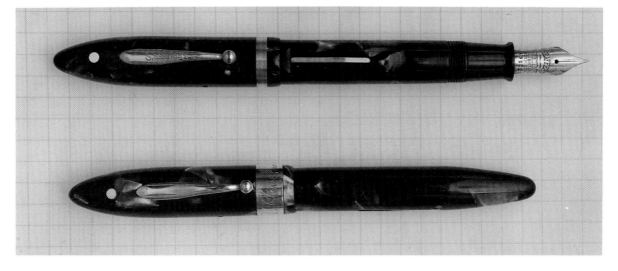

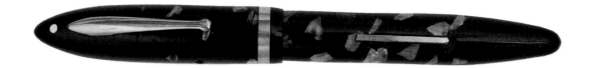

SHEAFFER, ca. 1935-1942. *Lifetime* lever filling *Balance* pen in ebonized pearl Radite. $175-300.

SHEAFFER, ca. 1934-1938. W.A.S.P. Vacuum-Fil pen. $50-75.

SHEAFFER, ca. 1935. Lever filling *Balance* demonstrator pen. $350-425.

SHEAFFER, ca. 1935. *Lifetime,* plunger filling, *Balance* demonstrator pen. An unusual demonstrator, this pen has been sawed in half to illustrate the mechanism. $200-250.

SHEAFFER, ca. 1937 advertisement.

SHEAFFER, ca. 1932-1935. Blue and black marble Radite 3-25, lever filling, *Balance* pen and pencil set. This color is not often found. $175-250.

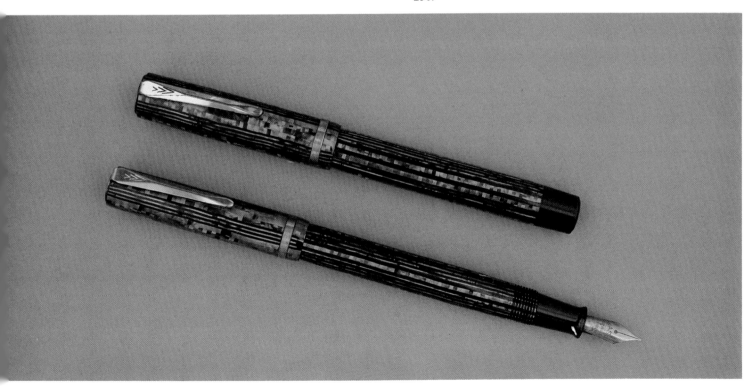

SHEAFFER, ca. 1934-1938. W.A.S.P. lever and plunger filling pens. The W.A.S.P. pen, which stood for W.A. Sheaffer Pen, was the budget priced line, along with the *Craig* line of pens. $40-60.

SHEAFFER, ca. 1934-1942. *Lady Sheaffer* lever filling *Balance* pen and pencil set in ebonized pearl Radite. This color was introduced in 1934. $125-150.

SHEAFFER, ca. 1931-1934. Black & pearl Radite, *Lifetime,* lever filling *Balance* pen/pencil combination. Of the major manufacturers, the combinations made by Sheaffer are the most often found. $150-200.

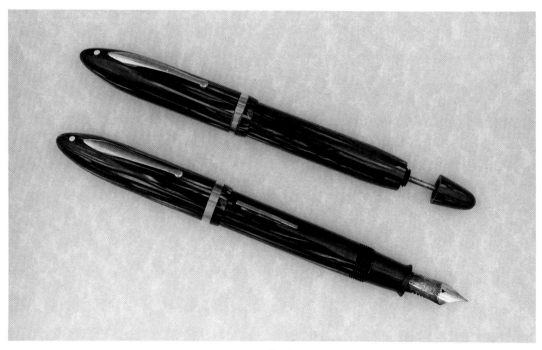

SHEAFFER, 1935-1945. "Premier", *Lifetime,* Vacuum-Fil *Balance* pen in marine green, and lever filling pen in golden brown Radite. During the 1930s and 1940s, Sheaffer produced pens available as either lever filling, or vacuum filling models. Other colors which were available at this time were: roseglow; pearl gray; and carmine. $75-175.

SHEAFFER. Comparison of the 1935-1936 flat ball clip on the left, and the 1937-1945 clip on the right.

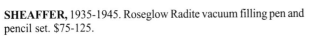

SHEAFFER, 1935-1945. Roseglow Radite vacuum filling pen and pencil set. $75-125.

SHEAFFER, ca. 1938. Vacuum filling demonstrator pen. $250-300.

SHEAFFER, ca. 1933. Four available sizes of *Balance* pen are illustrated.

SHEAFFER, 1942-1954. Sheaffer introduced the Triumph conical nib shown on the left in 1942, and thereafter pens were available with either the Triumph or conventional nibs.

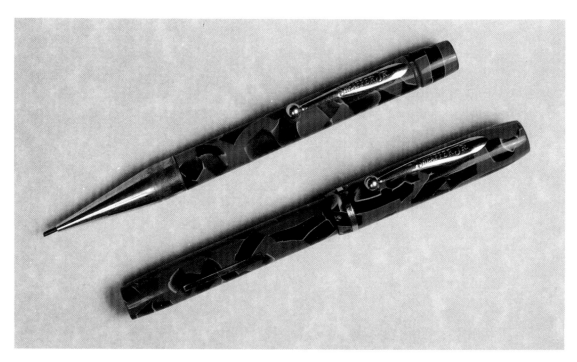

SHEAFFER, ca. 1932-1935. Sheaffer "Junior" lever filling pen and pencil set in blue and black marble Radite. $125-200.

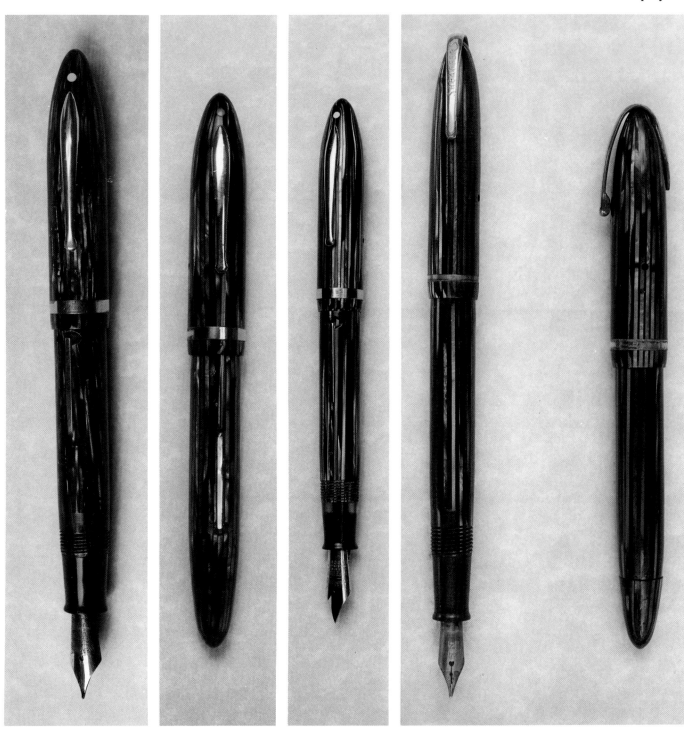

SHEAFFER, 1937-1945. "Premier", full size *Lifetime* pens in roseglow, golden brown, and pearl gray Radite. Sheaffer used many model names for their pens. These names were usually found on the price stickers, and in dealer material. The same names were carried over through the years, and served to designate the hierarchy of models. The "Premier", and "Statesman" were the top of the line of largest pens. The "Sovereign" the standard size. Terms such as "Excellence", "Autograph", and "Masterpiece" indicated some type of 14k gold trim. Lower priced pens had names such as "Admiral", "Craftsman", "Cadet", and "Junior". Left to right: $425-500; $150-200; $75-125.

SHEAFFER, 1941-1946. Military clip vacuum filling pens in marine green, and golden pearl Radite. Sheaffer introduced this clip style to comply with military regulations requiring shirt flaps be buttoned. Rather than design a new clip, Sheaffer mounted their regular clip upside down, and folded it over the top of the pen. $65-85.

SHEAFFER, 1937-1945. "Premier", *Lifetime,* vacuum filling pen in marine green Radite. $150-200.

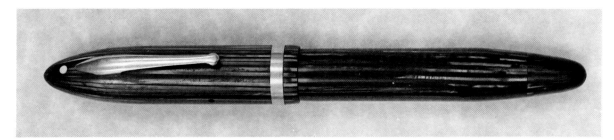

SHEAFFER, ca. 1937-1945. "Craftsman", lever filling pen in roseglow Radite. $40-65.

SHEAFFER, 1939. "Crest" model *Lifetime* lever filling pen with gold filled cap. This example with the barrel threads at the end of the section, was the first model "Crest", and inspired the rage for metal capped pens. $175-250.

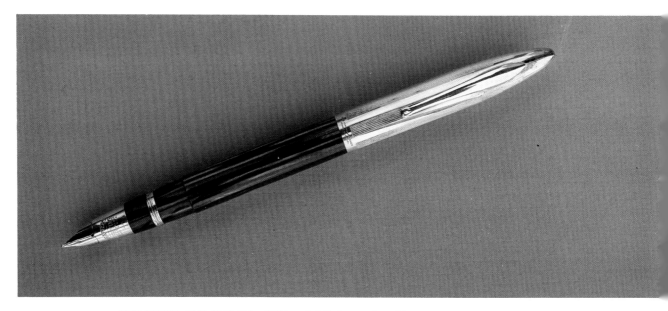

SHEAFFER, 1942-1945. "Crest" Triumph *Lifetime* pen in golden brown plastic. Available as either lever or vacuum filling pens, and with barrels in all the standard colors of the period. $75-100.

SHEAFFER, 1942-1945. Triumph 1250, White Dot *Lifetime* pens. Available as lever filling or vacuum filling, and in golden brown, marine green, pearl gray, carmine, and black plastic. $65-85.

SHEAFFER, 1949-1954. "Valiant", White Dot touchdown filling pens in burgundy, and persian blue plastic. The touchdown filling mechanism replaced the vacuum filling models, and for the most part the lever filling models as well. These pens were also available in burnt umber, evergreen, and black plastic. $40-65.

SHEAFFER, 1941-1946. Military clip, lever filling pen and pencil set in carmine plastic. $65-85.

SHEAFFER. Left to Right: 1914-1926 clip; 1927-1930 clip; 1930-1935 clip; 1937-1945 clip; 1945-1960 clip.

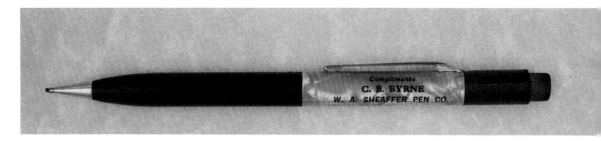

SHEAFFER, ca. 1943. Advertising pencil, often given away, usually with a company's name imprinted. $10-20.

SHEAFFER, 1944-1951. *Tuckaway* pens and pencil. These small pens were available in both vacuum filling and touchdown filling models, and in a variety of styles. $50-100.

SHEAFFER, 1952-1959. "Saratoga" model snorkel filling pens. Left to right: pastel green; pastel pink; pastel blue; burgundy; and pastel gray plastic. Also available in black plastic. The snorkel filling pens succeeded the touchdown filling mechanism, and was available in many variations such as white dot models, chrome cap models, and triumph nib models. $35-85.

SHEAFFER, 1945-1950. Triumph 1250 White Dot pens in marine green, and golden brown. These pens were available as lever filling or vacuum filling models. $65-85.

SHEAFFER, 1945-1949. "Admiral", lever filling pen and pencil set in carmine plastic. $25-35.

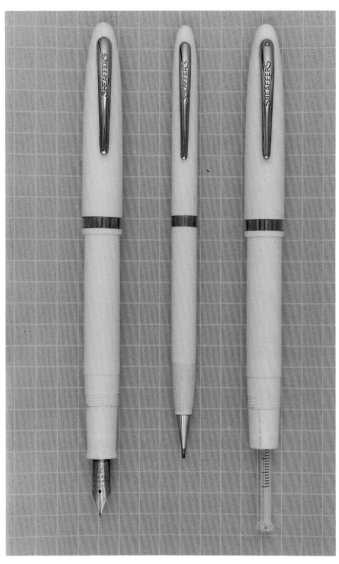

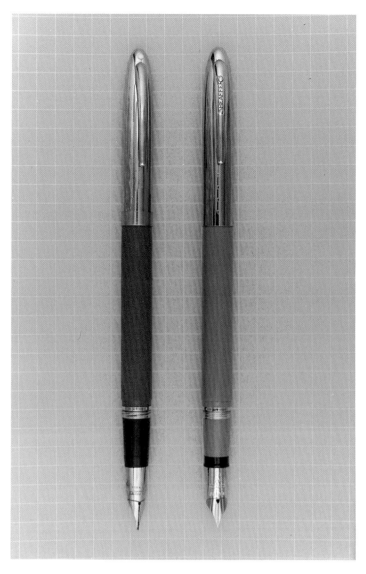

SHEAFFER, ca. 1952-1956. Doctor's set. A pen, pencil, and thermometer case in white plastic with gold filled trim, looked great in the doctor's white jacket. Note the small bump on top of the thermometer case's clip, so that the doctor didn't stick his pen in the patient's mouth. $200-300.

SHEAFFER, 1952-1959. "Sentinel" Deluxe snorkel filling pen in red; "Sovereign" snorkel pen in pastel gray plastic. $30-50.

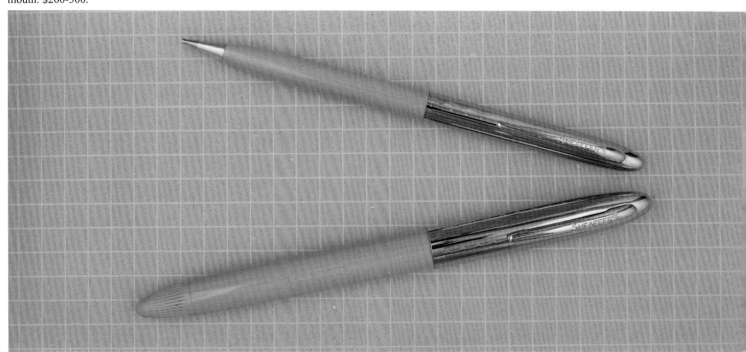

SHEAFFER, 1952-1959. "Sovereign" snorkel filling pen and pencil set in pastel pink. $45-60.

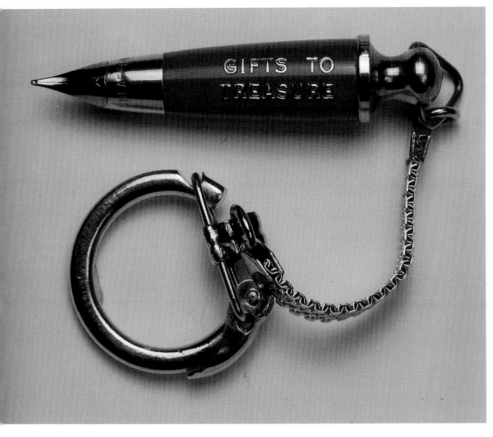

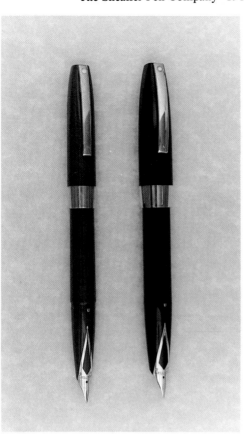

SHEAFFER, ca. 1957. Triumph snorkel keychain. This was presented to Sheaffer salesmen at one of their sales meetings. $45-75.

SHEAFFER, ca. 1960. PFM pen compared with standard size *Imperial* pen.

SHEAFFER, ca. 1955. Snorkel demonstrator pen. $175-235.

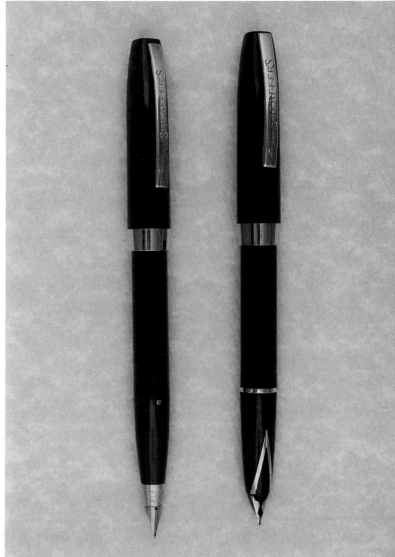

SHEAFFER *PFM*, 1959-1963. The Pen For Men, snorkel filling pens. The *PFM* pens were available in nine grades: *PFM* I: plastic cap and barrel, chrome trim, palladium silver nib; *PFM* II, brushed steel cap, plastic barrel, palladium silver nib; *PFM* III, plastic cap and barrel, gold filled trim, 14k gold nib; *PFM* IV, steel cap, plastic barrel, gold filled trim, 14k gold nib; *PFM* V, gold filled cap, plastic barrel, 14k gold nib; *PFM* VI, gold filled cap and barrel 14k gold nib; *PFM* VII, 14k gold cap, plastic barrel, 14k gold nib; *PFM* VIII, 14k gold cap and barrel, also called the "Masterpiece"; *PFM* "Autograph", plastic cap and barrel, 14k gold trim and nib. Left to right: $75-125; $150-225; $275-325.

SHEAFFER, ca. 1960. Sheaffer *Imperial* pens with Triumph and inlay nibs. $20-35.

SHEAFFER, 1958-1964. *Lady Skripsert* gold plated cartridge filling pen. Many varieties were available, all without clips. $40-300.

Chapter 7
The Wahl-Eversharp
Pen Company
1914-1957

The Wahl-Eversharp Pen Company started out in an entirely different manner than the preceding pen companies. Wahl was incorporated in September, 1905 as the Wahl Adding Machine Company, making adding machines. It was not a family business, but a corporation that was willing to invest in anything that would show a profit. Wahl entered the writing instrument field by buying the Ever-Sharp Pencil Company in 1914. Ever-Sharp was founded by Tokuji Hayakawa, inventor and producer of a metal mechanical pencil and later founder of the company that became Sharp Electronics. A factory was opened at 1800 Roscoe Street in Chicago, Illinois to make pencils.

The production of these Eversharp pencils was profitable and Wahl looked for a fountain pen company to acquire. A fountain pen line would compliment the pencil line and each would increase sales of the other. After looking at several companies, Wahl acquired the Boston Fountain Pen Company located in Massachusetts in late 1917. Boston Pen was a small, high quality pen company with a collection of valuable patents in addition to its machinery and personnel. Boston held patents on a comb feed, an inner cap design and on the rollerball clip. The Boston Pen operation was moved to Chicago.

In 1918, Wahl began selling the Wahl *Tempoint* pen, which was basically the unchanged Boston pen. Wahl's pen and pencil business was very successful and by 1920, Wahl was as big as, if not bigger than Parker and Sheaffer. In 1921, Wahl introduced an all metal pen to match its line of Eversharp pencils. It maintained its lead in pen sales until the mid-1920s when the other big pen companies began to produce their line of colorful pens. Competitive all the way, Wahl bought a rubber company and began to produce its own line of colorful pens.

In hind sight, this was a terrible mistake, as new lines of plastic pens were soon introduced by Sheaffer and Parker. Wahl was left, not only with a large supply of rubber pen parts, but a large rubber company. It continued to make hard rubber pens and sales began to fall. While not popular when introduced, to the collector, these pens made from 1926 to 1929 are some of the best balanced and greatest writing hard rubber pens ever made.

Wahl finally began to produce plastic pens in 1927. Their first plastic pen was similar to their hard rubber pens. Beginning in 1928, they introduced the *Personal-Point* pen. In 1929, a small gold seal with two check marks was placed on the cap to indicate that these were their best pens. It appears that this gold seal located in the same general area as the white dot on Sheaffer pens was created to cash in on the popularity of Sheaffer's white dot *Lifetime* pens. After a few years, Wahl entered the "lifetime guarantee" business and sold these gold seal pens as "guaranteed forever".

The *Personal-Point* feature of these new pens was that the nib and feed could be unscrewed from the main section of the pen and replaced easily. Their advertising told customers that the point could be changed to suit the personality of the writer. The *Personal-Point* was a successful seller. Again it seemed that the public wanted a large attractive pen that was distinctive and could be carried in their outside jacket pocket for show.

The stock market crash in 1929, had an impact on every pen company. With tens of thousands of people out of work, less pens were sold and with smaller pen sales, less money was available to invest in machinery and pen parts. The impact of the crash on most companies was to force them to rethink their advertising and redesign their pens. Streamlining was in vogue. Wahl streamlined its pens to keep pace. They produced a simple streamlined version (1930-

WAHL #76, ca. 1918-1922. *Tempoint* black chased hard rubber lever filling pen with gold filled cap band. $50-90.

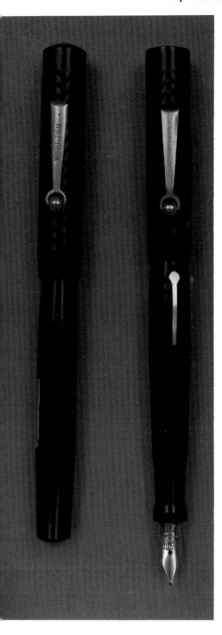

WAHL, ca. 1918-1922. *Tempoint* black chased hard rubber, lever filling roller clip pens, with nickel, and gold filled trim. $75-125.

1931) of their *Personal-Point* pens called the *Equipoised* and followed it with the *Doric* pen (1931-1941). The *Doric's* design was very "Deco" with its tapered twelve-sided shape. This design was copied by several other pen companies, but none had the grace and poise of the *Doric*. *Doric* pens used the roller ball clip until 1935, when a simpler Art Deco clip replaced it.

The large sized *Dorics* were discontinued in 1936, when Wahl introduced a large metal pen with plastic inserts called the *Coronet* (1936-1941). Incredibly, this large top-of-the-line pen was not called the *Coronet* in Wahl's advertising. It was referred to only in conjunction with the new "Repeating Pencil" and a feature of the pen called the "Safety Ink Shutoff". The "Safety Ink Shutoff" was a small metal tab that protruded from under the feed and pushed a plug into the ink channel when the cap was put on the pen. It did not work as advertised and was soon discontinued.

Wahl Pen Company and Eversharp Pencil Company were operated as two distinct entities. During the period from 1936 to 1940 the two companies had become uncoordinated and were losing market share to the other pen and pencil makers. Management did not know what was happening in the plant, sales did not know what production or planning was doing and the two companies were duplicating many management and production functions. To reorganize themselves, the two companies combined to become the Eversharp Company in 1940-41.

In 1941, Eversharp began production on a new pen that again brought the company around to profitability, the *Skyline* pen (1941-1949). The *Skyline* wrote beautifully, looked attractive, and was advertised not to leak in airplanes. This was in a period of increasing air travel. The *Skyline* was available in many colors, and price ranges, from the simple black to the solid gold "Command Performance" pen.

With the introduction of Parker's *51* pen, most pen makers tried to capitalize on the *51* hooded look. Eversharp was no exception. They introduced their *Fifth Avenue* (1943-1946) and then their *$64* pens, a 14kt gold capped version of the *Fifth Avenue*, named after a radio show of the same name that they sponsored, "The Sixty-Four Dollar Question" (first known as "Take it or Leave it"). The *Fifth Avenue* was not a popular model.

After the war, Eversharp made a drastic mistake that eventually lead to the demise of the pen writing instrument division. In 1945, they bought the rights to manufacture the new ballpoint pen designed by Biro, for one million dollars. The ballpoint pen idea had been conceived in the 19th century but like the problems with early ink, the technology of the day could not produce the necessary parts. In 1945, the technology developed during the Second World War led to a way of manufacturing the precision ball bearings necessary for the ballpoint's manufacture. At tremendous expense, Eversharp retooled their plants to produce this new ballpoint pen, but before they could begin production and coordinate advertising, a start-up company, Reynolds Pen, introduced their ballpoint pen to the public in October, 1945.

The Reynolds ballpoint pen was advertised as being able to write under water. It would make the fountain pen obsolete. The Reynolds was an instant best seller, selling $100,000 worth of pens in one store on the day of its introduction. Reynolds made millions of dollars over the next few months and captured the ballpoint market. To say that the other pen makers were jealous was an understatement. They were furious, enraged and embarrassed.

Production was rushed and Eversharp introduced their ballpoint pen, the *CA* ("Capillary Action"), before it was fully perfected. Sales were phenomenal. Eversharp sold millions of dollars worth of ballpoint pens in their first year. Unfortunately, most of them stopped working, leaked, or did not work at all. Being an established company with a fine reputation, Eversharp was forced to replace millions of defective pens. The Reynolds pen also stopped working, but they found it easier to dissolve the company when the going got tough.

Eversharp lost over 10 million dollars with their ballpoint pen. By the time they corrected the design of these pens to function properly, other companies had entered the market and driven the prices down. A battle among the management of Eversharp distracted the company even further and product development became uncontrolled. Many new products were introduced the *Symphony* (designed by Raymond Loewy), the *Envoy*, and the *Ventura* "burp" pen, but none of them was successful.

In December, 1957, Eversharp sold its writing instruments division to Parker Pen. The Wahl Company continues to this day however, making electric razors for barbers.

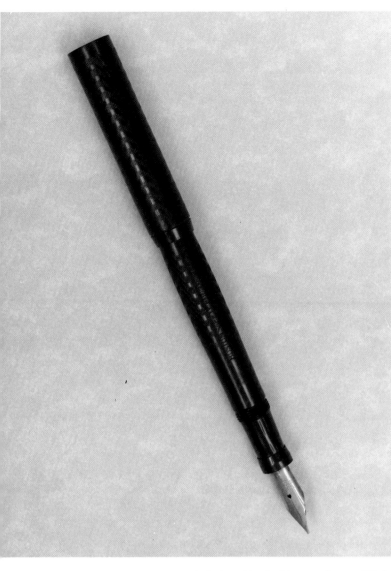

BOSTON, ca. 1915-1917. Red & black mottled hard rubber, lever filling lady's pen. The forerunner of Wahl's *Tempoint* line of pens, the Boston Pen Co. was purchased by Wahl in 1917. $40-65.

BOSTON, ca. 1914-1917. Black chased hard rubber, eyedropper filled pen. $40-60.

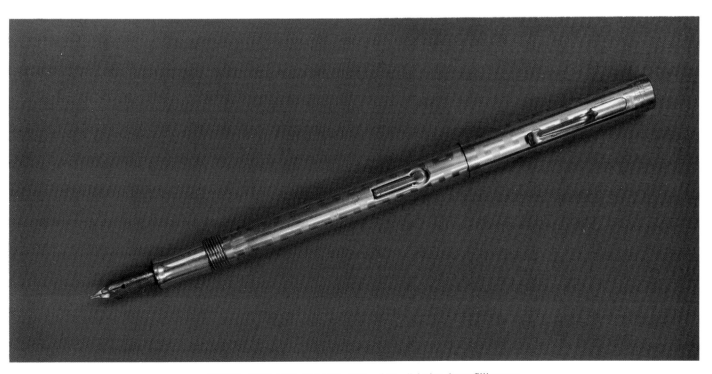

WAHL, 1922-1932. Gold filled "Greek Key" design, lever filling pen. Wahl produced some of the most beautiful metal pens during the 1920's, including enameled ones. $150-200.

WAHL, ca. 1918-1922. Black chased hard rubber, lever filling *Tempoint* pens. $35-60.

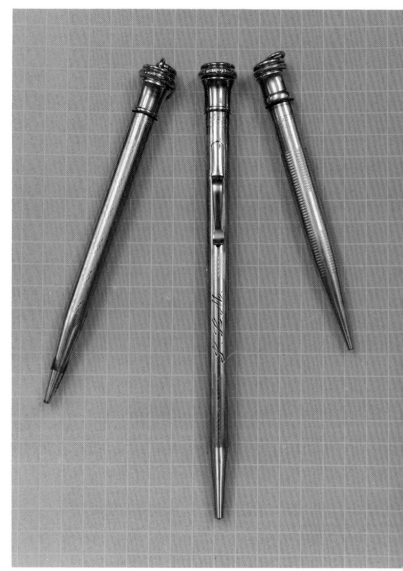

EVERSHARP, 1914-1932. Gold filled propel pencil. Eversharp pencils were available in many sizes, patterns, and materials during their period of manufacture. For the first ten years that Wahl was in business, these pencils represented the bulk of their sales. $20-50.

EVERSHARP, 1914-1932. Gold filled propel pencils. $20-50.

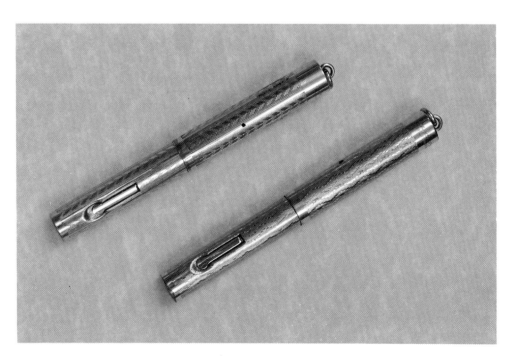

WAHL, 1922-1932. Gold filled, lever filling lady's pens. $45-75.

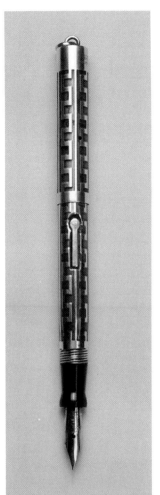

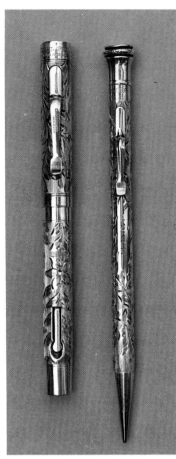

WAHL, 1922-1932. Gold filled, "Greek Key" design, lever filling lady's pen. $50-75.

WAHL, 1922-1932. Sterling silver, hand engraved design, lever filling pen and pencil set. $350-500.

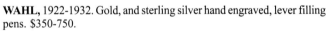

WAHL, 1922-1932. Gold, and sterling silver hand engraved, lever filling pens. $350-750.

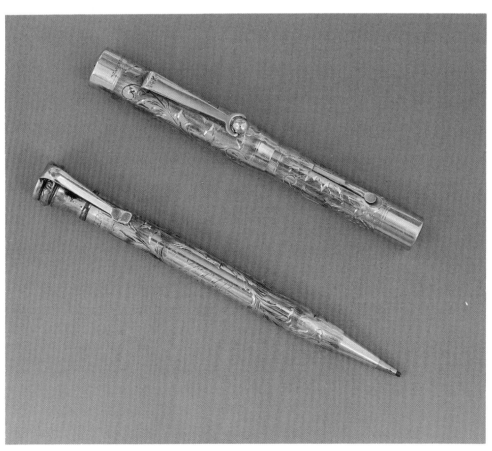

WAHL, ca. 1922-1932. Hand engraved design, short model, lever filling roller clip pen and pencil set in 14k gold. $400-550.

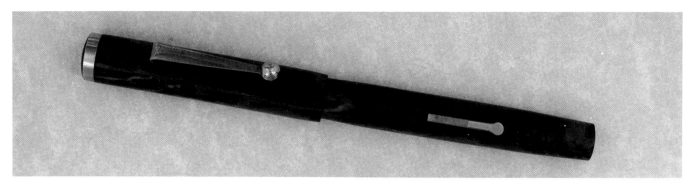

PARAMOUNT by WAHL, ca. 1924-1928. Red & black mottled hard rubber lever filling pen. Along with the Marathon, this was Wahl's budget priced pen. $50-75.

WAHL, ca. 1926-1929. Rosewood and black hard rubber lever filling, roller clip "Signature" pens. $200-400.

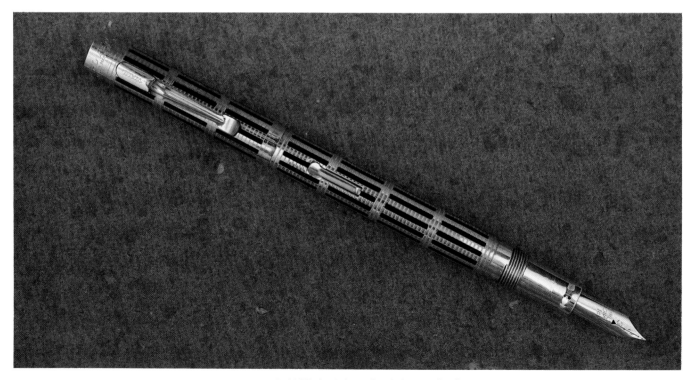

WAHL, 1925-1932. Gold filled, "Colonnade" design overlay, lever filling pen. $450-600.

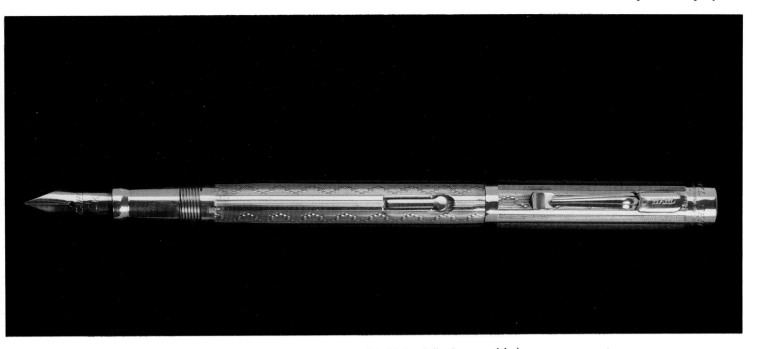

WAHL, ca. 1922-1930. Vermeil (gold plated silver) engraved design, lever filling pen. $400-600.

WAHL, ca. 1928. Olive woodgrain hard rubber lever filling desk pens in a marble base. $350-450.

WAHL, ca. 1925. Large brass advertising pen. $500-650.

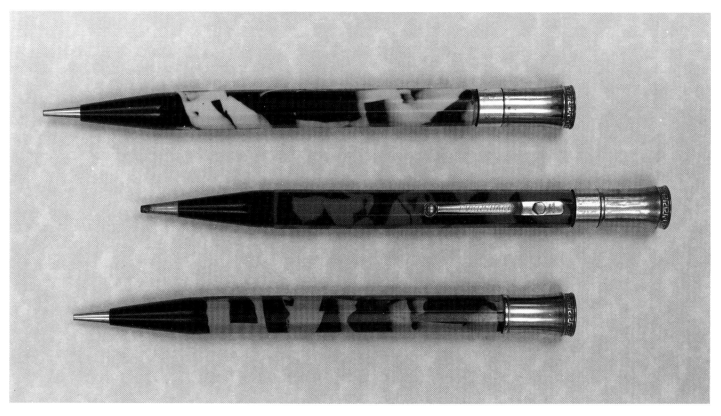

EVERSHARP, ca. 1929-1933. Propel pencils in unusual plastic colors.
$30-45.

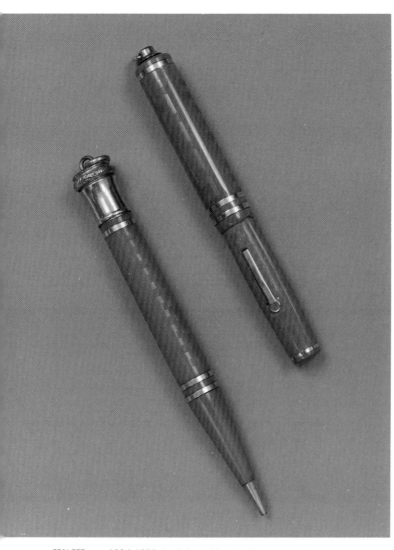

WAHL, ca. 1926-1932. Red chased hard rubber, lever filling, lady's pen and pencil set. $100-150.

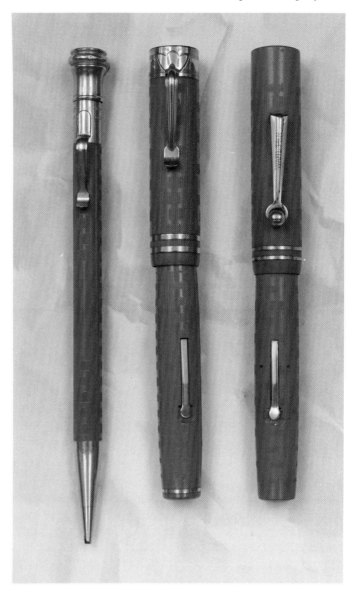

WAHL, ca. 1926-1932. Red chased hard rubber, lever filling "Student" model pens and pencil. Available without the double check Gold Seal, these lowered priced pens were advertised as being suitable for students. $200-275.

MARATHON by WAHL, ca. 1924-1928. Red and black hard rubber, lever filling pens. $100-150.

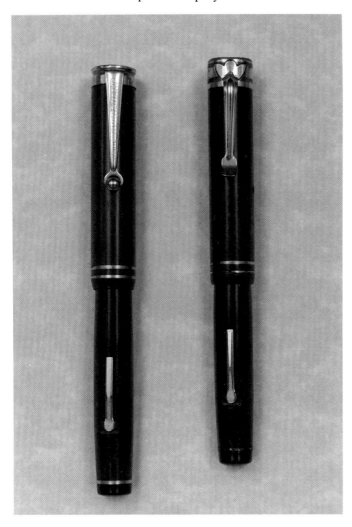

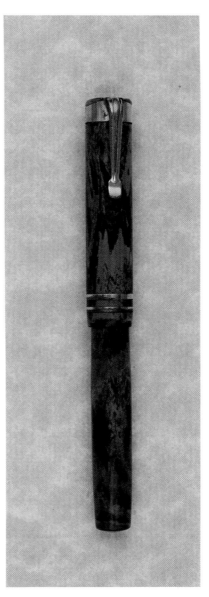

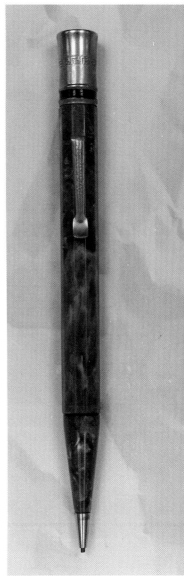

WAHL, 1927-1932. Roller clip and "Soldier Clip", lever filling pens in lazulitic blue plastic. $200-250.

WAHL, ca. 1923-1927. Red & black mottled hard rubber, lever filling "Soldier Clip" pen. Prior to the introduction of rosewood hard rubber, Wahl pens were of this mottled type. $50-100.

EVERSHARP, ca. 1929-1933. Propel pencil in pearl green marble plastic. $20-50.

WAHL, ca. 1929-1933. Unusual color plastic, lever filling lady's pens. $250-350.

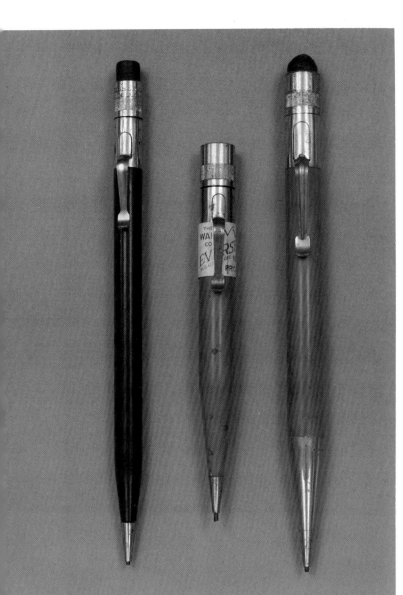

WAHL, 1927-1930. Black plastic lever filling, roller clip pen. $35-65.

EVERSHARP, ca. 1926-1932. Enamel metal propel pencils. $15-30.

WAHL, ca. 1934. Emerald green plastic lever filling "Palmer Method" pen. $100-175.

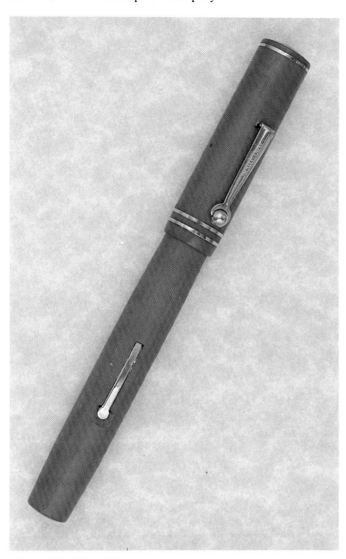

WAHL, ca. 1925-1928. Red chased hard rubber, lever filling, roller clip "Signature" pen. $300-450.

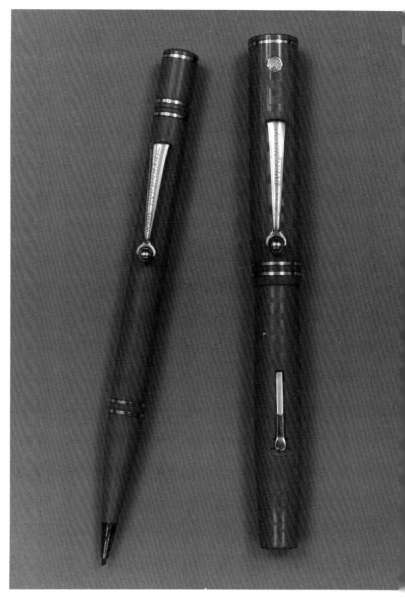

WAHL, 1929-1931. Red chased hard rubber, Gold Seal, lever filling pen and pencil set. $275-400.

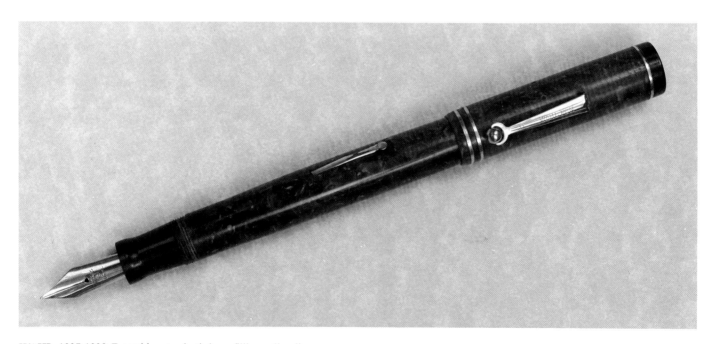

WAHL, 1927-1928. Emerald green plastic lever filling, roller clip pen. This large pen was the predecessor to the large Gold Seal, *Personal-Point* pens of 1929. In styling it resembles the hard rubber "Signature" pens. $200-300.

WAHL, 1927-1932. Gold Seal, *Personal-Point,* lever filling, "Soldier Clip" pens. Left to right: rosewood hard rubber; green & bronze plastic; black & pearl plastic; lazulitic blue plastic. Also available but not shown are: emerald green plastic; coral plastic; red, and black chased hard rubber; black plastic. $200-350.

WAHL, 1927-1932. Gold Seal, *Personal-Point,* lever filling, roller clip pens. Left to right: black & pearl plastic; rosewood hard rubber; emerald green plastic; lazulitic blue plastic; coral plastic; black chased hard rubber. Also available but not shown are: red chased hard rubber; black plastic. $150-300.

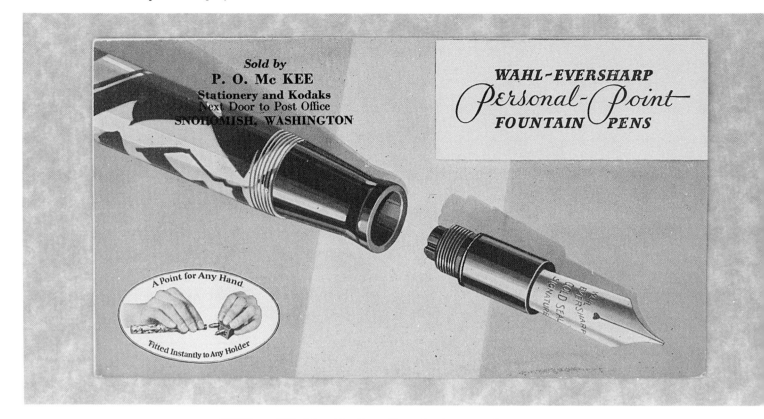

WAHL, ca. 1929. Advertising blotter illustrating the *Personal-Point* feature. $20-40.

WAHL, 1927-1932. Gold Seal, *Personal-Point,* lever filling lady's pens in green & bronze plastic; lazulitic blue plastic; coral plastic; black & pearl plastic; burgundy plastic. $100-200.

WAHL, 1929-1932. Oversize Gold Seal, *Personal-Point,* lever filling, roller clip "deco band" pens. Left to right: black plastic; green & bronze plastic; rosewood hard rubber; lazulitic blue plastic pen and pencil; black & pearl plastic; emerald green plastic. Black chased hard rubber not shown. These impressive pens were a serious challenge to the Parker *Duofold.* Left to right: $250-350; $350-450; $350-450; $100-150; $450-650; $275-375; $300-400.

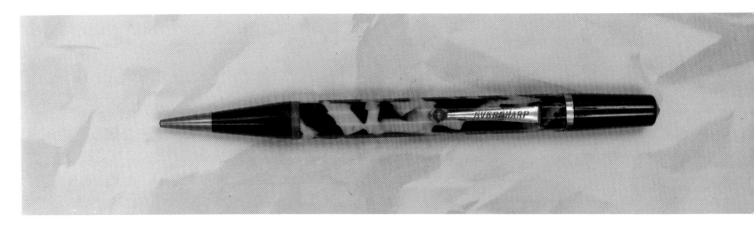

EVERSHARP, 1929-1932. Propel pencil in black & pearl marble plastic. $20-30.

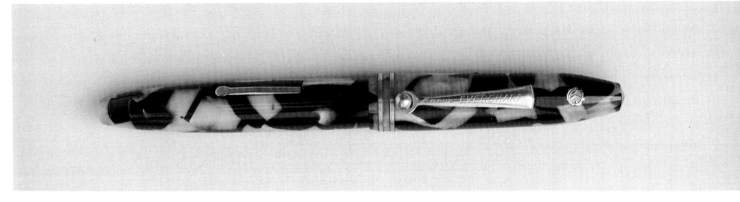

WAHL, 1929. Gold Seal, *Personal-Point,* lever filling, roller clip pen. Produced for only one year, Wahl termed this model *Equipoised.* It was available in the standard plastic colors. $100-175.

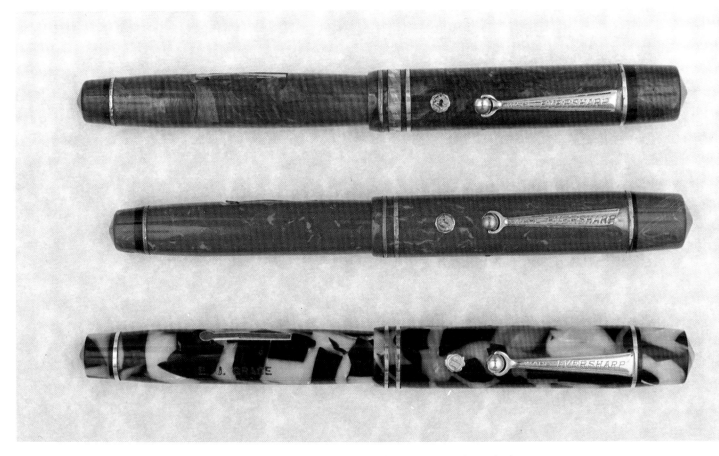

WAHL, 1929-1930. Gold Seal, lever filling, *Equipoised* type plastic pens. These transitional pens were produced for only one year prior to the introduction of the *Equipoised* line of pens. $400-500.

WAHL, 1930-1932. Full size Gold Seal, lever filling pen and pencil set in burgundy & black (Tunis) plastic. $175-275.

WAHL, 1930-1932. Green & bronze plastic Gold Seal, lever filling *Equipoised* pens. Top to bottom; Full size "Soldier Clip" pen; roller clip oversize pen. Top to bottom: $300-400; $350-500.

WAHL, 1930-1932. Oversize Gold Seal, *Equipoised,* lever filling, roller clip pens in green & bronze, and black & pearl plastic. The standard models were fitted with 14k gold warranted nibs, not Gold Seal nibs. $350-500.

WAHL, 1930-1932. Gold Seal *Equipoised* lever filling pens, illustrating the sizes available. Left to right: $300-500; $300-400; $200-350; $125-200.

WAHL, 1931-1934. Roller clip *Doric* on the left compared to a 1935-1941 *Doric* on the right. Left to right: $175-275; $100-175.

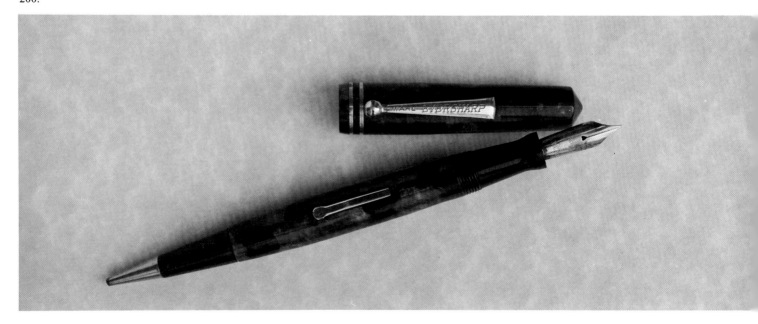

WAHL, 1930-1932. *Equipoised* lever filling roller clip, pen/pencil combination in burgundy & black plastic. $250-350.

WAHL, 1931-1932. Oversize *Doric* Gold Seal, Personal-Point, lever filling roller clip pen in black & pearl plastic. The rarest of the Dorics, this color is not generally associated with these later pens. $450-600.

WAHL, 1931-1934. Oversize *Doric* Gold Seal Personal-Point, roller clip, lever filling pens. Left to Right: Kashmir (silver pearl) plastic; Morocco (burgundy pearl) plastic; Cathay (silver green) plastic; jet (black) plastic; and Burma (green and black marble) plastic. $350-500.

WAHL, 1935-1941. Plastic plunger-vac filling pen. Jumping on the sacless bandwagon, Wahl's version like Sheaffer's, utilized a thin metal rod and washer. The mechanism in these pens is often found deteriorated, and is extremely difficult to repair. $50-75.

WAHL, 1935-1941. *Doric* plunger-vac, and lever filling pens, illustrating the available sizes. Pens were made in jet black; emerald green; silver shell; gold shell; sapphire blue; or garnet red plastic. Models of this time were available with either filling system. Left to right: $50-75; $100-175; $150-250.

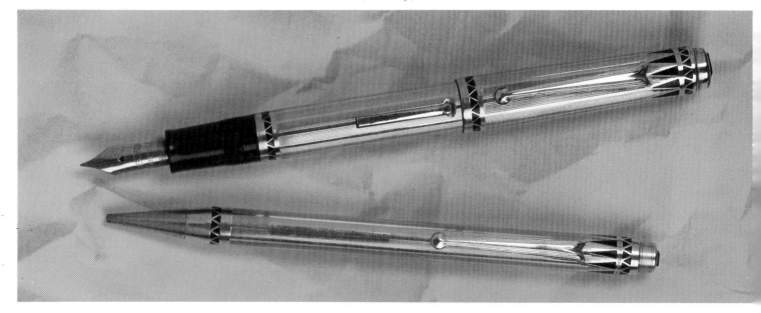

WAHL, 1936-1941. *Coronet* gold filled Personal-Point, lever filling pen and pencil set with jet Pyralin inserts. The most Art Deco styled pen produced by any manufacturer, it was also available with dubonnet (red) Pyralin inserts. $300-500.

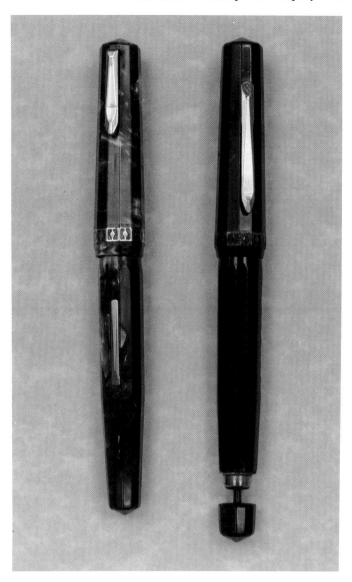

WAHL, 1935-1941. *Doric* plastic pens illustrating a lever filling, and plunger-vac filling model. $100-175.

WAHL, 1933. Midget plastic lever filling pen inscribed from the Century of Progress fair. $25-50.

WAHL, 1935-1941. Streamlined vacuum *Doric* bulb filling pen in silver web plastic. Thin and long, this unusual model was popular with stenographers. $125-200.

WAHL, 1936-1941. *Coronet* lever filling pens with gold filled, and rhodium plated caps. The pen on the top is fitted with the adjustable nib. $250-350.

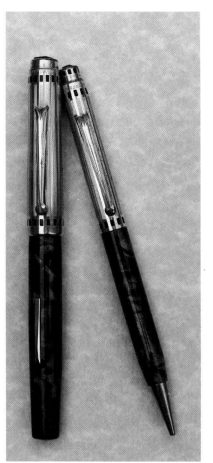

WAHL, 1936-1941. *Coronet* lever filling pen and pencil set featuring plastic barrels, and gold filled caps. This model *Coronet* was also available with rhodium plated caps, and various colored plastic barrels. $250-400.

EVERSHARP, 1936-1941. *Coronet* style repeater pencil in sterling silver. $25-50.

WAHL OXFORD, 1936-1941. The Oxford line of pens were budget models which did not feature a Gold Seal guarantee, or adjustable nib features. They were available as lever filling or plunger-vac filling models, in a variety of colors. $50-75.

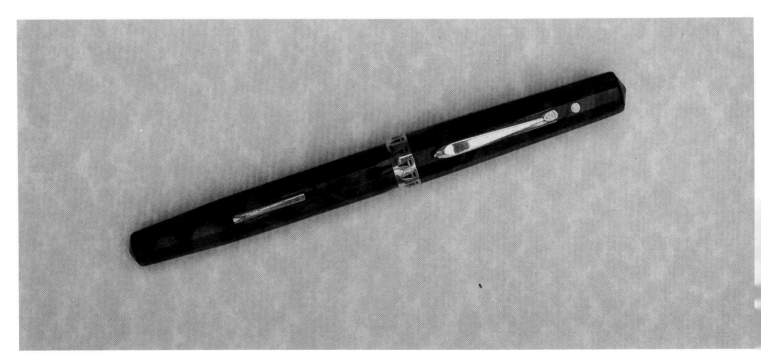

WAHL, 1935-1941. *Doric* Gold Seal, Personal-Point, lever filling pen in garnet red plastic. $100-175.

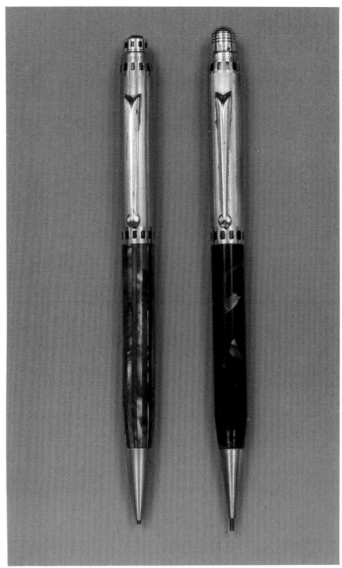

EVERSHARP, 1941-1949. *Skyline,* lever filling pens with gold filled derby caps in blue lines plastic. The extremely popular *Skyline* pen was available in many models, ranging from inexpensive plastic ones to solid 14k gold models. Illustrated here are two sizes: standard and short. A large Executive model was also made. $65-90.

EVERSHARP, 1941-1949. *Skyline,* lever filling pen and pencil set in gray lines pearl with wide gold filled band. This top of the line *Skyline* illustrates why these were such popular pens. $300-375.

EVERSHARP, 1936-1941. *Coronet* style repeater pencils with rhodium plated caps. $25-50.

WAHL, 1938-1941. Plastic lever filling pen and pencil set. $40-70.

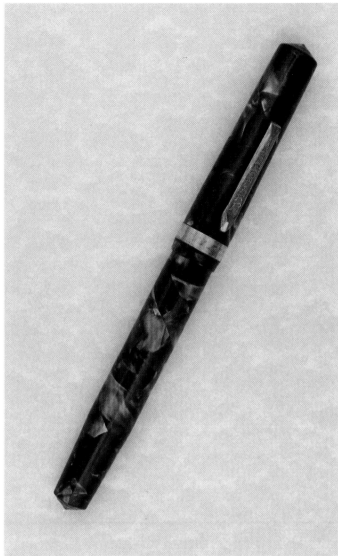

WAHL, 1938-1941. "Pacemaker," green plastic lever filling pen. This was the final Art Deco styled pen Wahl made, and was available in a variety of plastic colors. $50-75.

WAHL, 1938-1941. Blue marble plastic lever filling pen. $50-75.

EVERSHARP, 1940-1942. Gold Seal plastic lever filling pen. This was the first pen produced under the name Eversharp, the company having decided to merge the Wahl Pen and Eversharp Pencil divisions. $25-50.

EVERSHARP, 1941-1949. Lever filling *Skyline* pen with 14k gold cap, also referred to as the $64 pen. $150-225.

EVERSHARP, 1941-1949. *Skyline,* lever filling pen, in gold filled ribbed design. $150-225.

EVERSHARP, 1943-1946. "Fifth Avenue" $64 lever filling pen and pencil set with 14k gold caps and trim. Eversharp brought out this hooded nib pen to compete with the Parker *51.* It never lived up to expectations either in performance, or popularity, and was soon dropped. $200-300.

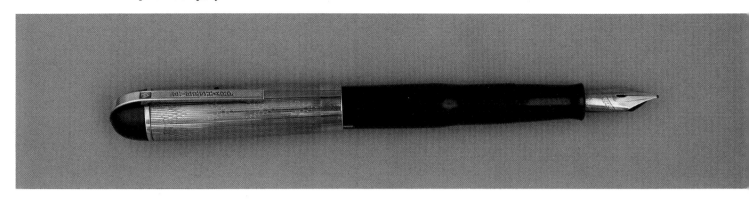

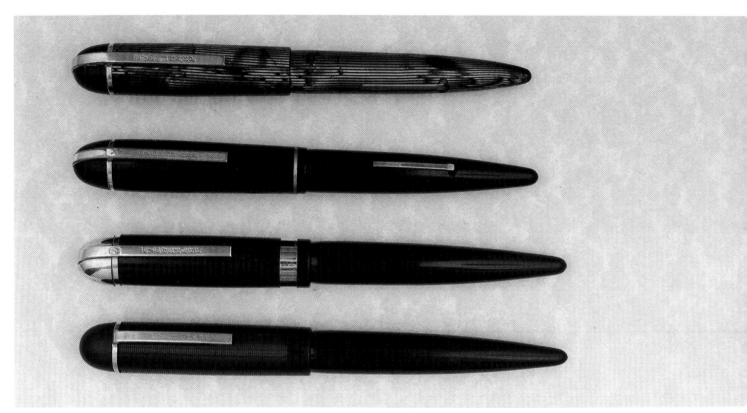

EVERSHARP, 1941-1949. *Skyline* lever filling pens. $60-90.

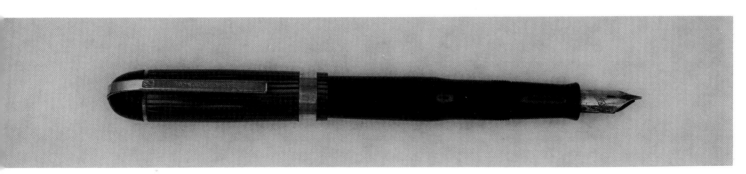

EVERSHARP, 1941-1949. *Skyline* lever filling pens. $60-90.

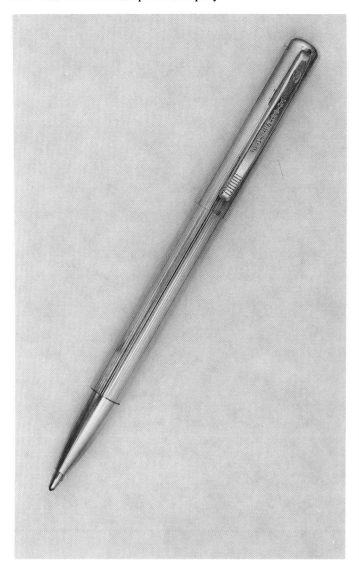

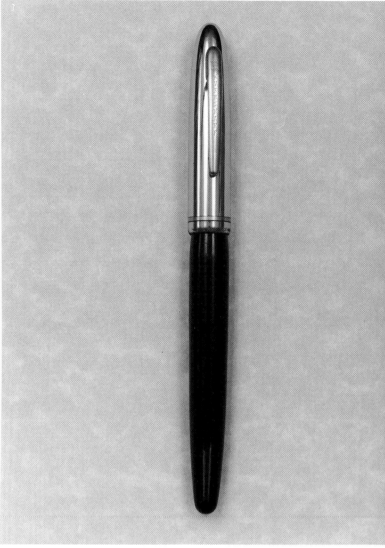

EVERSHARP, 1946-1950. *CA,* gold filled ballpoint pen. Eversharp, having obtained the rights to Lazlo Biro's rolling ball pen, hoped to revolutionize the industry with this pen. Unfortunately they were scooped in 1945 by Milton Reynolds, and although the ballpoint pen did revolutionize the industry, it was not the *CA* which did it. $25-50.

EVERSHARP, 1950-1954. Lever filling "Symphony" pen, designed by Raymond Loewy. $50-70.

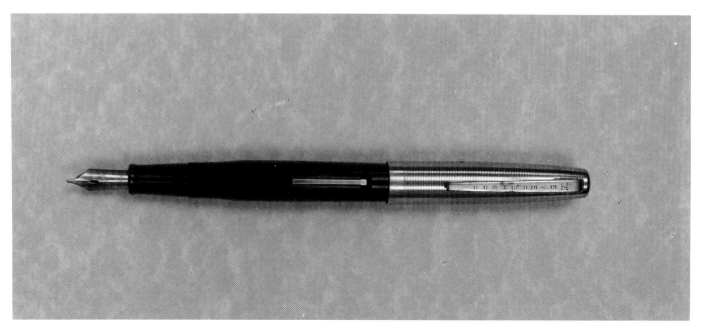

EVERSHARP, 1954-1957. Lever filling *Ventura* "burp" pen, with gold filled cap. The "pen that burps itself", was the last pen introduced by Eversharp prior to their purchase by Parker. $30-60.

Chapter 8

Montblanc

1908-Present

Montblanc's predecessor, the Simplo-Filler Pen Company was founded in 1908, in Hamburg, Germany, by a stationer, a banker and an engineer. Simplo-Filler began by making eyedropper filled models. About 1910-1911, Christian Lausen and Wilhelm Dziambor joined the company and the name was changed to the "Simplo Fountain Pen Company." Also at that time, Simplo began making a safety pen similar to the Waterman safety pen.

The top of the line of the Simplo pens was called the *Mont Blanc*. It was made with a red or black barrel and cap and a crown of white. In 1913, the white cap evolved into the white star design which was registered as a trademark and looked more like the snow-topped summit of the Mont Blanc mountain which it was supposed to symbolize. Mont Blanc's height was 4,810 meters. This height eventually was marked on the Montblanc pen nibs and indicated craftsmanship at its highest.

In 1914, during a period of German nationalism, the company changed its name to "Simplo Fullhalter Gmbh." and began to expand its line of pens. In the 1920s, Simplo began making pens with ink sacs inside and a simple filling system similar to the Parker *Duofold* button filler. The *Masterpiece* pen, which later became the *Diplomat,* was introduced in 1924. The Montblanc trademark was so successful that in 1934, Simplo Fountain Pen Company changed its name to the Montblanc Pen Company. Also about this time, they introduced the twisting piston filler which is still made today. The Montblanc pen evolved into the status symbol that it is today, but most collectors seek the earlier models. Many Montblanc pens were covered with precious metals whose design work is both beautiful and of the highest quality.

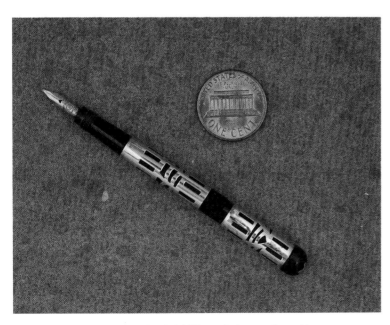

MONTBLANC, ca. 1915-1925. Gold filigree design overlay, midget safety pen. $1500-2250.

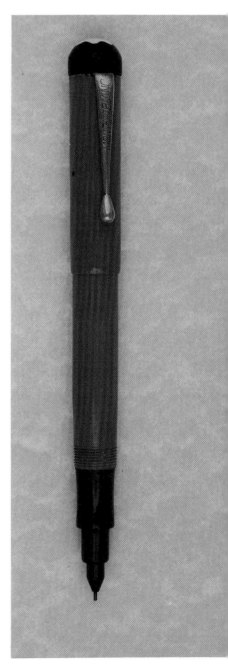

MONTBLANC, ca. 1915-1925. Red hard rubber stylographic pen. $200-350.

MONTBLANC #2M, ca. 1920-1930. Sterling silver web filigree design overlay, safety pen. $2000-3000.

MONTBLANC #1F, ca. 1920-1930. Sterling silver web filigree design overlay, safety pen. $2500-3000.

MONTBLANC #2M, ca. 1915-1930. Silver overlay safety pen. $1250-1750.

MONTBLANC #12H, ca. 1920-1930. Giant black hard rubber safety pen. $5500-6500.

MONTBLANC #6, ca. 1915-1930. Silver etched pattern overlay safety pen. $4500-6000.

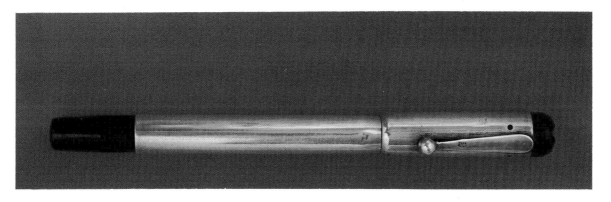

MONTBLANC, ca. 1915-1930. Silver overlay safety pen. $750-1000.

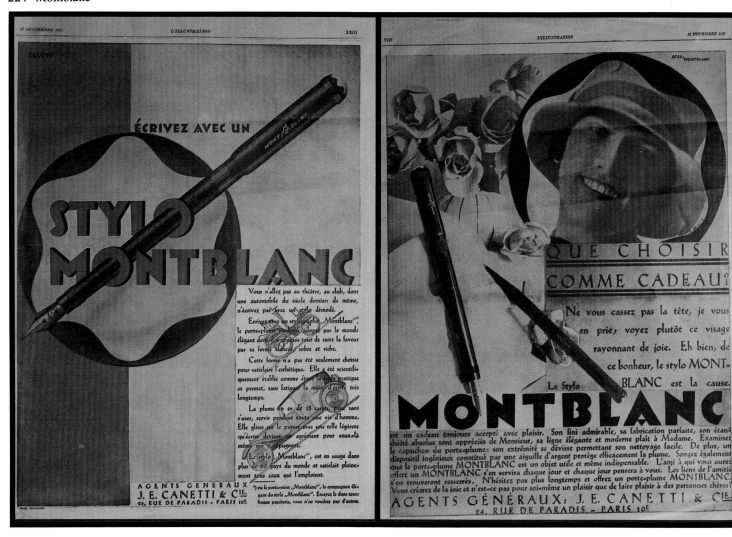

MONTBLANC 1927 advertisements.

MONTBLANC #46, ca. 1925-1935. Red & black hard rubber pencil.
$150-250.

MONTBLANC, ca. 1948-present. Black plastic #146, and #149 twist
filling "Masterpiece" pens. Top to bottom: $75-150; $100-175.

MONTBLANC, ca. 1925-1930. Black plastic stylographic pen. $125-200.

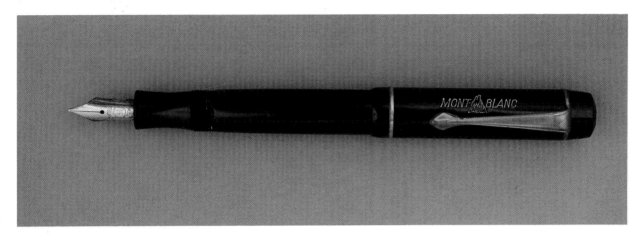

MONTBLANC #333, ca. 1935-1940. Black plastic twist filling pen. $150-300.

MONTBLANC #244, ca. 1950-1955. Striped plastic twist filling pen. $1000-1500.

MONTBLANC #146G, ca. 1949-1960. Green striped plastic twist filling "Masterpiece" pen. $750-1200.

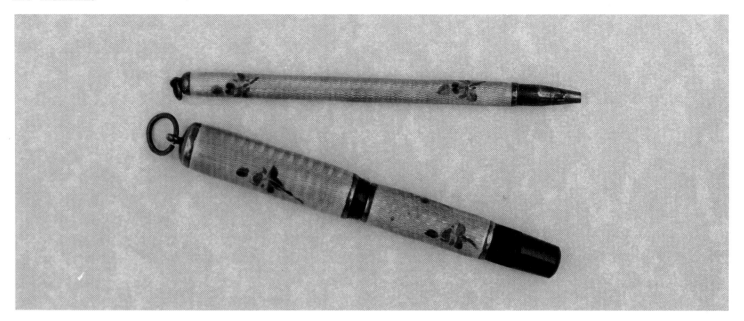

MONTBLANC (?), ca. 1920-1930. Enamel floral design overlay, midget safety pen and pencil set. Set not marked but matches other Montblanc pens of this type. $300-500.

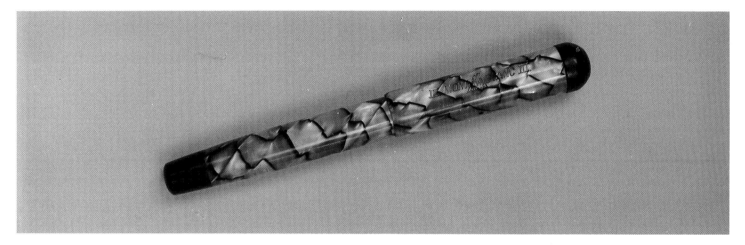

MONTBLANC, ca. 1930-1935. Black & pearl plastic safety pen. $300-500.

MONTBLANC #139, ca. 1938-1948. "Masterpiece" black plastic twist filling pen. This large pen was the predecessor to the current Montblanc "Masterpiece" pen. $500-700.

Chapter 9
Conklin Pen Company
1898-1947

The Conklin Pen Company was founded by Roy Conklin in 1898 in Toledo, Ohio. Conklin is best known for their "Crescent Filler" pens (1901-1928). The "Crescent Filler" was patented in 1901 & 1903 and consisted of a bar inside the pen attached to a crescent that protruded outside the barrel which contained an ink sac. Ink was drawn into the pen by pushing down on the crescent. The crescent was locked in place by a knurled hard rubber band that turned freely around a groove in the barrel. The design was simple, no eyedropper was necessary and the pen enjoyed great success in sales. Colors were usually black or mottle red & black with some models having silver or gold filled overlays. Conklin was among the four largest pen companies until Wahl took over that position in sales volume about 1924.

Dating Conklin Pens

Early Conklins had friction fit caps, but beginning in 1910, screw on caps were introduced to some models including the "Non-Leakable" style, introduced about 1910. "Crescent Fillers" made before 1908 had either no markings on the crescent or the words "Conklins Self Filling Pen". From 1908, the crescent was marked "Trademark" with the words "Crescent Filler" and after 1918 the crescent moon was used and the word "Conklin" added to the other side. With exceptions, you can also date Conklins by their numbering system. The early models (1903-1910) usually had an "S" and a number denoting size of the nib. The "Non-Leakable" models (1910-1918) used an "NL" or a "P" (for pocket models) and the "Standard" models (1918 and on) had numbers 20 through 75. Pens made before 1910 were marked "Conklin's" on the barrel which was changed to "Conklin" in late 1910. Pocket clips were introduced about 1916. Lever filler pens first appeared in late 1922—1923. It is believed that Conklin did not make any pens in red (orange) hard rubber until after 1922. The *Durograph* pen followed in early 1924 and in late 1924 they introduced their popular *Endura* model (1924-1932) which was "Unconditionally and Perpetually Guaranteed". The *Endura* was available in red or black, with "mahogany" introduced in 1925 and "sapphire blue" in 1926. By 1929 they were making "lime green", black and gold, and pearl and black. They continued to make the "Crescent Filler" pens unchanged except for a squared off cap (about 1924).

A handsome line of gold filled, silver and 14kt gold metal *Endura* style pens was made in the 1920s and plastic pens were introduced in 1926 with the sapphire blue model. In 1930, they introduced a streamlined pen called the *Symetrik* and in 1932 introduced their *Nozac* pen (1932-1938) designed by Louis Vavrik. It was available in a round or 10-sided version. The *Nozac* pen was different in that it had a twist filler similar to the Montblanc filling system. Some models had a word counter on the side of the transparent barrel that would tell the writer how many words worth of ink were left. These models were 12-sided at first and then were made 14-sided.

Conklin ran into financial difficulties during the Depression and sales lagged. In 1938, the company was sold to a syndicate in Chicago. This syndicate also made other pens: the *Park-O-Type*, the *Waltham*, the *Winchester* and the *Starr Pen*. The following from a 1944 Consumer's Research Bulletin sums up the quality of a Conklin pen of the 1940s, "One dollar. Iridium-tipped stainless-steel type alloy point. Transparent feed section. Writing quality, poor. Ink capacity, poor. The Federal Trade Commission has charged that the products of this company are of a grade inferior to the original Conklin, which was made by a well and favorably-known manufacturer of high-grade pens. Not Recommended."

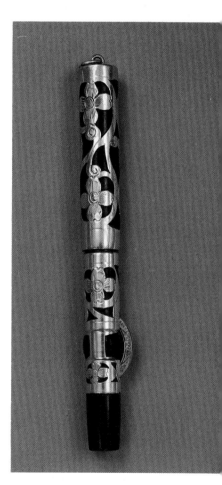

CONKLIN, ca. 1908-1918. Gold filled filigree design overlay, crescent filling lady's pen. $350-500.

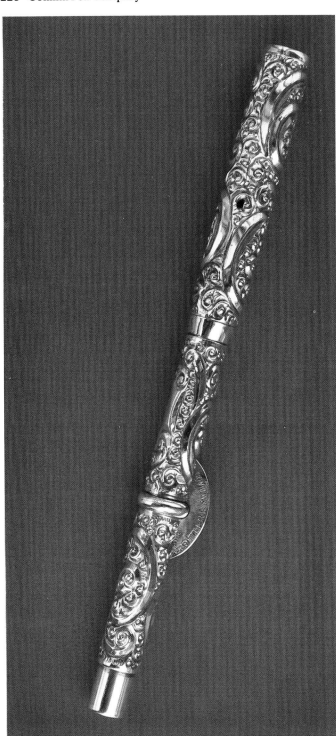

CONKLIN, ca. 1901-1903. Gold filled, and sterling silver crescent filling pens. These heavily embellished pens illustrate the earliest crescent filling mechanism, patented in 1901. These pens are the finest example of Roy Conklin's dedication to high quality pens. $3500-4500.

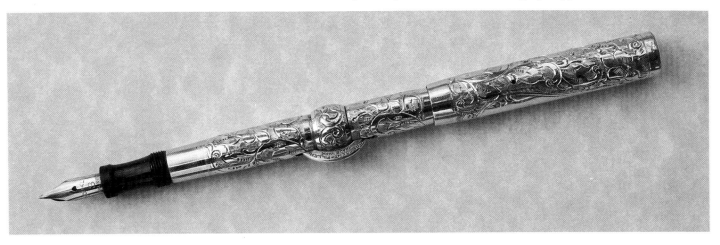

CONKLIN, ca. 1908-1918. Gold filled hand engraved design overlay, crescent filling pen. $650-850.

CONKLIN, ca. 1903-1908. Gold filled, and sterling filigree design overlay, crescent filling slip cap pens. Left to right: $850-1100; $900-1400.

CONKLIN, ca. 1908-1918. Gold filled filigree design overlay, crescent filling pen. $600-750.

CONKLIN, ca. 1908-1910. Black hard rubber crescent filling slip cap pen. $75-95.

CONKLIN, ca. 1903-1908. Black chased hard rubber crescent filling taper cap pen with two gold filled bands. $300-400.

CONKLIN, ca. 1918-1920. Gold filled filigree design overlay, crescent filling pen with military clip. $350-450.

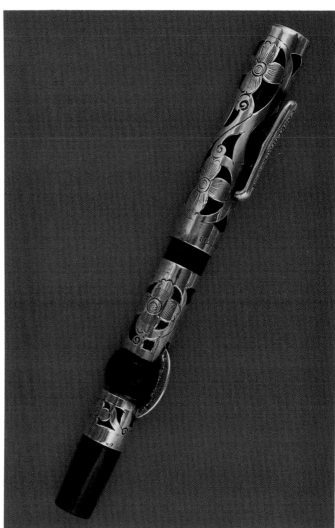

CONKLIN, ca. 1918-1926. Gold filled, and sterling silver filigree design overlay, crescent filling pens. Left to right: $250-400; $850-1100.

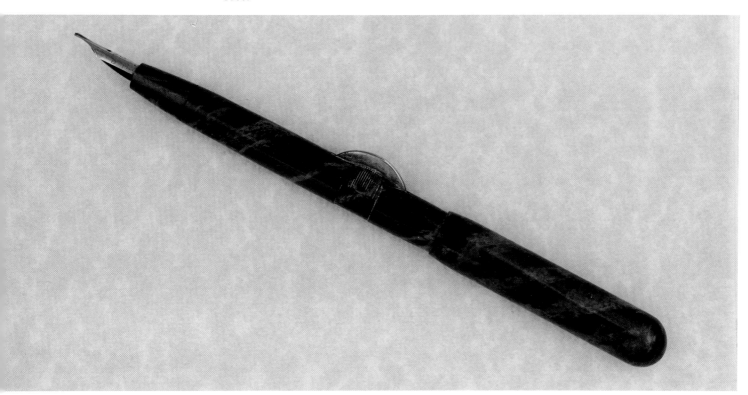

CONKLIN, ca. 1908-1910. Red & black hard rubber, crescent filling pen with slip cap. $400-550.

CONKLIN, ca. 1908-1918. Gold filled, and sterling silver filigree design overlay, crescent filling pens. Left to right: $300-500; $900-1200.

CONKLIN, ca. 1918-1920. Black chased hard rubber crescent filling pen with military clip. $50-75.

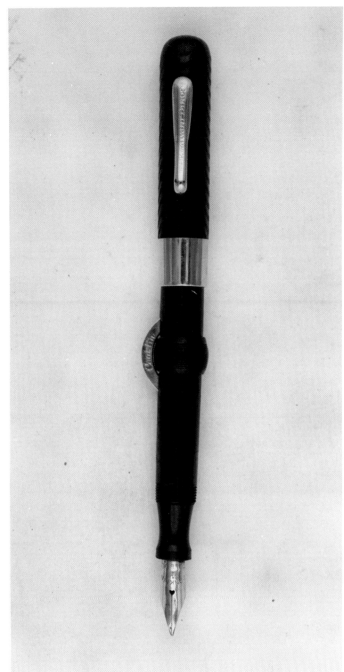

CONKLIN #50, ca. 1918-1924. Black chased hard rubber crescent filling pen with gold filled band. $200-275.

CONKLIN #8, ca. 1918-1924. Black hard rubber crescent filling pen with gold filled band. $300-450.

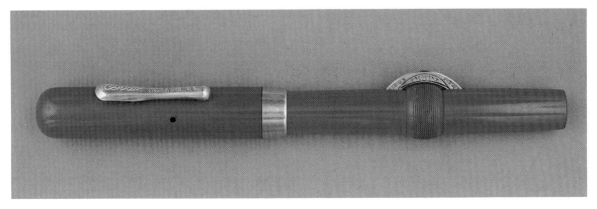

CONKLIN, ca. 1923-1926. Red hard rubber, crescent filling pen. $500-650.

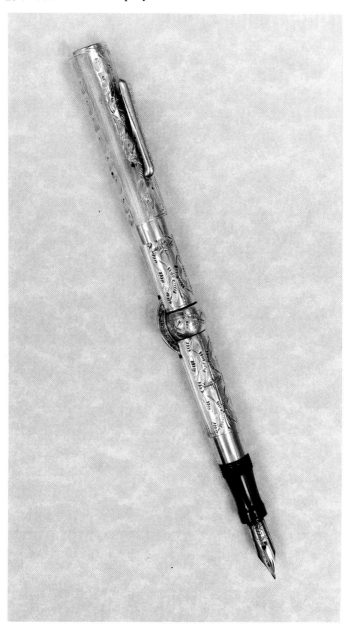

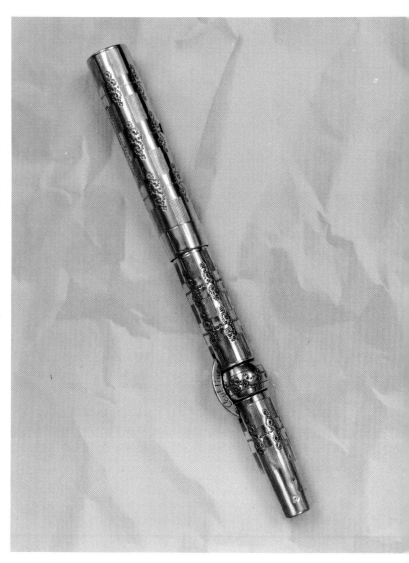

CONKLIN, ca. 1918-1926. Gold filled hand engraved design overlay crescent filling pen. $350-450.

CONKLIN, ca. 1918-1926. Gold filled engraved design overlay, crescent filling pen. $400-550.

CONKLIN, ca. 1924-1926. *Endura* large red hard rubber, lever filling pen and pencil set. $350-500.

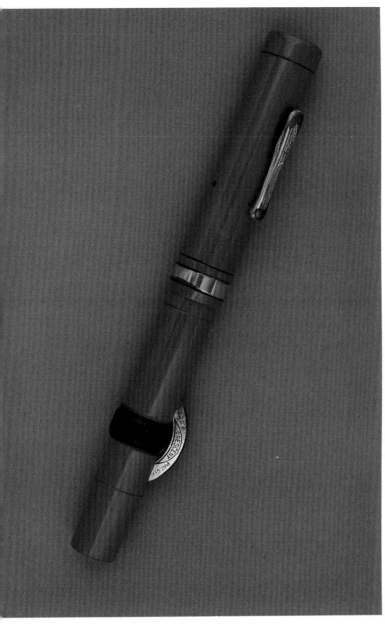

CONKLIN, ca. 1924-1928. Black chased hard rubber crescent filling pen. $50-75.

CONKLIN, ca. 1924-1926. *Endura* large crescent filling pen in red hard rubber. It is unusual to find crescent filling *Endura* pens. $400-600.

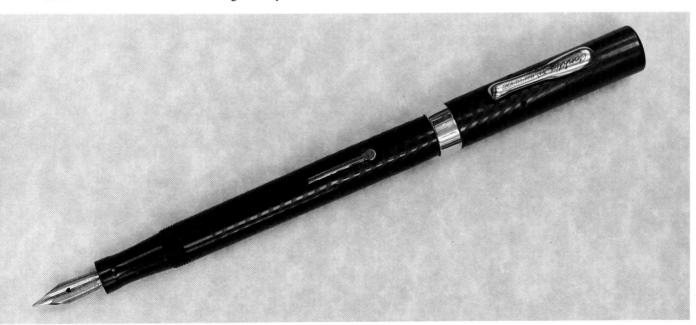

CONKLIN, ca. 1923-1924. Black chased hard rubber lever filling pen. This was Conklin's first lever filling pen. $75-100.

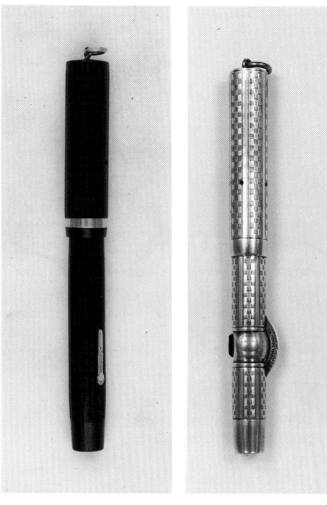

CONKLIN, ca. 1927-1932. *Endura* lady's lever filling pen in black plastic. $25-50.

CONKLIN, ca. 1918-1926. Sterling silver checkered design overlay, crescent filling lady's pen. $75-150.

CONKLIN, ca. 1925-1932. *Endura* lever filling mahogany hard rubber pen. $100-175.

CONKLIN, ca. 1923-1929. Sterling silver lever filling pen. This solidly made pen is typical of Conklin's line of metal pens made in the mid 1920s. $125-225.

CONKLIN, ca. 1927-1932. *Endura* large lever filling pen in black & pearl plastic. $225-300.

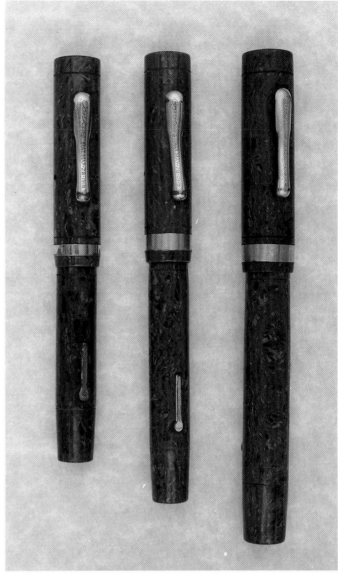

CONKLIN, ca. 1926-1932. *Endura* lever filling pens in sapphire blue plastic, illustrating the three sizes available. Left to right: $150-225; $175-275; $300-400.

CONKLIN, ca. 1927-1932. *Endura* large lever filling pens in lime green, red, and black & gold plastic. $275-400.

CONKLIN, ca. 1930-1932. *Ensemble* lever filling pen/pencil combination in black & gold plastic. $300-400.

CONKLIN, ca. 1934-1938. *Nozac* 12 sided herringbone design, twist filling plastic pens. Left to right: $175-275; $275-400.

CONKLIN, ca. 1940-1944. Chicago made model lever filling pen and pencil. Left to right: $25-50; $15-30.

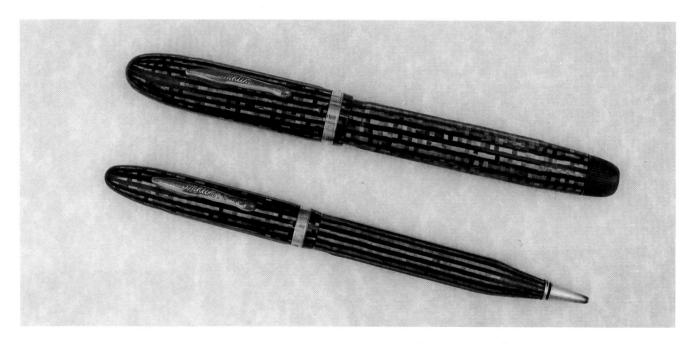

CONKLIN, ca. 1934-1938. *Nozac* 12 sided twist filling pen and pencil set. $275-400.

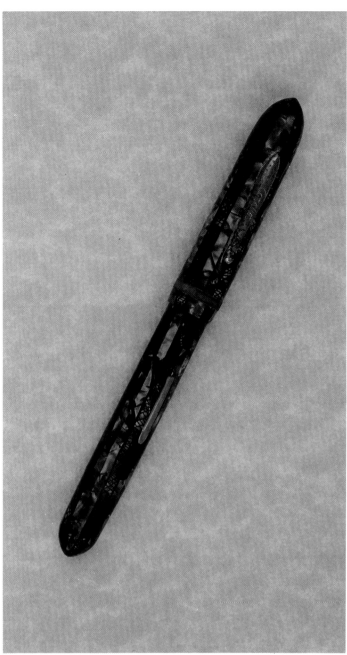

CONKLIN, ca. 1938-1940. Early Chicago made, lever filling pens fitted with 14k gold nibs, in marblized plastic. $25-50.

CONKLIN, ca. 1932-1934. *Nozac* green marble plastic twist filling pen with round barrel. The round design was used for the first *Nozac* pens. $75-125.

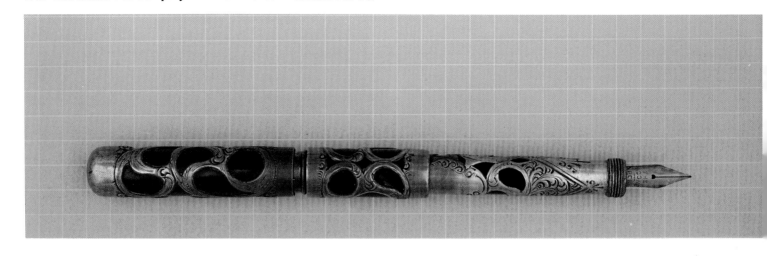

MOORE, ca. 1900-1910. Fancy sterling silver, and gold filled overlay, safety pens, made by American Fountain Pen Co. under Moore's patent. These are examples of the ornate designs used by Moore early in the century. Top: $950-1200. Left to right: $650-850; $600-800; $350-500.

Chapter 10

The Moore Pen Company
1896-1956
and The American Fountain Pen Co.
1899-1917

The Moore Pen Company story is somewhat unusual in that a pen was produced that was designed by Mr. Moore, but Mr. Moore was never a part of the company that began production. Morris W. Moore of Holyoke, Massachusetts patented a pen with a retractable nib on September 8, 1896. It was similar in design to the Waterman safety pen as the nib retracted into the barrel and was filled with an eyedropper. The pen was different in that a separate lower barrel was slid upward to push the nib straight up to writing position. To close the pen, the nib was withdrawn by sliding the lower barrel downward. The cap sealed the barrel and the pen did not leak. It was a workable design that held a sizable quantity of ink.

Moore began looking for someone to produce his pen and a partnership was soon entered into with Francis C. Brown to make the pen in New York City. There is no evidence that any pens were ever produced by Brown and Moore and the partnership ended in 1899 with Francis Brown getting the patents on the pen.

The first Moore pens were produced by the American Fountain Pen Company of 711 Boylston Street, Boston. American Pen was founded by a group of Boston businessmen in 1899. Among them was Walter F. Cushing, a partner in the stationery firm of Adams, Cushing and Foster. Adams, Cushing and Foster was at that time the sales agent for the A.T. Cross pen, a leading maker of stylographic pens. American Pen had acquired the patents to Moore's *Non-Leakable* pen and began producing the *Non-Leakable* line of Moore's Pens in late, 1899. The pen was a good seller and the company made a reasonable profit selling the same pen basically without modification.

1917 was a big year for American Pen. They changed their name and acquired some new pen patents. They were reorganized as the Moore Pen Company with Walter F. Cushing becoming its president after his short stay in another management position. Also in 1917, the Boston Pen Company, a quality competitor of American Pen, was offered for sale. The new Moore Pen Company was one of the bidders and acquired a few bits and pieces of Boston Pen. Included were the employees who did not wish to move to Chicago, some large machinery that was not practicable to move to Chicago, the rights to use a patent for a form of lever filler and a comb feed. Boston Pen, you will recall, was sold to the Wahl Adding Machine Company which wanted to acquire a going pen manufacturer to enable it to get into the fountain pen business.

The Moore *Non-Leakable* pen remained virtually unchanged during its lifetime (1899-1929). One change was invisible to the user but did stop a great deal of nib damage caused by the original design of the pen. The nib of the *Non-Leakable* could break if the user forgot to retract the nib when closing the pen. The tip of the nib would catch in the cap and twist and bend. In 1919, Moore installed a pusher rod in the cap. This rod pushed down the nib, feed and inner section when the cap was closed, thereby protecting the point from damage.

Moore began making lever filler pens under the Boston patent in 1918. They resemble the early Wahl *Tempoints* and the predecessor Boston pens. Nothing new was added to these pen designs. It could be said that Moore lacked innovation. Their product line in the 1920s and 1930s had little to offer over the other quality pen manufacturers except, perhaps, price. Their

MOORE, ca. 1918-1922. Black chased hard rubber eyedropper filled pen with gold filled band. $30-60.

MOORE, ca. 1918-1924. Black hard rubber lever filling ladies pen. $35-50.

pens were very well made and the company stood behind their product, but they began to reproduce what the other pen makers produced. When Sheaffer came out with a white dot to signify their lifetime models, Moore came out with a "Red Dot" (1925-1929). When Parker made a "Big Red", Moore made a big red pen. After Eversharp introduced the *Doric*, Moore, in 1932, introduced its ten-sided pen. Moore, however, was slower to follow the leads of the other pen makers into plastic. They began to make plastic pens about 1927, three to four years after Sheaffer's first plastic pen.

Moore pens were not substantially cheaper than their competition's. One can compare and contrast the difference between Eagle Pencil Company copies and Moore copies. The Moore copies were made just as well as the other companies' original pen and sold for a price that was 65% to 75% as much. When given the choice, the customer bought the Waterman or Sheaffer for a little more money. Eagle's tactic was to offer a look-alike pen at less than half as much money. The pens were well-made but nowhere near the quality of the original. Where money was a deciding factor in a purchase, the cheaper look-alike pen was the one that made the sale. Moore's copying did nothing to distinguish their pens from these cheaper copies and their sales suffered as a result.

During the 1920s and 1930s, Moore exhibited a lack of direction and indecision similar to that which plagued the Wahl-Eversharp Company in the 1930s and 1940s. Numerous pen lines were produced to cater to every whim of the consumer. Pens appeared, lasted a few years, and disappeared. Several lines overlapped, being produced at the same time as another competing Moore pen. Moore was actually trying to compete with all of the pen manufacturers at the same time.

In 1946, Moore attempted to produce a pen that would compete with the Parker 51 and the Sheaffer *Triumph*. They created the *Fingertip Pen* (1946-1950), a Buck Rogers-like, spaceship-shaped pen. It was an appealing pen that, when opened, looked as if it were from another world. Unfortunately for Moore, it was not a best seller. It may have been that the thin look was in and the *Fingertip* was not a thin pen. Once it was closed, it looked just like any other pre-Parker 51 pen. The *Fingertip* was made in many sizes and colors and although it is not easy to find, it makes a good addition to any collection of pens from the 1940s.

Moore's last pen was the *Specialist* (1950-1956). It was a cheap, brass capped pen with an aerometric filler. Moore decided to close down its operations without having ever made a ballpoint pen. When the ballpoint pen caught on, the fountain pen business stopped.

MOORE, ca. 1900-1910. Gold filled chased design overlay, safety pens, made by American Fountain Pen Co. Top to bottom: $300-400; $650-850.

MOORE, ca. 1905-1917. Black chased hard rubber safety pens made by the American Fountain Pen Co. Left to right: $30-65; $40-75; $40-75.

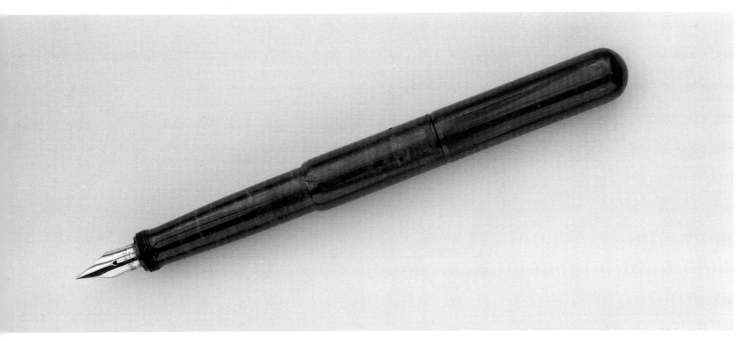

MOORE, ca. 1908-1917. Large red & black mottled hard rubber safety pen made by American Fountain Pen Co. $300-400.

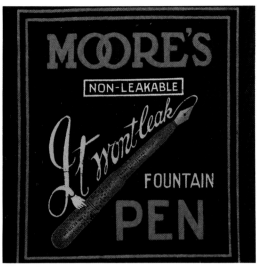

MOORE, ca. 1915. Felt counter mat. $150-175.

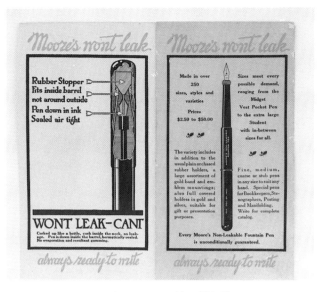

MOORE, ca. 1920. Safety pen pamphlet. $35-60.

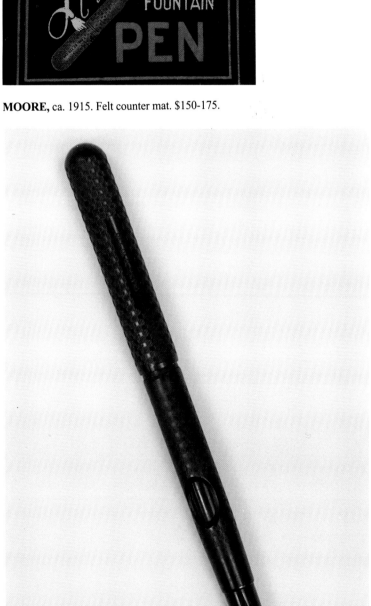

MOORE, ca. 1917-1926. *Banker* model black chased hard rubber safety pen. This pen was unusual in that it could be closed with the nib exposed, or retracted. $50-75.

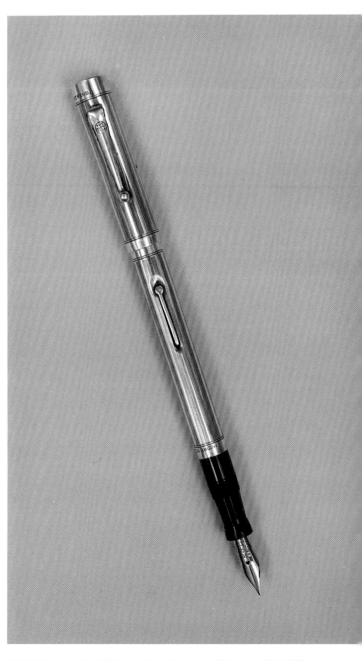

MOORE, ca. 1922-1930. Sterling silver lever filling pen. $150-250.

MOORE, ca. 1929-1935. *Maniflex* lever filling pens in brown, green marble, and black & pearl plastic. Top; $75-125, bottom left; $100-150, bottom right; $100-150.

MOORE, ca. 1930-1935. *Maniflex* streamlined lever filling pens in marble plastic. Left; $50-75, right; $50-75.

MOORE, ca. 1930-1935. *Maniflex* lever filling pen and pencil set in black & pearl plastic. Top; $75-100, bottom; $75-100.

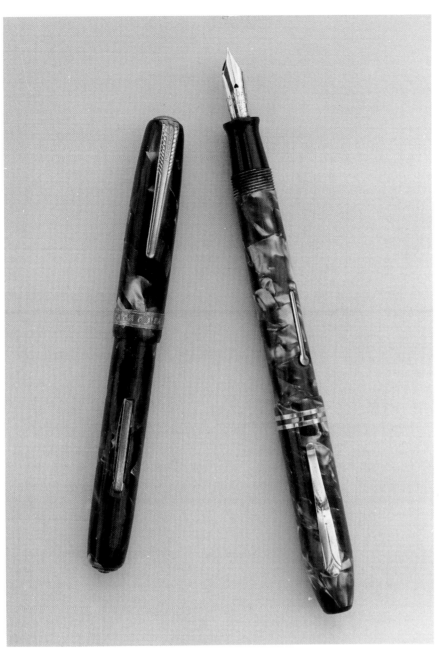

MOORE, ca. 1938-1946. Plastic lever filling pens in marble plastic,
illustrating the various pens available. $40-65.

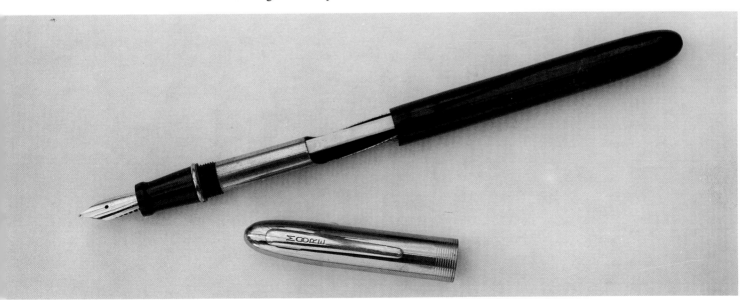

MOORE, 1950-1956. *Specialist* aerometric filling pen with brass cap.
The final model produced by Moore, a sad end for an illustrious
company. $30-40.

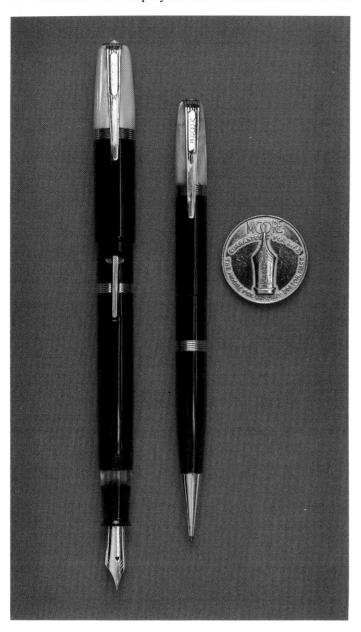

MOORE, 1939-1946. Lifetime *Maniflex* lever filling pen and pencil set with lifetime guarantee coin. A difficult pen to find, this model was brought out to compete with Sheaffer's Lifetime guarantee. $100-150.

MOORE, ca. 1946-1950. *Fingertip* model lever filling pen with chrome cap. $150-250.

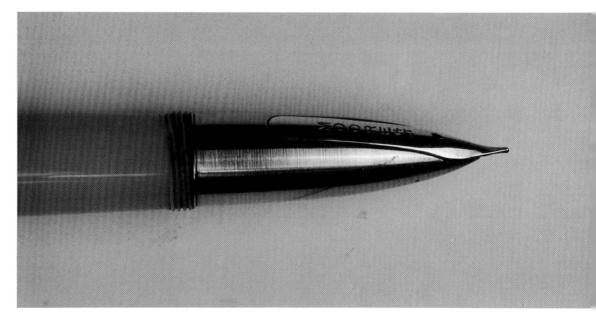

MOORE, ca. 1946. Closeup of the *Fingertip* nib.

Chapter 11
A.A. Waterman Pen Co.
1897-1920

The A.A. Waterman Pen Company was founded about 1897 in New York City by Arthur A. Waterman, who was no relation to L.E. Waterman. A.A. Waterman was known for their *New Lincoln* pen (1904-1907) which was a regular eyedropper filler pen, their middle joint filler pen (1902-1907) and their *Modern Automatic Self Filler*, a twist filler (1902-1920). There are some exceptionally beautiful models made in gold filled metal and silver. Arthur A. Waterman was pushed out of his company in 1905 when Frazier & Geyer successfully sued him and took over the company. About 1912, L.E. Waterman also sued the A.A. Waterman Company and forced them to put a disclaimer stating, "Not connected with the L.E. Waterman Co." on all of their pens and advertising. The A.A. Waterman Pen Company began to fade away about 1916 and was just a memory by the 1920s. The company is believed to have been sold to the Chicago Safety Pen Company.

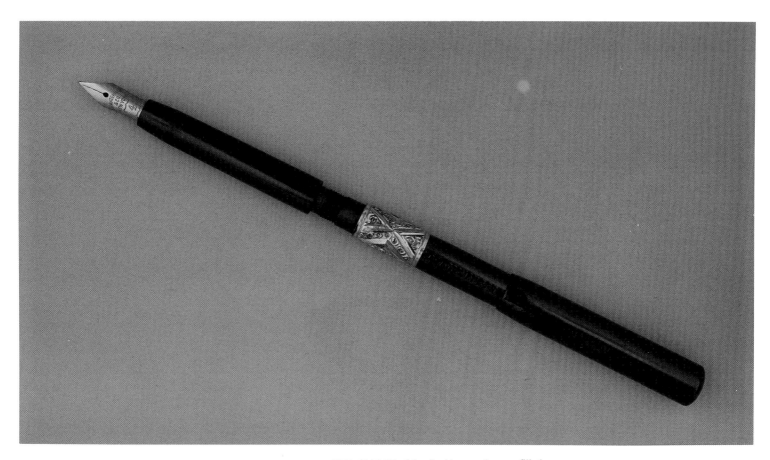

A.A. WATERMAN, ca. 1902-1907. Black hard rubber eyedropper filled middle joint pen with gold filled band. $60-90.

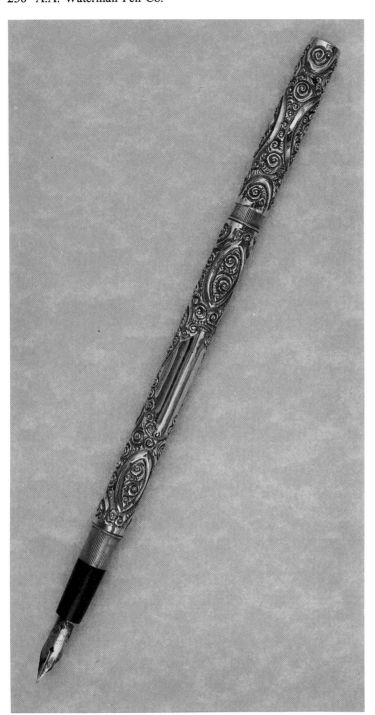

A.A. WATERMAN, ca. 1902-1905. Gold filled, and sterling silver chased design overlay, eyedropper filled pens. Left to right: $600-800; $500-650.

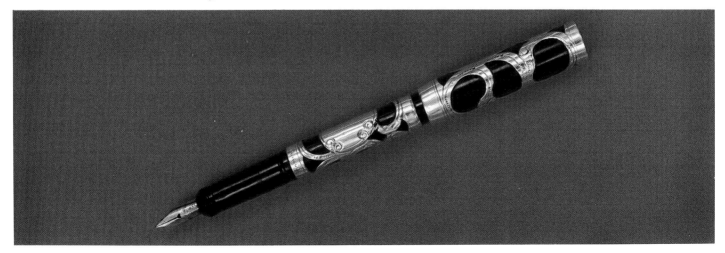

A.A. WATERMAN, ca. 1905-1912. Gold filled overlay, eyedropper pen. $75-125.

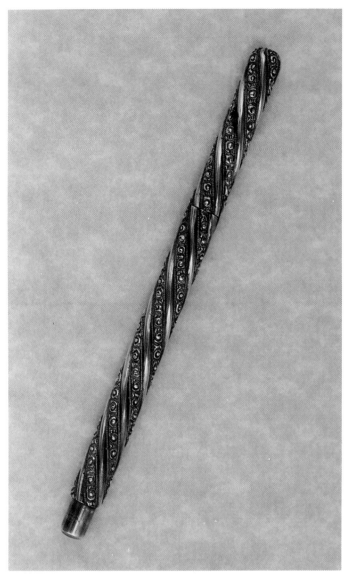

A.A. WATERMAN, ca. 1905-1910. Sterling silver cable chased design overlay, eyedropper filled pen. $650-850.

A.A. WATERMAN, ca. 1902-1907. Gold filled chased design overlay, eyedropper filled taper cap pen. $600-800.

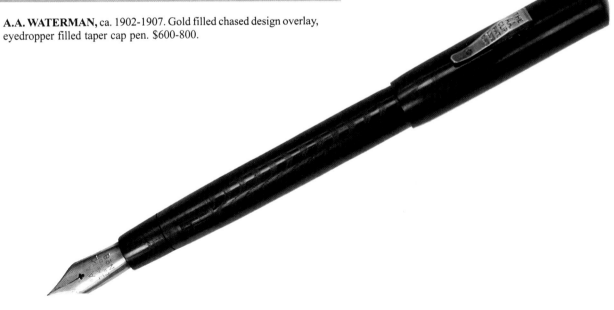

A.A. WATERMAN #8, ca. 1912-1915. Black chased hard rubber eyedropper filled pen. $175-225.

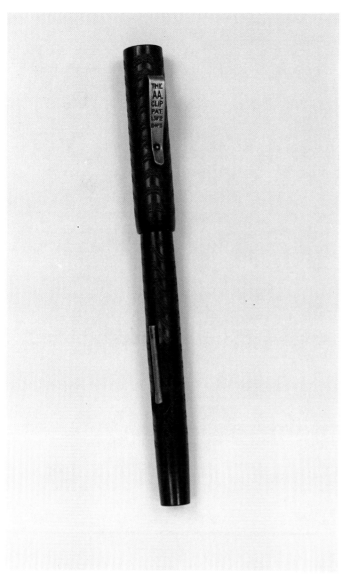

A.A. WATERMAN, ca. 1915-1920. Black chased hard rubber lever filling pen. $40-60.

A.A. WATERMAN, ca. 1905-1912. Gold filled overlay, twist filling pens. Left to right: $500-750; $450-650.

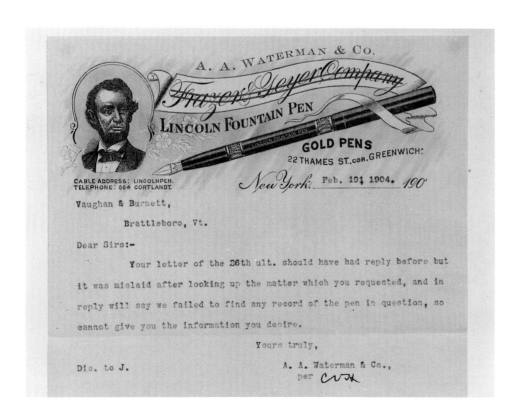

A.A. WATERMAN, 1904. Letterhead illustrating the company's origins. $65-85.

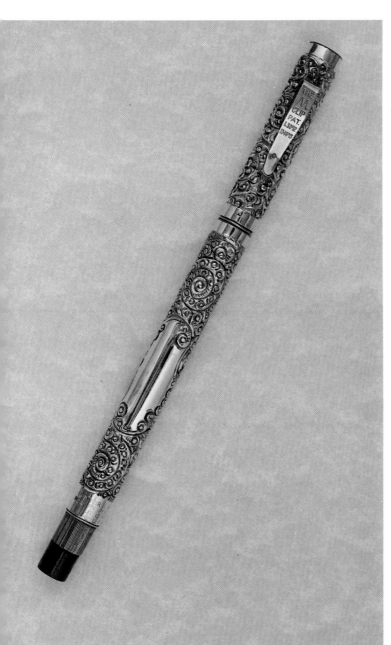

A.A. WATERMAN, ca. 1912-1915. Elaborate floral and chased design
gold filled overlay, twist filling pens. Left to right: $400-600; $650-850.

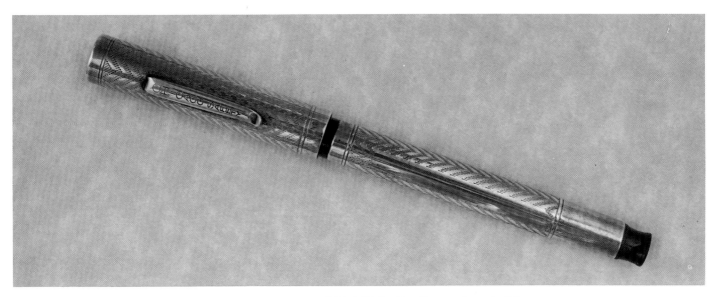

A.A. WATERMAN, ca. 1921-1923. Sterling silver overlay, twist filling
pen, marked "Chicago Safety Pen". $150-225.

A.A. WATERMAN #8, ca. 1912-1915. Red & Black mottled hard rubber eyedropper filled pen. $350-500.

A.A. WATERMAN, ca. 1915-1920. Black chased hard rubber safety pen. $75-100.

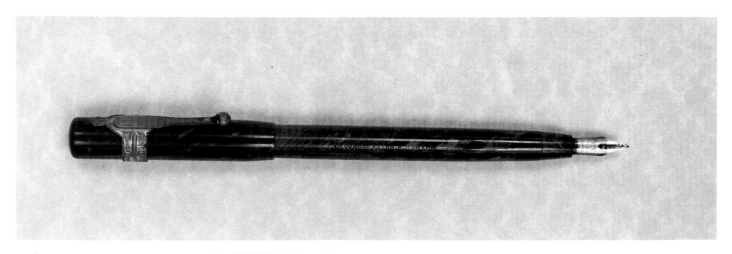

A.A. WATERMAN, ca. 1905-1912. Red & black mottled hard rubber eyedropper filled pen. $50-100.

Chapter 12

Crocker Pen

1902-1931

and Chilton Pen

1923-1941

The Crocker Pen Company was started about 1902 in Massachusetts by Seth S. Crocker. Crocker Pen was a small company that made very high quality eyedropper filled and blow filler pens. Crocker's first blow filler pen was patented on July 16, 1901. It had a simple hole in the end of the barrel. One simply blew into it. The air collapsed the sac and the ink was drawn into the pen. Another blow filler was patented on August 9, 1904. This one had the hole on the side of the end of the pen.

Crocker was originally located at 88 Broad Street in Boston and moved to 163 Oliver Street about 1903. The pens marked "S.S. Crocker Pen" were most likely made in 1905 & 1906. Seth S. Crocker's son, Seth Chilton Crocker, took over the company about 1907, renaming it the "S.C. Crocker Pen Company". He moved the company to 79 Nassau Street, New York City. Crocker made an improved blow filler pen and a hatchet filler. His blow filler pen was patented on May 2, 1916. The hatchet filler was a long lever filler. It worked like the standard lever filler but the lever was secured to the barrel by screwing down a blind cap connected to the end of the lever. The name and patents of the Crocker Pen Company were sold to Nicholas Zaino in 1930-31.

In 1923, Seth C. Crocker started another pen company, the Chilton Pen Company, of Boston, Massachusetts and began using a new patented pump filler pen. These early Boston Chiltons are very nicely made pens. To fill the pen, the barrel would be pulled up from the section exposing a metal tube which contained an ink sac. Pushing down the barrel compressed the ink sac with air pressure. This design enabled the Chilton to hold a larger ink sac and more ink.

CROCKER, ca. 1916-1920. Red & black mottled hard rubber "Ink-Tite" blow filling pen. $50-75.

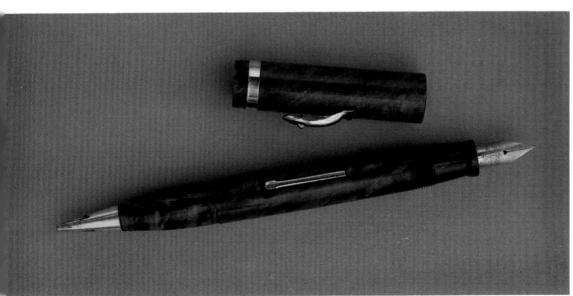

CROCKER, ca. 1927. Red & black mottled hard rubber lever filling pen/pencil combination. $200-350.

The company moved to 10-20 51st Avenue, Long Island City, New York in 1926, and apparently combined production of the Crocker and the Chilton lines. They began to make Chilton pens out of plastic in early 1926, which gave them access to new colors. In early 1927, the filler was slightly changed so that instead of the entire barrel moving up to pump, the end of the barrel was attached to a thick metal tube, with an air hole in the end, that slid out of the barrel which contained the ink sac. This later pump filler resembles the Sheaffer pump filler of 1949.

A very attractive line of Chilton pens, the *Wingflow* (1935-1938), was made in colored plastic with inset metal lines and initials. The *Wingflow* used a nib that was wrapped around and locked into the feed. Supposedly it looked like a wing. The quality of Chilton pens declined over the next few years. Chilton Pen moved to Summit, New Jersey in 1939 and folded about a year and a half later, selling its remaining stock and tools to local jobbers. The reason that these pens are difficult to find is that they never considered themselves to be making pens for the world market. They were satisfied selling to smaller regional markets. Look for these pens in the Northeastern United States.

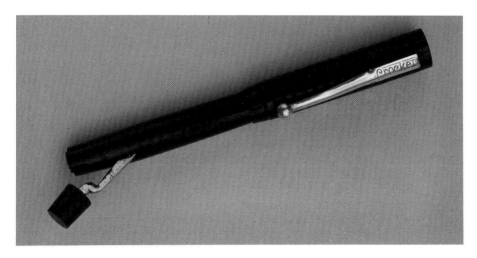

CROCKER, ca. 1916. Black chased hard rubber hatchet filling pen. $50-75.

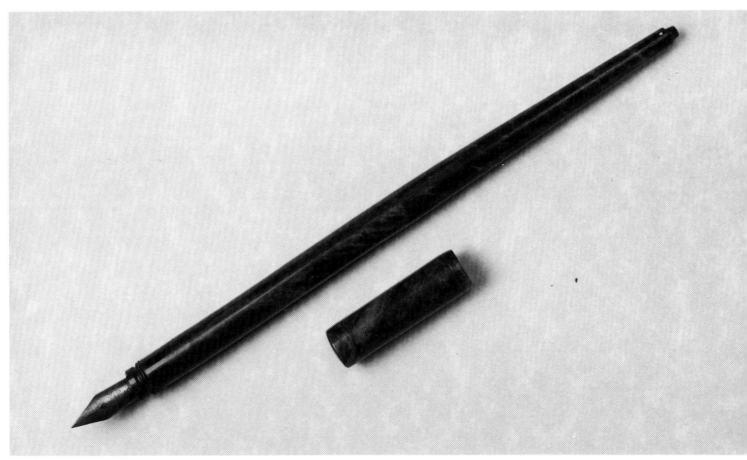

CROCKER, ca. 1903-1906. "Ink-Tite" blow filling desk pen in red & black mottled hard rubber. $100-150.

CHILTON, ca. 1927-1934. Marble plastic pump filling pens. Note the filling buttons at the bottom of the barrels. Top left; $125-200, top right; $350-500, bottom; $40-70.

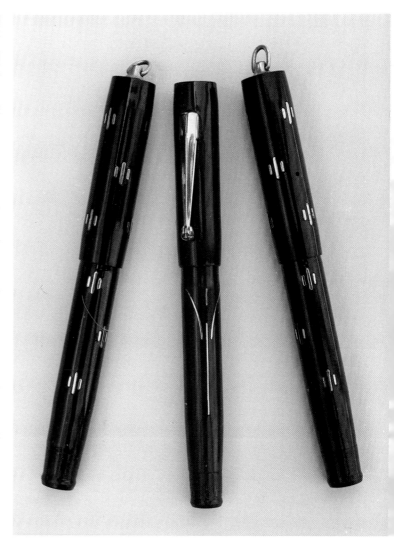
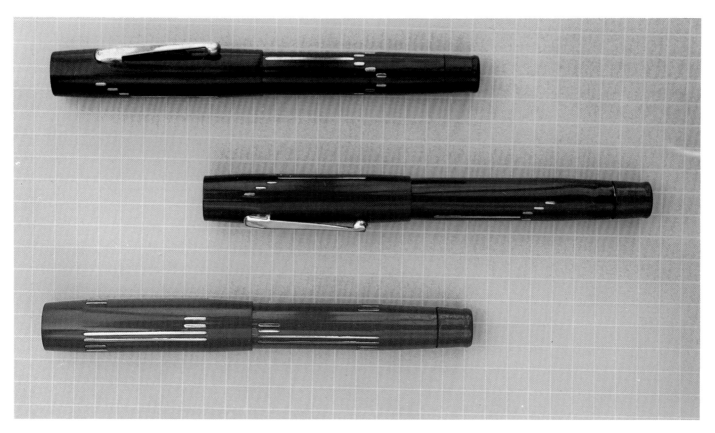

CHILTON, ca. 1935-1937. Inlay plastic *Wingflow* pump filling pens and pencil. These pens featured a wraparound *Wingflow* nib and many different inlay patterns. Top left: $350-500; Top right: $275-350; Bottom: $300-500.

CHILTON, ca. 1924-1926. Alligator covered Boston-made pen. Examples of these pens have been found covered in elephant, lizard, ostrich, and snakeskin. $175-275.

CHILTON, ca. 1924-1926. Black hard rubber, red hard rubber, and green marble plastic pump filling pens. The Chilton filling system utilized air pressure to fill the pen. $300-425.

CHILTON, ca. 1923. Red & black mottled hard rubber pump filling pen. This large pen is a good example of the quality pens made in Boston by Chilton. $300-450.

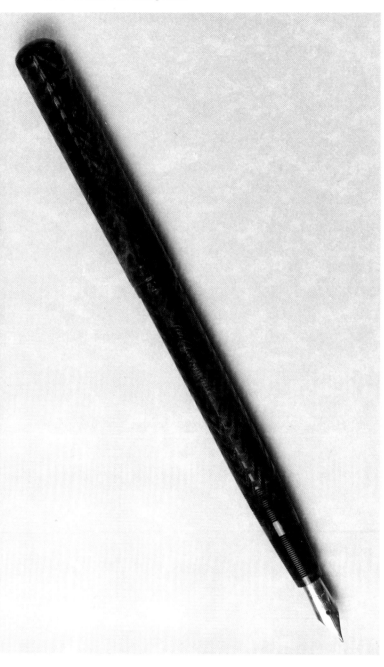

CAMEL, ca. 1935-1938. Red & gray marble ink pellet filling pen. The Camel pen company begun by Joseph V. Wustman was out of business by 1938. $100-150.

AUTOFILLER, ca. 1905. Red & black mottled chased hard rubber pen. $50-75.

CAMEL, ca. 1936-1938. Clear demonstrator pen. $150-250.

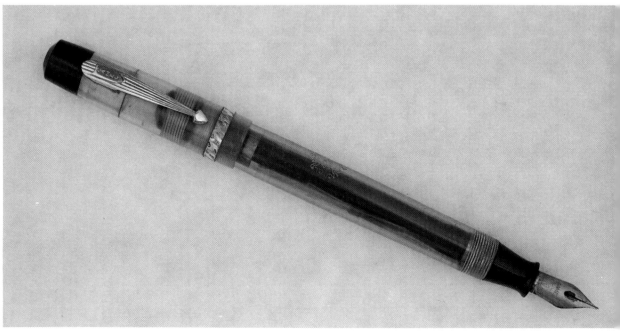

Chapter 13
Other Pen Companies

There were hundreds of pen companies. Some lasted only a few years while others made millions of pens that were sold through mail order catalogs or sold in only a regional area. Those listed below made either quality pens or interesting pens that can be found throughout the country. Any information that we have about them follows:

ARTCRAFT PEN
Birmingham, Alabama

BETZLER & WILSON
New York City

BLAIR'S FOUNTAIN PEN CO.
25 Maiden Lane, New York City.
These pens had an ink cartridge inside the barrel and were filled with water.

BOSTON SAFETY PEN, Successors to Colonial Pen Co.
319 Washington St., Boston, Mass. Made the *Dewey Pen*

WM. BOLLES CO.
106 Jefferson Ave., Toledo, Ohio

CAMEL PEN CO., 1935-1938
Joseph V. Wustman came up with the idea of a pen that would fill with water and write with ink without adding ink pellets. His company, Camel Pen, started in 1935, a particularly bad year to start a company due to the depressed state of the country's economy. It was situated at 13 Central Avenue, Orange, New Jersey.

The pen contained an ink pellet in a mixing chamber attached to an ink sac that attached to the feed section of the pen. The pen was filled by unscrewing a blind cap at the end of the barrel and pushing the end in. This compressed the sac and drew in the water. The water would mix in the mixing chamber and the pen would write in ink. Unfortunately the ink was too thin when the pen first started writing and too thick when it was about out of ink. The ink pellet was expected to last about a year. The pen itself was very well made and the Camel insignia, two camels on hind legs drinking from a glass of water with a straw, was certainly appealing, but the pen was a flop and the company was soon out of business. After bankruptcy, Wustman started the Newark Pen Company with the equipment bought from Camel.

CAREY PEN COMPANY, 1890-1915
Not much is known about the Carey Pen Company. In 1910, Carey was located at 196 Broadway, New York City. They made very high quality pens and distribution appears to have been primarily in the New York area. Known examples are eyedropper filled pens (regular and middle joint) in black or red & black hard rubber and gold foil and sterling silver overlays on black hard rubber. They are rare and desirable.

CAREY, ca. 1910. Heavy sterling silver floral design overlay, middle joint eyedropper filled pen. $1500-1750.

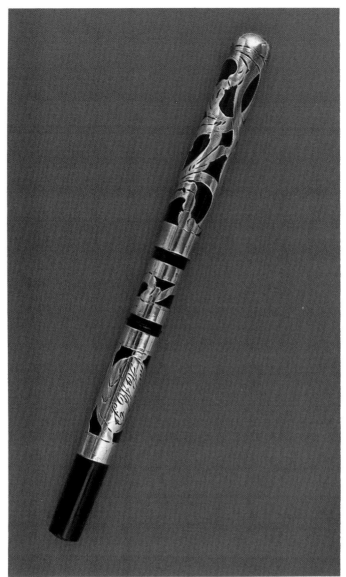

CAREY, ca. 1910. Sterling silver filigree design overlay, red & black mottled hard rubber, and black hard rubber middle joint eyedropper filled pens. Left to right: $650-750; $400-600.

CAREY, ca. 1905-1910. Gold filled filigree design overlay, eyedropper filled pen. $400-600.

CAREY ?, ca. 1900-1910. Sterling silver floral design overlay, eyedropper filling pen. $125-200.

CARTER PEN CO., 1926-1931

John W. Carter founded a company in Boston, Massachusetts in 1857 that would later become the Carter Ink Company. Carter was best known for its ink products but made very nice fountain pens during the 1920s and 1930s. Fountain pen manufacture began about 1926 with what is believed to be the remains of the Laughlin Pen Company's patents and stock of parts. Carter pens appeared in some very unusual colors that other pen manufacturers did not use. There were unusual shades of green, blue, and orange, and a white pearl. The effects of the Depression made selling fountain pens very difficult. Carter abandoned the pen business about 1931 and returned to just selling ink products.

CAW'S PEN AND INK CO., 1890-1915

Located at 76 Duane St., New York City, Caw manufactured stylgraphic, eyedropper filling and safety pens.

CENTURY PEN COMPANY

Whitewater, Wisconsin

CHICAGO SAFETY PEN, ca. 1921

538 South Clark St., Chicago, Illinois. Believed to have purchased the A.A. Waterman Company.

COLONIAL FOUNTAIN PEN CO.

Made the *Warren N. Lancaster* pen at its 882 Park Ave. headquarters in Baltimore, Md.

A.T. CROSS, 1846-Present

The A.T.Cross company had its roots in the jewelry business. Alonso Townsend Cross, born 1846, entered the business through the firm of Richards & Cross of Attleborough, Massachusetts, his father's company, silversmiths and pencil case makers. By 1858 they had moved to Providence, Rhode Island. About 1880, A.T.Cross was involved in a patent infringement case with his former partner, Duncan MacKinnon. MacKinnon had patented a stylographic pen in 1875. Cross perfected it, and patented his pen in January, 1878. The pens were very similar in appearence, but the Cross pens worked better, and he won the case. In 1916, Cross sold the company to Walter Russell Boss, Sr., who continued and expanded the company. Walter Boss's sons joined the company and eventually became its officers. The Boss family is involved in the company today.

DIAMOND POINT PEN CO.

Located at 39 W. 19th St., New York City, Diamond Point Pen Co. made the *Blofil* and *Protector* pens

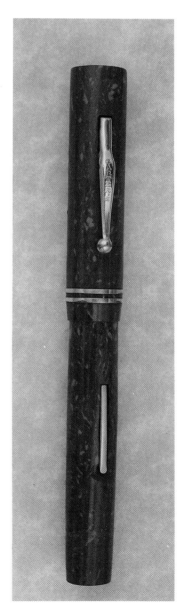

CARTER, ca. 1928-1930. Salmon marble plastic lever filling *Inx* pen. $250-350.

CARTER, ca. 1926-1927. Red & black mottled hard rubber lever filling pen. $225-400.

CARTER, ca. 1930-1931. Blue marble, and black plastic lever filling *Inx* pens. These streamlined pens were Carter's final models. Left to right: $275-425; $125-175.

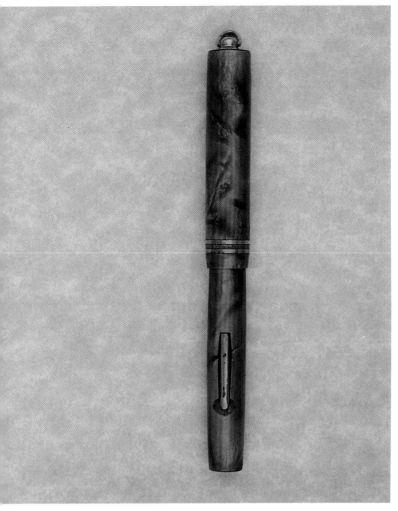

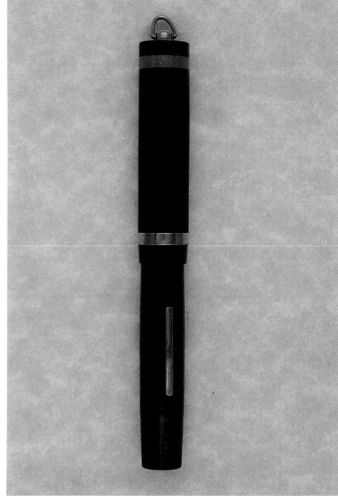

CARTER, ca. 1929-1930. "Pearltex" blue plastic lever filling lady's pen. $75-100.

CARTER, ca. 1926-1928. Black hard rubber lever filling lady's pen. $60-90.

CARTER, ca. 1918. Advertising blotter. $15-30.

CAW, ca. 1905-1908. "Courage" model, black chased hard rubber safety pen. $75-125.

CAW, ca. 1905-1908. Black chased hard rubber safety pen. The nib is exposed by placing the small cap on the back of the pen and turning it. $75-125.

CAW, ca. 1905-1908. Black chased hard rubber stylographic pen. $75-125.

SANFORD & BENNETT, ca. 1915. Gold filled engraved design rotating barrel and sleeve filling pens. By rotating the barrel, the sac was exposed and the pen was filled by pressing on it. This is one of the many early versions of the sleeve filling mechanism. $350-500.

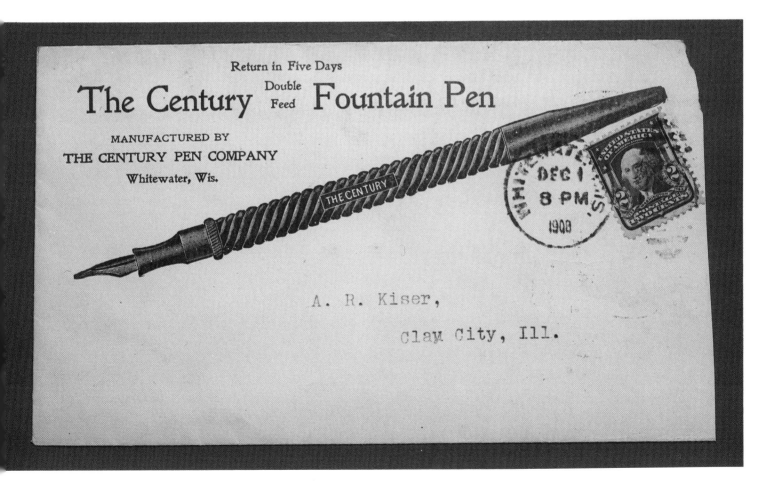

CENTURY, ca. 1908. Advertising envelope. $25-50.

COLUMBIAN, 1893. Black hard rubber safety pen sold during the Chicago Columbian exposition of 1893. $50-75.

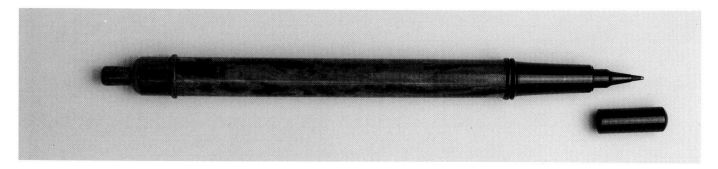

A.T. CROSS, ca. 1880. Red & black mottled hard rubber stylographic pen. $100-150.

A.T. CROSS, 1930-1937. Gold and enamel fountain pen. The earliest Cross nib style fountain pen was made about 1892, and was similar in appearance to the Wirt pen of the period. A 1904 model resembled the Swan over-under feed pen. The pen illustrated, produced during the great depression, is rarely found today. $750-950.

MACKINNON, ca. 1879. Black chased hard rubber stylographic pen. $75-125.

DIAMOND POINT, ca. 1925-1928. Mahogany hard rubber lever filling pen. $50-100.

DIAMOND POINT, ca. 1915. Silver filigree design red & black mottled hard rubber eyedropper filled pen. $125-175.

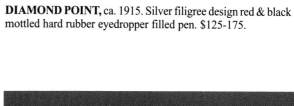

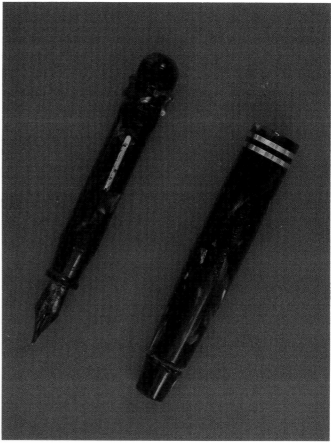

DIAMOND MEDAL, ca. 1929. Green marble plastic lever filling pen. $75-125.

DIAMOND POINT, ca. 1930-1935. *Long & Short* model lever filling pen in green marble plastic, when closed the barrel was concealed almost completely within the cap. $60-90.

DUNN, ca. 1921-1924. Silver plated pencil. $20-40.

DUNN, ca. 1921-1924. *Camel* model pump filling black hard rubber pen. $100-175.

EAGLE, ca. 1895-1913. Black hard rubber eyedropper filling pen. $25-40.

EAGLE, ca. 1930. Blue marble plastic lever filling pen. $20-40.

DUNN PEN COMPANY, 1921-1924

One of the shortest-lived companies, Dunn Pen, was founded in 1921. Its main office was 300 Madison Avenue, New York City. The Dunn was a pump filler and was identifiable by its red section at the back end of the barrel. The pen held a great deal of ink due to its filling system. Advertisements of the day claimed that it could hold a month's worth of ink. Quality was high but few of these pens work today due to the hardening of the rubber pump parts.

Many of the parts for the Dunn pen were made by Julius Schnell of *Schnell Penselpen* fame. It was the failure of Dunn in 1924 that convinced Schnell that he could not rely upon one large company for all his business. It caused him to start his own company. The directors of the Dunn Corporation did not include anyone named Dunn. Dunn went out of business after a prolonged strike by its employees.

EAGLE PENCIL (and Pen) COMPANY, 1860-Present

Eagle was founded in 1856 by Henry Berolzheimer, Leopold Illfelder and Joseph Reckendorfer in Furth, Bavaria. When Henry Berolzheimer brought his company and family to New York in 1860, they wanted an American symbol for the company. They chose the eagle. The Berolzheimers shortened their name to Berol. The Eagle Pencil Company was first located at 600 West 27th Street, New York City. Some time later they moved to Yonkers near the mouth of the canal leading into the Hudson River. Although offices were eventually located in other places; 73 Franklin St.(1876) and 377-379 Broadway (1910), the main factory was located at 13th & 14th Streets and Avenues C & D (1896). It covered an entire city block.

Eagle's main business was pencil manufacturing. To ensure an adequate supply of cedar wood, they purchased and owned forests, lumber companies, saw mills, trucking companies, and the factories that made the pencils. Fountain pen manufacturing began about 1887.

Their first successful, innovative pen was the glass cartridge pen of 1890. The pen came with a small glass vial filled with ink. The vial was inserted in the barrel and the section (nib, feed & collar) was connected to the ink vial with little mess. The body of the pen was either aluminum or painted brass. Another popular pen was their pen/pencil combination similar to that which most other pen makers produced in the 1930s. Eagle produced their first pen/pencil combination in 1890. They had been making dip pen/pencil combinations since 1870. This pen/pencil combination was a simple black hard rubber item.

By 1913, Eagle had a full line of fountain pens in different styles, sizes and shapes. There were eyedropper fillers, twist fillers, plunger fillers, safety fillers, stylographic pens and handsome mother-of-pearl overlay pens. The line was generally inexpensive but fairly well made. Eagle also made pens for other companies in other countries that were sold under the other company's name, such as the Martinez Pen of Manila in the Philippines.

By the 1920s, their pens reflected the styles of the pens of the day. They produced copies of most popular pens such as the Parker "Big Red", Sheaffer "Green Jade" and Eversharp style pencils. About 1930, Eagle cut back its line of Eagle pens and began to produce the *Epenco* line. The bright colors and clever designs of these plastic *Epenco* pens makes them a desirable addition to any collection. Two examples are the *Gleam* pen and the Popeye pen. The *Epenco* pens only cost 25 cents to a dollar when they were new. They are inexpensive pens with gilt (gold wash) fittings, gold plated nibs and a soft plastic barrel and cap that can easily warp if heated. A nice collection of Eagle pens should be fairly easy to put together and reasonably priced.

In 1970, Eagle, which had expanded to produce a full line of pencils, pens, mechanical pencils, pencil sharpeners, templates, magic markers, etc., began to use the Berol name. Family members are still involved in the company which is now located in Brentwood, Tennessee.

ECLIPSE PEN

New York City company believed to have purchased the Keene Pen Co.

EDISON PEN CO.

Petersburg, Virginia. Made the *Edison* pen.

THOMAS A. EDISON, JR. CHEMICAL CO.

14 Stone St., New York City. Made the *Edison Jr Wizard* pen.

JOHN FOLEY

New York City (out of business by 1915). Made the *Writeright* pen.

GESSNER PEN

New Orleans, Louisiana. An example seen was an eye dropper, gold filled overlay similar to a Carey

EAGLE, ca. 1915-1917. Brass coin filling pen. $30-50.

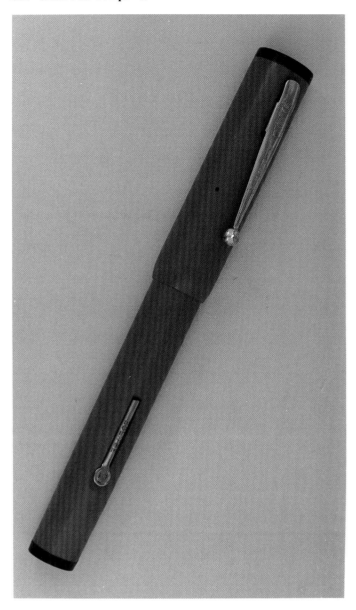

ECLIPSE, ca. 1924. Red hard rubber lever filling pen, made to look like a Parker *Duofold*. $40-75.

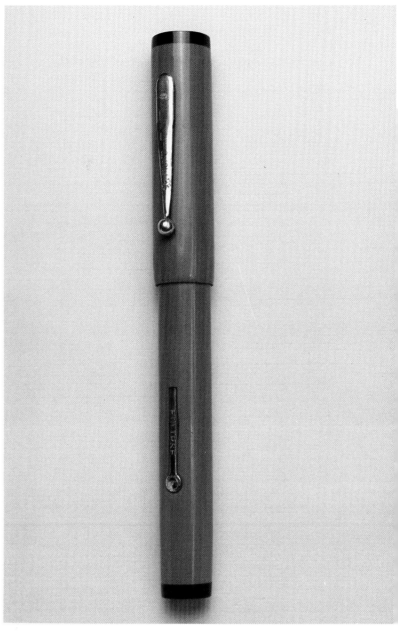

ECLIPSE, ca. 1926. Red plastic lever filling pen. Another example of a *Duofold* copy. $40-75.

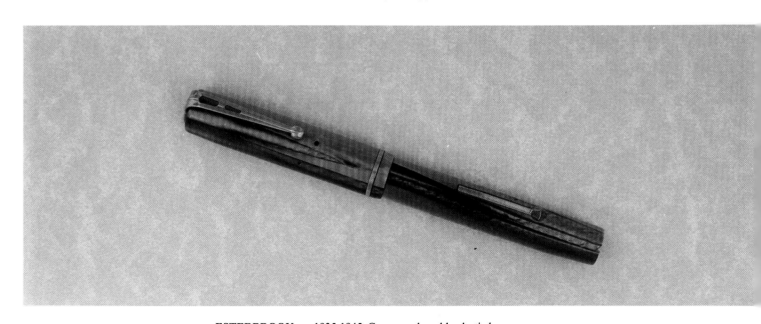

ESTERBROOK, ca. 1935-1945. Green pearl marble plastic lever filling pens. $15-35.

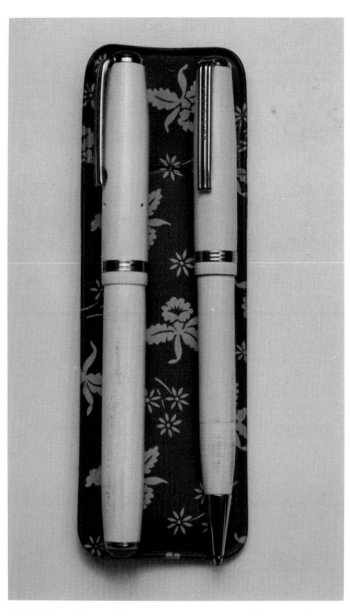

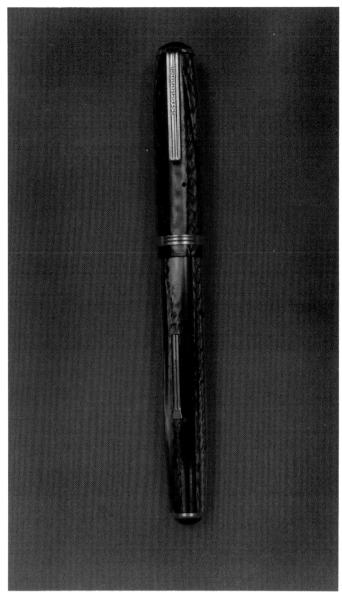

ESTERBROOK, ca. 1948-1956. White plastic lever filling nurse's pen and pencil set. $75-150.

ESTERBROOK, ca. 1946-1956. Green marble pearl plastic lever filling pen with interchangeable steel nib. $15-35.

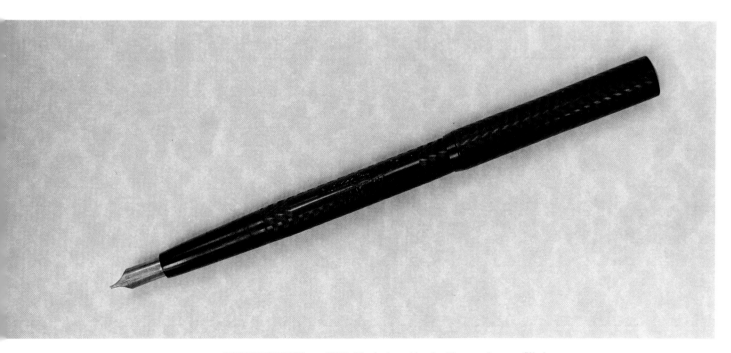

ESTERBROOK, ca. 1920. Black chased hard rubber eyedropper filled stenographer's shorthand pen. $65-90.

 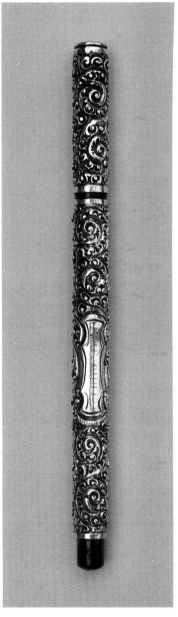 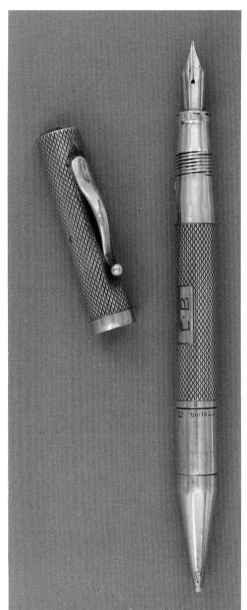 

HAUTON, ca. 1915. Black chased hard rubber eyedropper filled pen with perpetual calender in the cap. The trim on this pen is 14k gold. $100-150.

W.S. HICKS, ca. 1900. "The Quill" sterling silver chased design overlay eyedropper filling pen. Note the similarity between the Aiken Lambert chased design and this one. $300-400.

W.S. HICKS, ca. 1928. Sterling silver lever filling pen/pencil combination. Hicks made many gold and silver pens for Tiffany & Co. Many of their pens produced for Tiffany can be identified by the turned-up clip. $175-250.

JOHN HOLLAND, ca. 1895-1905. Black hard rubber eyedropper filled taper cap pen with two gold filled bands. $100-150.

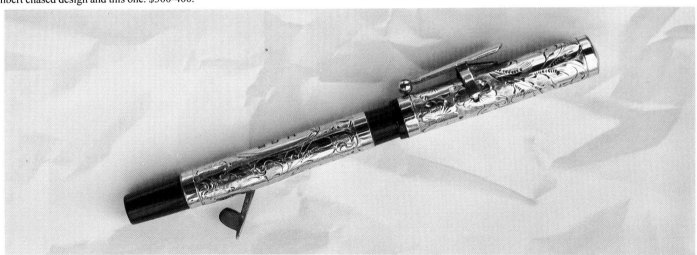

JOHN HOLLAND, ca. 1908-1910. Gold filled engraved design overlay, hatchet filling pen with unique style Holland clip. $350-500.

GRIESHABER CO.
116 N. State St., Chicago, Illinois

JOHN HANCOCK
Boston, Mass. Made a high quality cartridge filler pen.

GEORGE W. HEATH & CO.
208 1st St., New York City. Made the *Tribune* and the *Thames* pen and made silver and gold overlays for other pen companies including Parker during the period from 1900 to about 1915.

W. S. HICKS' SONS
235 Greenwich St., New York City. Made high quality pens, many in gold and silver. Also made many of Tiffany & Company's pens.

HOUSTON PEN COMPANY, 1911-1924
The Houston Pen Company of Sioux City, Iowa, was founded by William A. Houston. The style of the pen set it apart from other pens. It looked like a desk pen with a lady's style cap (no clip) with a safety chain attached. Filling systems were an eyedropper filler and a pump filler which was replaced by an unusual, modified matchstick filler system about 1915-1916. In the modified matchstick filler, a portion of the tapered end of the barrel unscrewed and was screwed into a hole in the side of the barrel. This was then pushed in to compress the ink sac. The pen was later modified to a simple matchstick filler with the cap having a protrusion to push into the hole.

Houston appears to have also made the "Jiffy Pen Co." pump filler pen of the same style. He became the manager of Jiffy Pen in 1917. Houston Pen became the General Manufacturing Co. in 1920 which manufactured the *Snapfil Fountain Pen*. Houston Pen claimed to make the "Largest and Smallest Fountain Pens in the World". They did in fact make a 2⅛" (55 mm) long pen and a 7¼" (18.5 cm) long pen. They had a good sense of humor.

JOHN HOLLAND PEN CO., 1841-1950
The John Holland Pen Co. of 127-129 East Fourth Street, Cincinnati, Ohio was one of America's oldest pen makers. The predecessor company, started by George Shepard and transferred in full to John Holland about 1862, began making gold nibs for dip pens in 1841. The company was incorporated in 1885. It became a Holland family business. In 1909, the president was John Holland, the vice-president was James Holland and the secretary was John A. Holland. Holland claimed to have begun manufacturing the first American fountain pens in 1869.

Holland pens are of the highest quality and rather rare. An innovative Holland model was their *Self Filling* pen (1906-1914). It had a metal half ring in the middle of the barrel that when lifted away from the barrel, pulled up a pressure bar under the ink sac, compressing it. It appeared rather unsightly, but did the job it was supposed to do. Holland also made a sleeve filler called the *Eureka* from 1906 to 1912. The "hatchet" filler was another filler used from about 1908 to 1912. By 1920, all of their pens were lever fillers.

A little known fact about Holland is that they made the *MacKinnon Pen* which was a very popular 1878-1880s stylographic pen. The company's output decreased in the 1930s and they ceased production of pens after the second World War.

Pen names used were *Clymax, Columbia, Dexter, Duplex, Durand & Co., Fountgraph, Geo. W. Sheppard, W. B. Snow, MacKinnon, Victor* and *Imperator*.

HUTCHEON BROS.
Little is known of the Hutcheon Brothers except what can be gleaned from the pens and pencils that they left behind. The brothers, one of whom was named Alfred, worked in New York City. They manufactured pencils with a clutch mechanism to hold the lead called the "Hutch Clutch". Their pencils exhibit the highest quality, were often made of silver and came in some innovative shapes. In 1910 they made "Magazine" pencils under a June 7, 1910 patent. Their pens appear about the turn of the century, They included eyedropper filled, sliding sleeve type fillers, and later, lever fillers. A mystery exists about the brothers. Their pen uses the same ladder feed, the same clip (with the same patent date) and have the same groove on the collar as Mabie, Todd's Swan pens. Their magazine pencils in sterling silver are identical to the Swan's, right down to the patent date, and their *Fine Pointe* made in the 1910s sounds remarkably similar to Mabie, Todd's *Fyne Poynt* made in the 1920s.

JOHN HOLLAND, ca. 1906-1910. Sterling silver filigree design overlay, pull filling pen. $400-600.

JOHN HOLLAND, ca. 1928. Black plastic lever filling *Jewel* pen. $40-80.

JOHN HOLLAND, ca. 1900-1905. Gold filled floral design overlay, eyedropper filled pen. $450-650.

JOHN HOLLAND, ca. 1925. Red hard rubber lever filling pen. $75-125.

JOHN HOLLAND, ca. 1900-1905. Gold filled floral design overlay, eyedropper filled pen. $200-300.

JOHN HOLLAND, ca. 1900-1905. Mother-of-pearl covered barrel black hard rubber eyedropper filled pen. $100-150.

JOHN HOLLAND, ca. 1905. Red & black mottled hard rubber eyedropper filled pen. $100-150.

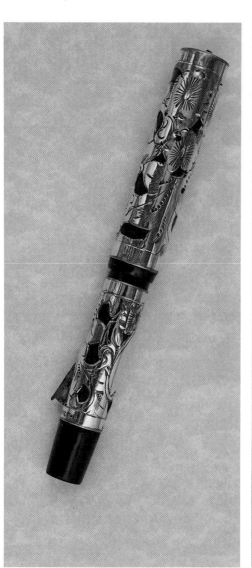
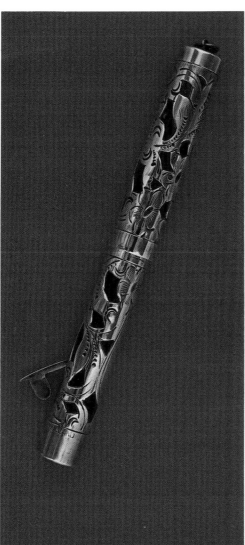
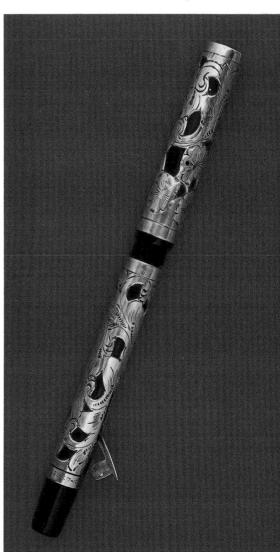

JOHN HOLLAND, ca. 1908-1912. Gold filled and sterling silver filigree design overlay, hatchet filling pens. Left to right: $300-450; $350-500; $275-450.

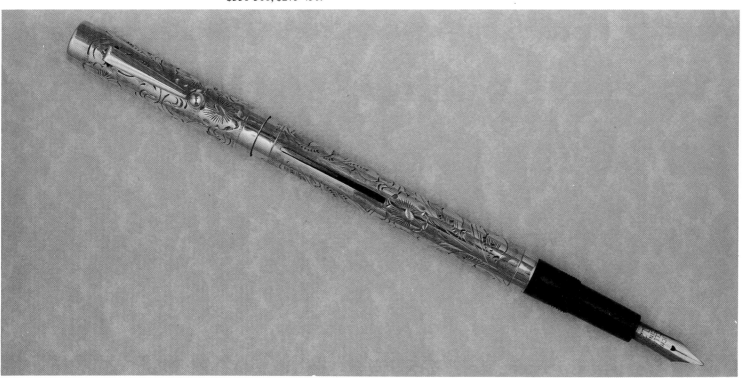

JOHN HOLLAND, ca. 1908-1912. Gold filled engraved floral design overlay, hatchet filling pen. $300-400.

JOHN HOLLAND, ca. 1900-1905. Sterling silver Art Nouveau filigree design overlay, eyedropper filled pen. $250-350.

JOHN HOLLAND, ca. 1905-1907. Gold filled filigree design overlay, pull filling pen. $400-500.

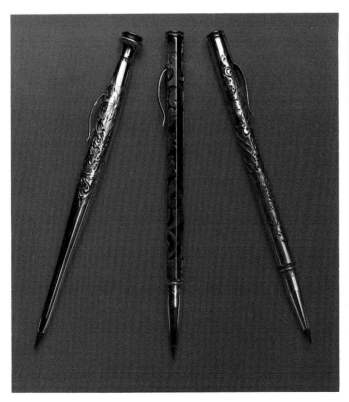

HUTCHEON BROS., ca. 1910-1916. Sterling silver etched, and engraved "Hutch Clutch" magazine pencils. $75-150.

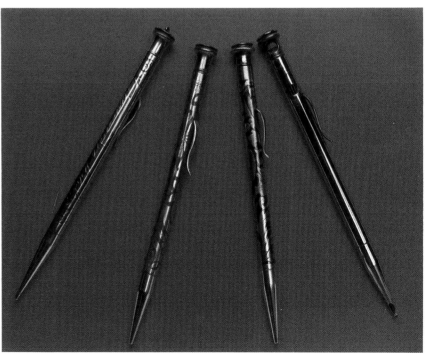

HUTCHEON BROS., ca. 1917-1925. Sterling silver etched design *Fine Pointe* pencils. Pencil illustrated on the right is a cutout demonstrator model. $75-150.

INDIAN, ca. 1933. Plastic pen/pencil combination with plated trim and nib. They featured striking colors and a design in the style of Navaho Indian rugs and blankets. A rather inexpensive pen, possibly made to sell to tourists visiting Indian reservations in America's southwest. During the 1920s and 1930s there was an increased awareness of Indian artwork and design. Magazine featured Indian jewelry, pottery, baskets and weaving. Those with money swarmed to the reservations, buying everything old that was available. Those with less to spend, bought the new Indian items. $75-100.

INGERSOLL, ca. 1925-1930. Brown plastic button filling pen. $25-50.

KEENE PEN
New York City company which made eyedropper and match filler pens. Later purchased by Eclipse Pen Company.

AIKIN LAMBERT PEN CO., 1864-1932
The Aikin Lambert Company was begun in 1864 in New York City. It initially made gold pen points for dip pens and began to make fountain pens in the 1890s at 10 Cortland Street, New York City. The majority of Aikin Lambert's pens were high quality, with many of them having beautiful silver and gold filled overlays similar to pens made by L.E. Waterman. Also many styles of pens were made including Waterman safety style, eyedroppers and lever fillers. Few know that L.E. Waterman's pencils were made by Aikin Lambert until about 1920. They merged with Waterman Pen Company about 1932.

LAPP & FLERSHEM
Chicago, Illinois. Made the *Banner*, *Lakeside*, and *Remington*. These names may have been sold to another company as L & F appear to have gone out of business by 1915. The *Lakeside* pen was sold in Montgomery Ward catalogs in the 1920s.

LAUGHLIN PEN COMPANY, 1880-1925
The Laughlin Manufacturing Co. was located on Griswold Street in Detroit, Michigan. Laughlin made medium and high quality pens similar to John Holland pens and also a line of inexpensive pens. In 1904 they claimed to be the "Largest Fountain Pen Makers in the World", a claim that appears to be pure fiction unless perhaps they made a 12 foot (4 meter) long pen.

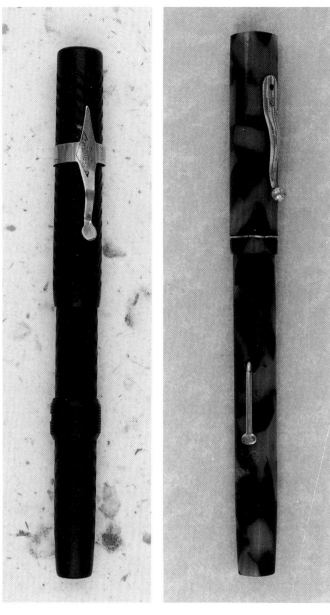

KEENE, ca. 1915-1920. Black chased hard rubber matchstick filling pen. $20-40.

AIKIN LAMBERT, ca. 1926-1930. Black & pearl plastic lever filling pen. $30-60.

AIKIN LAMBERT, ca. 1900-1910. Gold filled chased, and floral design overlay, eyedropper filled pens. These early overlay pens of Aikin Lambert are often mistaken for L.E. Waterman pens due to their similarity. Left to right: $1000-1500; $250-450; $650-1000.

AIKIN LAMBERT, ca. 1905-1910. Gold filled basket weave design filigree overlay, eyedropper filled pen. $300-500.

They made an interesting eyedropper filled fountain pen in 1900 that contained a fever thermometer. The highest quality Laughlin pens are hard to find. It is believed that Laughlin's machinery, stock and patents were sold to Carter's Ink Company to create their pen company.

LE BOEUF
Springfield, Massachusetts. Le Boeuf made very high quality pens in some unique colors. They included sleeve fillers and lever fillers. Sleeve fillers often are found cracked or discolored.

THE LINCOLN PEN CO., 1895-1906
The *Lincoln* pen was first introduced in 1895. It was a simple unassuming pen that was very well made, cost one dollar, and had a gold nib. Lincoln Pen was located at 108 Fulton Street, New York. In 1899 it was sold to the Frazier & Geyer Company which was located at 36 Gold Street, New York. Frazier & Geyer expanded the *Lincoln* line to include different priced pens, including a solid gold overlay pen.

In 1904, they entered into a partnership with the A.A. Waterman Pen Company and began to sell the *Lincoln* and later, the *New Lincoln* pen, under the A.A. Waterman banner. The *New Lincoln* was A.A. Waterman's standard eyedropper pen line. This differentiated it from A.A. Waterman's middle joint pen and their *Modern Automatic Self Filler*, a twist filler. Apparently after several uneventful selling years, the *New Lincoln* was lost to obscurity. A *Lincoln* pen resurfaced in the 1920s made by the National Pen Company of Chicago, Illinois. The 1920s pen was comparable to an *Eclipse* or *Gold Medal* pen, a standard pen that was not exceptional in any way.

MONROE, 1930s
New York City. A high quality very Art Deco pen in great colors. Hard to find.

MOONEY PEN, 1875-1917
Chicago, Illinois manufactured pens usually found as blow fillers. Started by Frank H. Mooney, who was originally a gold pen maker. These pens are usually marked by a crescent moon on the barrel.

NATIONAL PEN CO.
Chicago, Illinois. Made the *Gold Bond, National, Gold Medal, Lincoln* and others.

PERRY PEN
Milton, Wisconsin

PICK PEN
Cincinnati, Ohio

POSTAL PEN
New York City. Made a bulb filler that held a large load of ink.

THE RELIANCE TRADING CO., successor to the Post Fountain Pen Co.
120-124 W. 14th St., New York City. Made the *Post* pump filler pen

J.G. RIDER PEN COMPANY, 1905-1925
The J.G. Rider Pen Company was established in Rockford, Illinois in 1905 and incorporated in 1907. The original officers were J.G. Rider, President, H.A. Merlien, Vice President, E.W.Parker, Secretary, and A.C.Horton, Treasurer. Sales were so good for such a new company that in 1908 Rider added a factory which made the *Perfection* pen. In 1910 the company employed 20 people and produced 25,000 pens. Most of its business was in the central states, the west and part of the south. In 1921, Jay D. Rider became the president but in 1925, strangely enough, the family and company left Rockford and disappeared.

Rider pens are very attractive. Many had long, gracefully curved clips, while others had long flat clips. Both clips had a ball at the end. The clip served a purpose other than attaching the pen to your pocket. It was used to remove the pen's unusually long feed by hooking a tab located under the nib on the feed. With the feed removed, the pen could then be filled with an eyedropper. It was a novel, but messy method. A rare pen today, it has been found in many sizes, from a jumbo as large as a Waterman #20 to a thin, standard length pen in black or red & black hard rubber.

AIKIN LAMBERT, ca. 1900-1905. Sterling silver chased design overlay, eyedropper filled pen. $500-750.

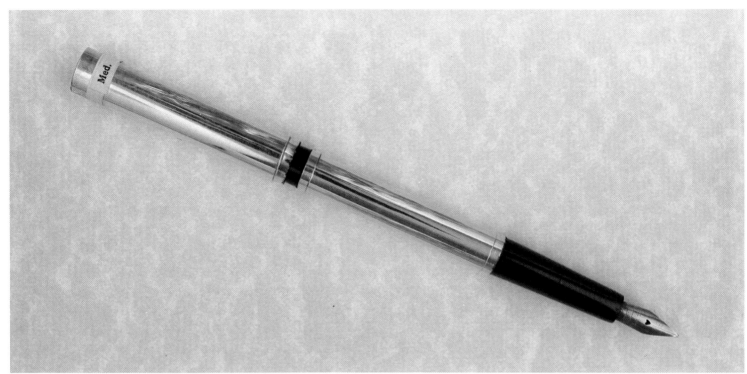

AIKIN LAMBERT, ca. 1910-1915. Gold filled overlay, eyedropper filled pens. $200-300.

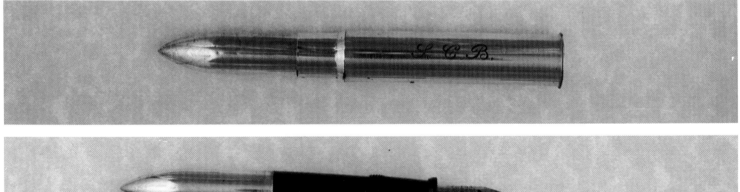

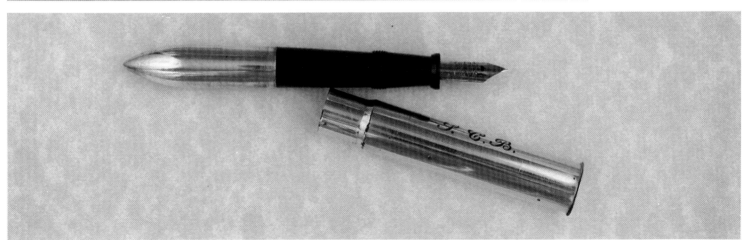

AIKIN LAMBERT, ca. 1917. Silver & brass "bullet" eyedropper filled pen. Other companies also produced bullet shaped pens around the time of World War I. $200-275.

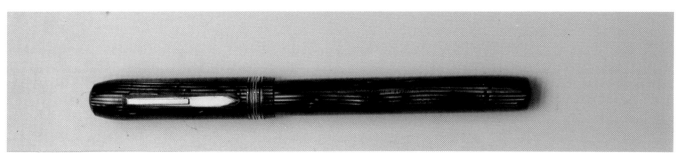

AIKIN LAMBERT manufactured by **L.E. WATERMAN,** ca. 1930-1931. Green striped plastic lever filling pen. $20-40.

LAUGHLIN, ca. 1905-1915. Red & black mottled hard rubber eyedropper filled pen with two gold filled bands. $75-100.

LAUGHLIN, ca. 1905-1915. Black hard rubber eyedropper filled pen with two gold filled bands. $50-75.

LAUGHLIN, ca. 1900-1910. Black hard rubber eyedropper filled pen with threaded section and two gold filled bands. $50-75.

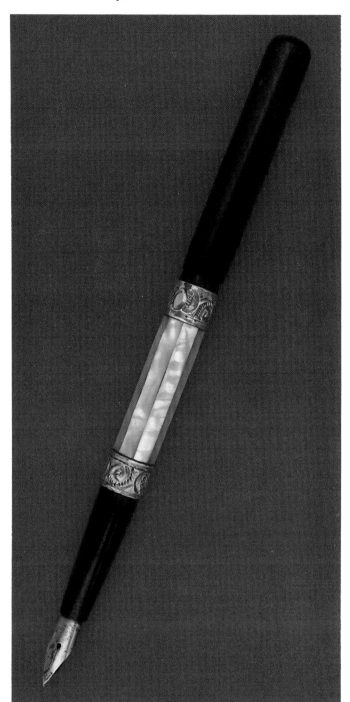

LAUGHLIN, ca. 1910-1915. Mother-of-pearl covered barrel eyedropper filled pen. $75-125.

LAUGHLIN, ca. 1900-1910. Sterling silver filigree design overlay, eyedropper filled pen. $175-300.

LE BOEUF, ca. 1930. Blue pearl marble sleeve filling pen, open to show filling mechanism. $250-350.

LE BOEUF, ca. 1932. Blue marble plastic button filling pen and pencil set. $300-400.

LE BOEUF, ca. 1926-1928. Blue marble plastic lever filling lady's pen with original ribbon. $100-150.

LE BOEUF, ca. 1928. Gold marble plastic lever filling pen. $200-250.

LE BOEUF, ca. 1927. Gray & black swirl plastic lever filling lady's pen. $100-200.

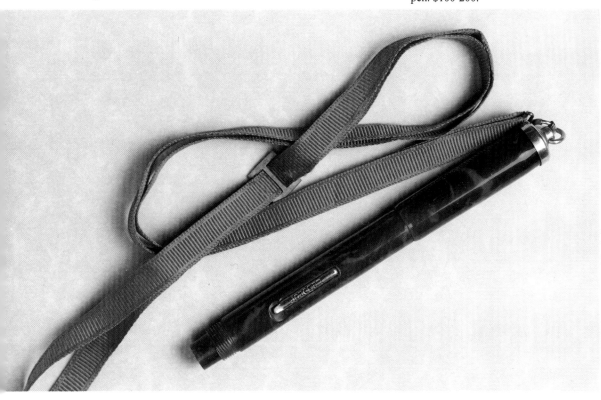

LINCOLN, ca. 1897-1899. Red & black mottled hard rubber eyedropper pen. The Lincoln Pen Company was sold to Frazier & Geyer in 1899. $50-75.

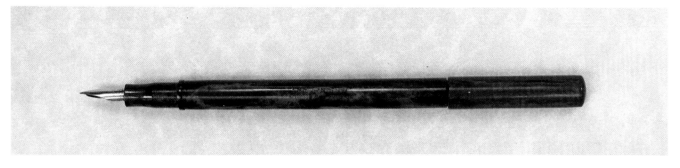

LINCOLN, ca. 1897-1899. Red & black mottled hard rubber eyedropper filled pen. $50-100.

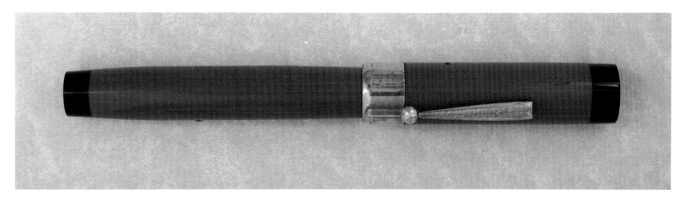

MORRISON, ca. 1926. *Tourist* red hard rubber lever filling pen. $60-90.

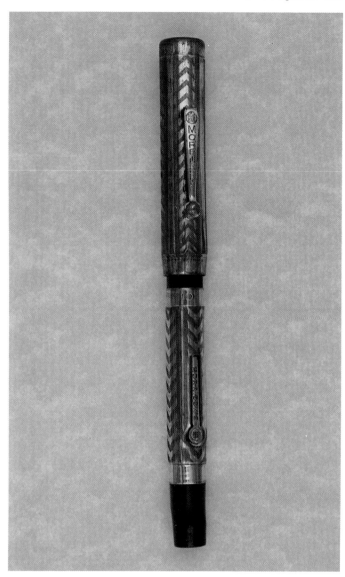

MORRISON, ca. 1943. Red plastic lever filling pen with American and British flag insert in the cap top. $30-60.

MORRISON, ca. 1925. Gold plated overlay, lever filling pen. $40-80.

MOONEY, ca. 1905-1910. Sterling silver filigree ribbon design overlay, eyedropper filled pen. $500-650.

MOONEY, ca. 1900-1910. Gold filled engraved design overlay, blow-filling pen. Frank H. Mooney was a gold pen maker in the 1880s and sold his pens through stationers. $375-475.

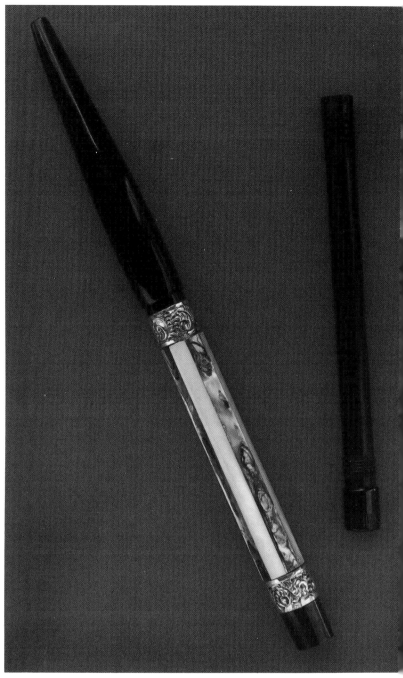

MYERS, ca. 1905. Mother-of-pearl covered barrel, taper cap, ink reservoir pen. Ink reservoir removed from the pen for illustration. $175-275.

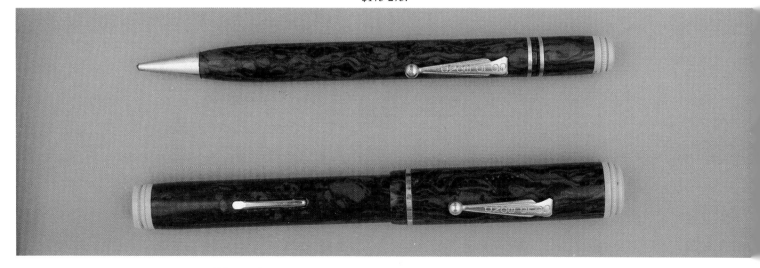

GOLD BOND made by NATIONAL PEN CO., ca. 1930. The *Gold Bond,* a red & black mottled plastic lever filling pen and pencil set. $175-250.

LINCOLN made by NATIONAL PEN CO., ca. 1925. The *Lincoln,* a black plastic lever filling pen. $20-35.

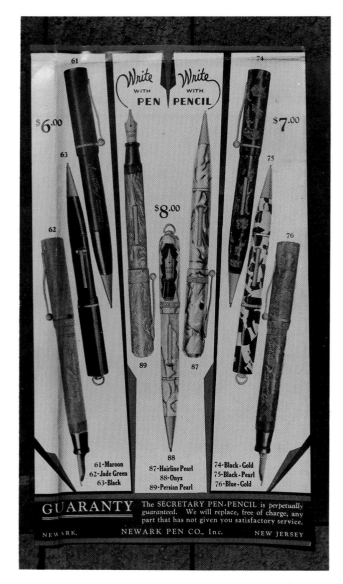

NEWARK, ca. 1938-1945. Advertisement for the *Secretary* pen/pencil combination. With the demise of the Camel Pen Company, Joseph Wustman formed the Newark Pen Co., and produced a complete line of plastic, and hard rubber pens, in addition to the *Secretary* combination.

ONOTO, ca. 1930-1935. Black plastic *Duofold* style pen made in England. Many companies at this time copied the design of the extremely popular Parker *Duofold.* $75-125.

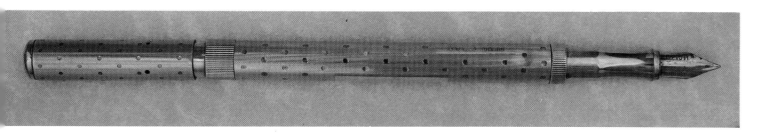

ONOTO, ca. 1910. Solid 9k gold self-filling "dot" pattern pen with English hallmarks. $600-850.

ONOTO, ca. 1910. Black chased hard rubber self filling pen with over-under feed. Onoto's self-filling mechanism consisted of a hard rubber piston and rod. $50-75.

PACKARD, ca. 1933. Marble pearl plastic lever filling pen/pencil combination. This is a typical pen/pencil combination of the 1930's. $25-50.

PELIKAN #100N, ca. 1935-1940. Gray striped and black plastic piston filling pen. $175-250.

PERRY, ca. 1915. Gold filled filigree design overlay, eyedropper filled pen. $250-350.

PILOT, ca. 1970. Black plastic, and wood cartridge filling pens. $75-100.

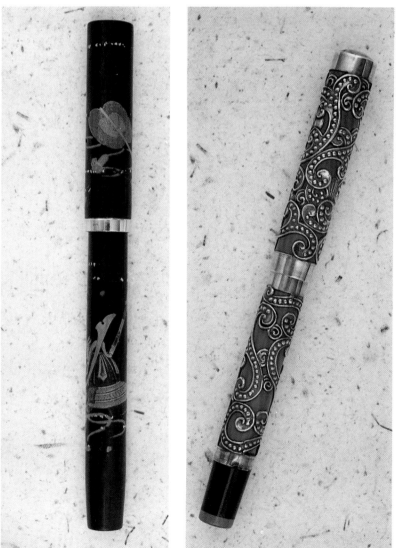

PILOT, ca. 1935. Hand painted lacquer design lever filling pen. $500-750.

PILOT, ca. 1938. Highly decorated sterling silver filigree design overlay, red hard rubber pen. $600-850.

POSTAL, ca. 1927 Postal Reservoir pen advertisement.

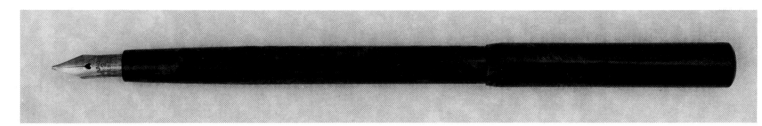

J.G. RIDER, ca. 1907. Red & black mottled hard rubber eyedropper filled pen. $75-125.

J.G. RIDER, ca. 1910. Gold filled filigree design overlay, eyedropper filled pen. $450-600.

J.G. RIDER, ca. 1910. Red & black mottled hard rubber eyedropper filled pen. $400-600.

J.G. RIDER, ca. 1910. Black hard rubber eyedropper filled pen with chased gold filled trim. $150-200.

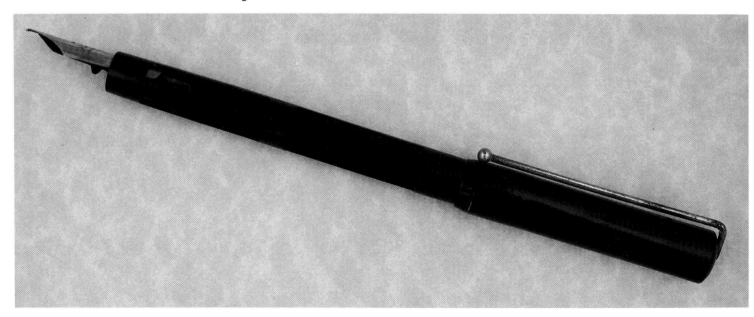

J.G. RIDER, ca. 1910. Black hard rubber cutout demonstrator pen. $250-400.

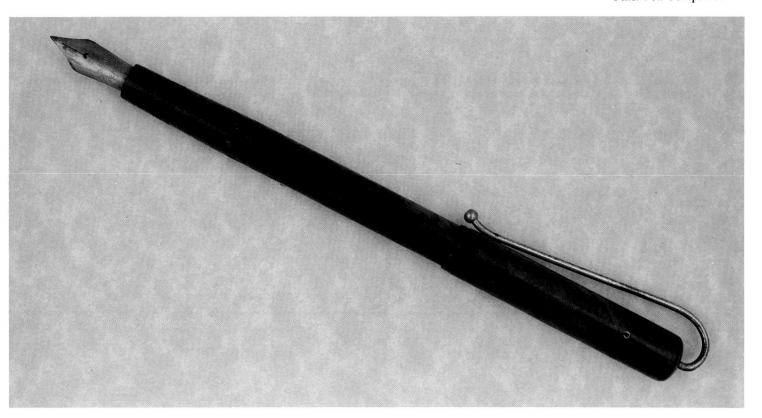

J.G. RIDER, ca. 1910. Red & black mottled hard rubber eyedropper filled pen. The long clip was used to remove the feed for filling the pen. $125-200.

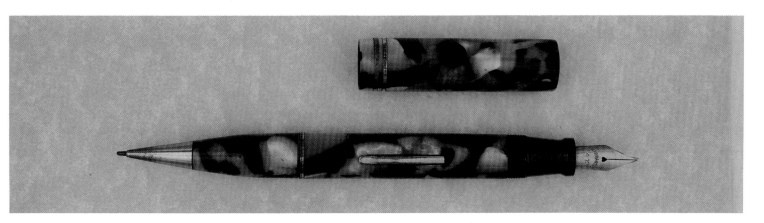

ROOSEVELT, ca. 1935. Black & pearl plastic lever filling pen/pencil combination. $35-65.

SALZ, ca. 1932-1937. Red marble pearl plastic lever filling pen. $5-15.

SANFORD & BENNETT, ca. 1915. Gold filled sleeve filling pen. $100-175.

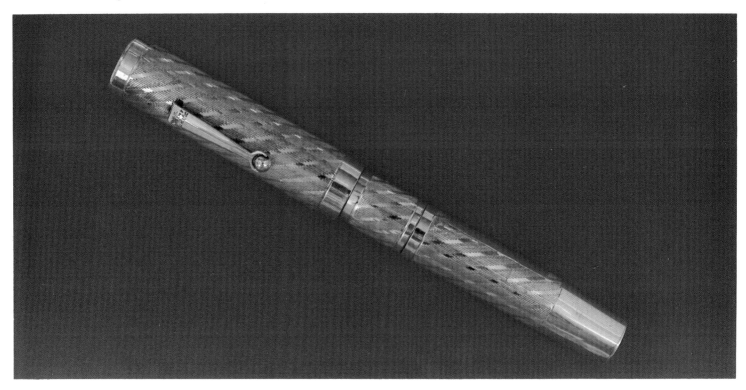

SANFORD & BENNETT, ca. 1915. Gold filled sleeve filling pen.
$275-400.

SCHNELL, ca. 1930. Marble plastic, slide lever pen/pencil combinations. $400-650.

SAGER PEN
New York City

SALZ PEN
New York City. Salz made the *Peter Pan* pen.

WILLIAM SANFORD PEN CO.
New York City. Made high quality pens with unusual filling systems such as a Chilton type pump filler that used the cap as a pump. It probably was not related to a (1909) company with a similar name in Cleveland, Ohio.

SANFORD & BENNETT
51 Maiden Lane, New York City. Made the *AutoPen*, a high quality blow filler as well as a sleeve filler pen. They took over the Sanford Pen Co. about 1921.

SCHNELL
Julius Schnell claims to have invented the fountain pen/pencil combination in 1890. Born in 1869, he was trained as a machinist and tool maker. In 1890, he began working for the Weidlich Pen Co., then moved to John Holland and then to Swan. In 1905, he set up his own shop making parts for Edward Todd & Co., Conklin, and Dunn. Around 1915 he produced the "Julius L. Schnell" pen. The only example known is a sterling silver overlay matchstick filling pen, similar to the Weidlich. A skilled craftsman and inventor, he began production of the Schnell *Penselpen* in early 1929. A high quality pen/pencil combination throughout, its distinguishing characteristic was an airplane shaped clip whose design was inspired by Charles Lindbergh's recent flight to Paris. The pen also featured a sliding switch to compress the sac. Parker, which used an airplane theme in its advertising, tried to buy the clip patent for $10,000. Schnell turned them down. The *Penselpen* was made for only five or six years.

SERVO PEN
Boston, Mass.

STAR PEN
Cincinnati, Ohio

SOPER & SEIVEWRIGHT
89 Fulton St., New York City. Made the *Keystone*.

STERLING FOUNTAIN PEN CO.
Davicson Rubber Co., 19 Milk St., Boston, Mass. Made high quality middle joint pens

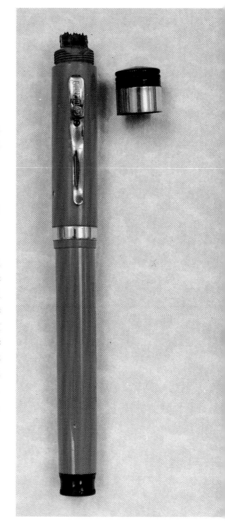

SECURITY, ca. 1922. Red hard rubber twist filling pen with check protector. A small metal roller hidden in the cap was rolled over the signature on a check to prevent alteration. $175-275.

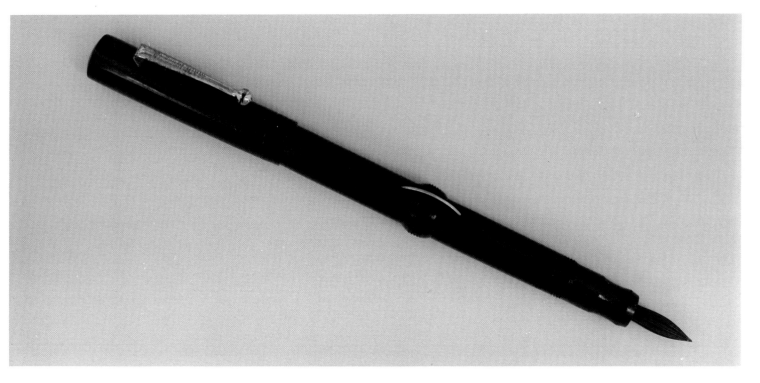

SPORS, ca. 1930. Black plastic crescent filling glass nib pen. $10-25.

EDWARD TODD & CO.

1 W. 34th St., New York City. Made the *Paragon, Peerless, Scholar's Companion, Traveler, Triumph, Universal* and high quality gold and silver pens for Tiffany & Company.

TRIAD PEN

Pawtucket, Rhode Island. Made a beautiful three-sided pen that unscrewed by turning the top of the cap.

J. ULLRICH & CO.

27 Thames St., New York City. Made the *Star, Elk, Independent, Juco* and *Vulcan.*

WEIDLICH SIMPSON PEN CO., 1895-1921. Successor to the Wright Pen Co. of St. Louis, Mo. (before 1915)

5th & Sycamore Sts., Cincinnati, Ohio. Made the *Simplo Match Filler* and an eyedropper filler before 1915. Believed to have merged into Star Pen and Pick Pen in 1921.

WELLCOME PEN

Made a gold filled safety pen about 1918.

PAUL E. WIRT FOUNTAIN PEN CO., 1878-1930

The Paul E. Wirt Fountain Pen Company was started by Paul E. Wirt in Bloomsburg, Pennsylvania. Wirt patented his first pen design in 1878 and made a few pens by hand. He went on to design machinery to build the pen parts and opened his first factory in 1885. Wirt made a popular, simple and reliable pen that was picked up by several major retailers such as Sears & Roebuck. His advertising claimed that he had sold 350,000 pens by April, 1891, 450,000 by August, 1891 and one million by 1894. Wirt pens were sold worldwide. They were handsome pens and examples have been found in heavy silver and gold filled overlays. Sales began to slip by the early 1920s due to increasingly stiff competition from other pen companies and Wirt's involvement in interests outside of making pens. The company finally closed about 1930. Wirt also made the *Phenix* pen.

YANKEE PEN

Minneapolis, Minn.

EDWARD TODD, ca. 1928. Gold filled lever filling pen/pencil combination. Todd made gold and silver pens for Tiffany & Co. $100-150.

EDWARD TODD, ca. 1923. Black chased hard rubber lever filling lady's pen. $40-60.

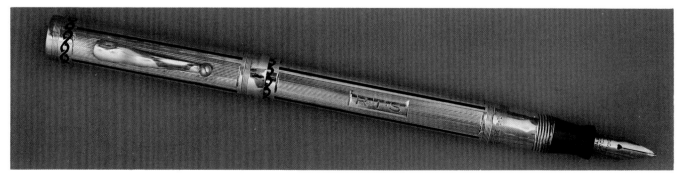

EDWARD TODD, ca. 1923. Solid 14k gold lever filling pen with black enamel trim. $950-1100.

Unknown, ca. 1910. Sterling silver "Magazine" pencils, hallmarked with an "M" in a box. Made for Alfred Hutcheon. $200-275.

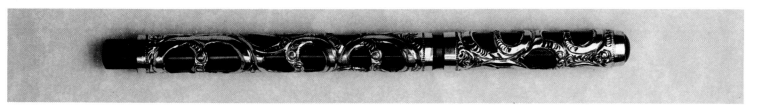

UNKNOWN, ca. 1900. Gold filled filigree design overlay, eyedropper filled pen. $250-350.

Unknown, ca. 1900. Sterling silver filigree design overlay, eyedropper filled taper cap pen. This beautiful overlay is marked with the hallmark. $500-750.

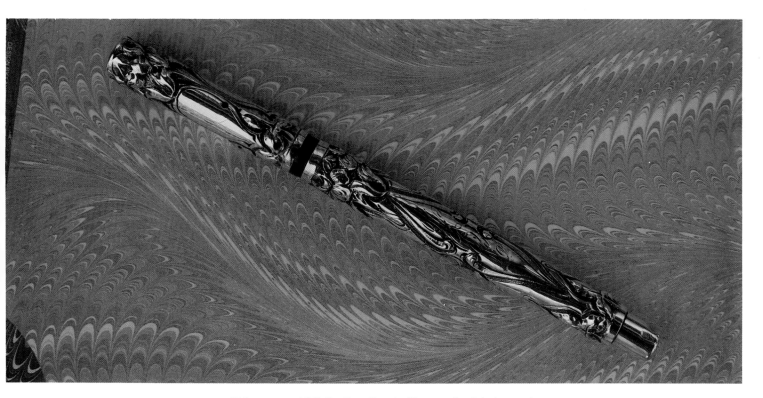

Unknown, ca. 1900. Sterling silver Art Nouveau floral design overlay, eyedropper filled pen. $650-850.

Unknown, ca. 1930's Lever filling pen in laminated plastic. $15-30.

Unknown, ca. 1910. Red hard rubber stylographic pen with sterling silver filigree design overlay. The overlay is marked with the Heath hallmark and is identical to the Parker #14 overlay. $125-200.

WEAREVER, ca. 1940's. Red & gray plastic lever filling. A low-priced pen. $5-15.

WEAREVER, ca. 1940's. Red marble plastic lever, and button filling pens. $5-15.

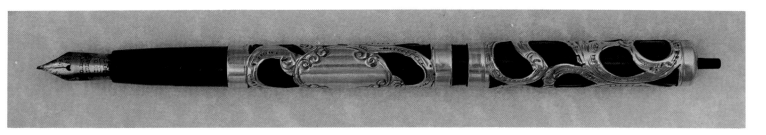

WEIDLICH, ca. 1910. Gold filled filigree design overlay, matchstick type filling pen. $250-350.

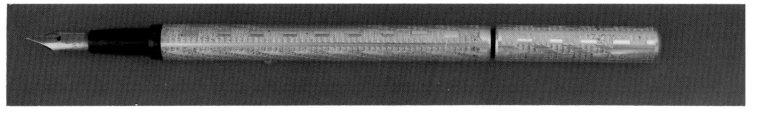

WEIDLICH, ca. 1905. Aluminum overlay, eyedropper filled pen. Aluminum was considered a rare metal at this time and was touted as better than silver as it would not tarnish. $450-650.

WEIDLICH, ca. 1910. Sterling silver filigree, and mother-of-pearl barrel matchstick filling pens. The top of the cap was used to fill the pens. $200-500.

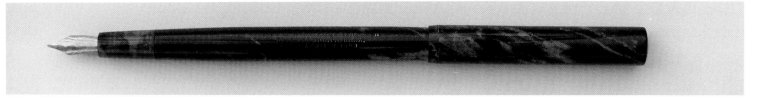

WIRT, ca. 1905-1915. Black & red mottled hard rubber eyedropper filled pen. Note the typical unvented nib. $75-100.

WIRT, ca. 1908. Gold filled filigree design overlay, eyedropper filled pen. $200-300.

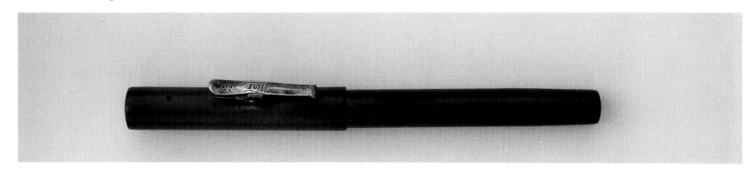

WIRT, ca. 1910-1915. Black hard rubber eyedropper filled pen with an unusual Wirt clip. $25-50.

WIRT, ca. 1908-1912. Black hard rubber eyedropper filled pen with chased band and safety cap. $25-50.

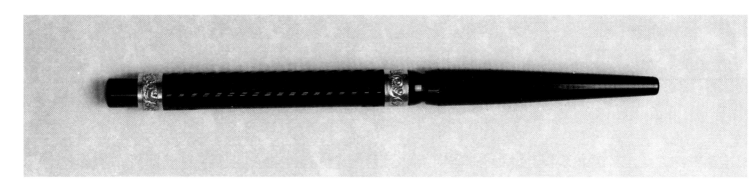

WIRT, ca. 1895-1905. Black chased hard rubber taper cap eyedropper filled pen with two gold filled bands. $50-75.

WIRT and PHOENIX, ca. 1905-1912. Black hard rubber pens. $65-95.

WIRT, ca. 1895-1905. Gold filled chased design overlay, eyedropper
filled taper cap pens. $300-500.

WIRT, ca. 1900-1908. Gold filled filigree design overlay, eyedropper
filled pen. $100-150.

WIRT, ca. 1895-1905. Sterling silver filigree design overlay, eyedropper
filled pens. $400-600.

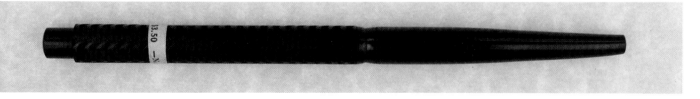

WIRT, ca. 1895. Black chased hard rubber eyedropper filled taper cap
pen. $50-75.

WIRT, ca. 1905-1910. Sterling silver filigree design overlay, eyedropper
filling pen. $400-500.

WIRT, ca. 1890-1898. Black chased hard rubber overfeed eyedropper
filled pen with two gold filled bands. $75-100.

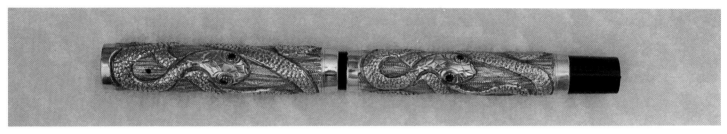

WIRT, ca. 1908. Gold filled snake design overlay, eyedropper filled
pen. $7500-9000.

WIRT, ca. 1898-1903. Red & black mottled hard rubber cable design,
eyedropper filled pen. $250-350.

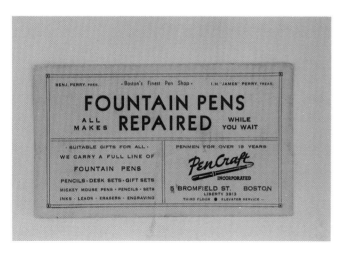

WHITE RUBBER CO., ca. 1940's. Aluminum sac size gauge. $10-20.

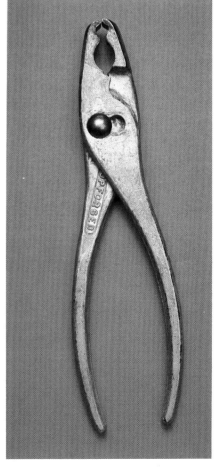

Advertising blotter. $5-10.

Section Pliers, ca. 1930's. One of the most useful tools for the pen
repairman is smooth jawed pliers, used for gripping and removing the
pen's section. $50-60.

Chapter 14

Novelty Pens

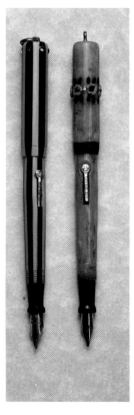

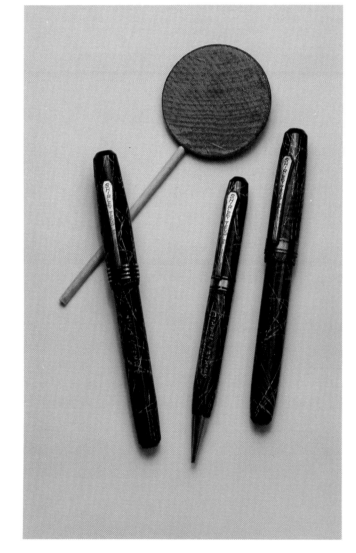

SHIRLEY TEMPLE, ca. 1936. The Shirley Temple pen and pencil were made by the Wearever Pen Company. Endorsements by Shirley Temple helped to sell them. These glittering pens came in an assortment of colors such as red, green, blue, or brown, and had Shirley's name stamped on the clip and barrel. There was also a shorter solid color version of the pen. $75-125.

NOVELTY PENS, ca. 1935. The New Clip jumbo pen, 6½" long and ½" in diameter, and the Peter Pan pen, 3" long, were novelty pens. Generally novelties were poorly made and never intended as serious writing instruments. The illustrated examples were exceptions. They showed signs of quality workmanship and had 14k gold nibs. The original artwork on the New Clip is of Japanese origin. The Peter Pan pen, manufactured by Salz, was made in many decorative styles—flowers, rhinestones, colors, and patterns—while maintaining its small size. Left to right: $150-300; $30-60.

MELVIN PURVIS, ca. 1933. This plastic pen/pencil combination features Melvin Purvis, the G-Man. $75-125.

MICKEY MOUSE, ca. 1935. The Mickey Mouse pen and pencil set was made by the Inkograph Company, 200 Hudson St., New York City. It was a simple black plastic pen, with a metal Mickey Mouse head stick on the top. The pen and pencil said Mickey Mouse on the clip, and each had a decal of Mickey. With even moderate use the decal was easily damaged making it difficult to find one in perfect condition. Mickey cost 75 cents in 1935, $1.00 in 1936, and 69 cents in 1937. The Mickey Mouse pen in the box was made in 1936 in a fatter style, also with the Mickey head. It came in a Disney decorated character box. Both pens were made for children. Originally "thin" Mickey was sold through the mail, while "fat" Mickey was sold in store. These comic character pens were cheaply made and never had gold nibs, but are actively sought by comic character collectors and pen collectors alike.

POPEYE, ca. 1935. The Popeye pen and pencil set was made by Epenco—Eagle Pencil Company of New York—in 1935. It had the name and picture of Popeye on the clip and a circle of decals of Popeye covered by a gilt band around the bottom of the cap. As the band loosened and turned, it scratched off the decal, making it difficult to find one in perfect condition. A different version of the Popeye pen was made in 1937. It was available in red, yellow, green, black, or blue, with Popeye on one side of the clip and Olive Oyl on the other. Unlike the earlier Popeye pen, Epenco embedded Popeye in the plastic. Pens were sold on a display card of ten or twelve pens. A rather inexpensive pen when made, few have survived. Top: $200-300; Left to right: $125-200; $70-90.

MERLIN or GLEAM ca. 1937. The Merlin pen and pencil set was made by Epenco. It was available in brown with gold stars, or red, blue, or green with silver stars, and cost 25 cents. Epenco's adverting read, "for scintillating beauty, there is nothing to equal this distinctive new pen. By an entirely new method of lamination, sparkling metal stars and crescent moons are permanently fixed beneath the surface of the barrel against a background of softly gleaming colored pyralin. Fitted with gilt clip, bands, and levers, and sturdy gold plated nibs." $25-40.

BABE RUTH, ca. 1932. The Babe Ruth pen and pencil was made by the Diamond Point Pen Co. of New York. This rare pen is actively sought by pen and baseball collectors alike and has an interesting story to go with it. After the start of the depression, millions of Americans were out of work with little money to spend on new fountain pens. Diamond Point, a maker of Medium quality pens, was struggling for existence. The director of sales tells this story:

"In December, 1930 I was on a train going to Chicago. I struck up a conversation with a stranger, during which I told him of our company's hard times. He said that he had a friend who might be in a position to help us. We walked over to a corner of the car and I was introduced to his "friend"—Babe Ruth. The stranger was his business manager. We worked out a deal where Babe would endorse one of our pens. Sealed with handshake, that endorsement was a major factor in our surviving the depression. The pen did not do well in department stores, but is sold like hotcakes for $1.00 at the ballparks". $150-250.

STATUE OF LIBERTY, ca. 1935. A souvenir of a visit to the Statue of Liberty in the 1930s, this very cheaply made pen satisfied the tourists looking to take home a remembrance of their visit to "the lady". $20-40.

SUPERMAN, ca. 1940. The rarest comic character fountain pen. This model features a decal of Superman with his name on the clip. An inexpensive pen, it originally sold for 59 cents. Superman did not lend his good name to just any pen, this Superman pen could only be purchased by one true of heart and willing to fight for truth, justice, and the American way. $130-170.

ROY ROGERS and **HOPALONG CASSIDY,** ca. 1950. If you appeared on television, someone would want your fountain pen. Roy Rogers and Hopalong Cassidy both wrote with their official fountain pens from the back of their horses. Hopalong more often is found as a ballpoint pen. The fountain pen was made by Stratford and the ballpoint by Parker. Left to right: $50-75; $65-85.

PEPSI COLA, ca. 1937. A promotional piece given out by Pepsi Cola. It's clip was in the shape and colors of a Pepsi bottle. The colors of the pen held up over time, but the clip usually rusted or rubbed away. Could there have been a Coca Cola pen? None has surfaced to date. $75-100.

Glossary

Aerometric filler—So named by Parker in 1948, variations of this filler had been used for years. The pen is filled by pressure from the hand by pressing on a metal bar laid across the ink sac.

Barrel—The part of the pen which holds the ink, either directly, or within a rubber sac, or cartridge. It also contains the filling mechanism in self-filling pens.

Bayonet cap—Found primarily on early Swan pens, the cap is held on the pen by means of a pin in the section which fits into a groove on a rotating ring on the cap. By turning the ring slightly, the cap is locked in place.

Blind cap—The small cap over the end of the button on button filling, or vacumatic filling pens.

Blow filler—The ink sac was depressed by air pressue by the simple expedient of blowing through a hole in the barrel.

Breather tube—A thin hollow tube attached to the end of the feed, which is used to equalize the pressure between the inside and outside of the pen. Especially useful when the pen is carried in airplanes.

Button filler—Used primarily by Parker, the ink sac is depressed by pushing a button at the end of the barrel. The button is attached to a pressure bar inside the barrel which pushes against the sac.

Cap—The part of the pen which either screws onto threads of the barrel, or is friction fit onto it. It covers the nib and section and keeps the nib from drying out.

Capillary attraction—The filling method employed in the Parker *61*. It consisted of a plastic coated Filler tube containing a cellophane-like material rolled around a breather tube. When the point of the pen is held in ink, the ink is drawn into the pen by capillary attraction, and is trapped between the layers of cellophane.

Chased—This refers either to a pattern of lines machined onto the surface of many hard rubber pens, or in the case of overlay pens, it describes a particular design which was used by almost all the pen manufacturers. This latter design is composed of many decorated spirals.

Cone cap—The standard friction fit cap used on early Parker, and Waterman pens. There is no inner cap, and the inside of the cap is tapered like a cone for a better fit over the section.

Crescent filler—A metal crescent protruding from a slot in the barrel, and held in place by a rotating ring is attached to a pressure bar. By rotating the ring to its open postion, the crescent and bar are pushed in to depress the sac. Used primarily by Conklin.

Ebonite—See *Hard Rubber*

Eyedropper filler—The earliest type of filling method, the entire pen barrel acted as the ink reservoir, and was filled by means of an eyedropper, usually supplied with the pen.

Feed—This channels the ink to the tip of the the nib from the ink reservoir by means of narrow slits along its surface. Usually located on the underside of the nib, on early pens it was placed on top, (referred to as an overfeed pen), or both above and below. It also usually contains some type of trapping pockets to hold any overflow of ink from the pen.

Hard rubber—The first material used for construction of fountain pens, it is comprised of natural latex rubber vulcanized with 32% sulfur. The primary dyes used to color it were carbon black which also gives the rubber tensile strength, and iron oxides for red hard rubber. Because of the lack of carbon black, red rubber is more brittle than black, and cracks easily.

Hatchet filler—A version of the lever filler used by John Holland. A metal bar shaped like a hatchet is used to depress the ink sac.

Ink-Vue filler—A Sacless barrel filler where a small rubber bulb is depressed by a lever to draw ink into the barrel, very much like squeezing the bulb of a eyedropper.

Inner cap—An insert in the cap which when the pen is closed, seals the pen with an ink tight fit. The bottom of the inner cap usually rests on the lip of the section when the pen is closed.

Jewel—A trim piece of either real or synthetic stones, or plastic, which is mounted in the cap top or the bottom of the barrel.

Lady's pen—A generic term for small pens, or more generally, ring cap pens which were supplied with a ring at the top of the cap for hanging the pen from a ribbon or chain worn around the neck, or from a lapel pin.

Lever box—Used primarily on L.E. Waterman pens, the lever mechanism is a self-contained unit made up of the lever and a small metal frame which is held in the barrel by small tabs.

Lever filler—Filling mechanism utilizing a lever attached to the pen barrel, and a pressure bar. By lifting the lever, the bar depresses the ink sac.

Matchstick filler—A small hole in the side of the barrel, is used for insertion of a matchstick, which depresses a bar over the sac.

Montblanc type—A sacless piston filling method where the ink is drawn directly into the barrel Filler or into a separate filling unit by the action of a cork or plastic piston operated on a spiral.

Overlay—A metal covering applied to hard rubber, or plastic pens, usually silver, gold filled metal, or solid gold which usually has a design stamped or engraved into it., but also may be plain.

Permanite—The trade name used by Parker for Dupont's nitrocellulose Pyroxylin plastic, and first used by them in 1926.

Piston filler—Also known by many trade names such as Vacuum Fil, Plunger Vac, etc., it is a sacless system utilizing a piston composed of either rubber washers, or cork attached to a thin metal rod which is withdrawn from the back of the barrel, and then pushed into the pen creating pressure which is released at the end of its travel allowing ink to be drawn into the pen.

Plastic—Pyroxylin (Celluloid) or nitrocellulose, replaced during the 1940s by lucite and cellulose acetate plastics, which were less flammable.

Plunger filler—See *Piston filler.*

Pressure bar—A metal bar used to depress the ink sac.

Propel-Repel pencil—A pencil mechanism where the lead can be advanced or withdrawn by turning part of the pencil.

Pull filler—A metal tab on the outside of the barrel attached to a pressure bar. Pulling on the tab squeezes the the sac between the pen barrel and the bar.

Pyroxylin—The name used by Dupont for nitrocellulose plastic. Called Celluloid by Celenese Corp. This plastic is highly flammable!

Radite—The trade name used by Sheaffer for Dupont's nitrocellulose Pyroxylin plastic, first used by them in 1924.

Repeater pencil—A pencil mechanism where the lead can be advanced in small increments by pushing on the top of the pencil. Sometimes referred to as a "clicker" pencil.

Ring cap—See *Lady's pen.*

Safety pen—A retracting nib pen. The nib and feed are attached to a rod which holds them in the pen barrel when the pen is closed. The entire barrel is used as the ink reservoir, and the nib must be pushed up to use the pen.

Section—The part of the pen which holds the nib and feed, and is either screwed into the pen barrel, or friction fit. It is also the portion of the pen where the fingers rest while writing.

Sleeve filler—An early type of aerometric filler, a metal or plasic sleeve covers the sac and pressure bar, which is depressed by hand.

Snorkel filler—A sac filling system employed by Sheaffer from 1952-1962. A metal snorkel tube is withdrawn from the feed, and inserted in the ink. The sac is then collapsed by air pressure then released , drawing the ink into the pen through the tube.

Straight cap—The first style of cap used by Waterman and many other companies , it is a small bullet shaped cap about two inches long.

Taper cap—A long tapering cap fit on early style pens.

Tassie—A metal or plastic trim ring at either end of the pen.

Touchdown filler—A sac filling system utilized by Sheaffer from 1949-1954. The ink sac is collapsed by air pressure, which is then released while the nib is in the ink, drawing it into the pen.

Twist filler—A method of filling the pen by means of a knob attached to the end of the barrel which wrings the sac to empty and then fills it.

Vacumatic filler—A sacless system which utilizes a rubber diaphragm to create air pressure to draw ink into the barrel. Used on Parker pens of the 1930s and 40s.

Vent hole—The small hole in the nib of the pen which allows air to be drawn into the pen to replace ink as it is used, thus avoiding the creation of a vacuum in the reservoir.

Washer clip—Used by Parker, the clip is attached to the cap by means of a washer fitted between the top of the cap, and a screwed on button, which is also the inner cap on these pens.

Index

Houston Pen Company

Baby Grands in Plain Gold and Gold Filigree

Standard only

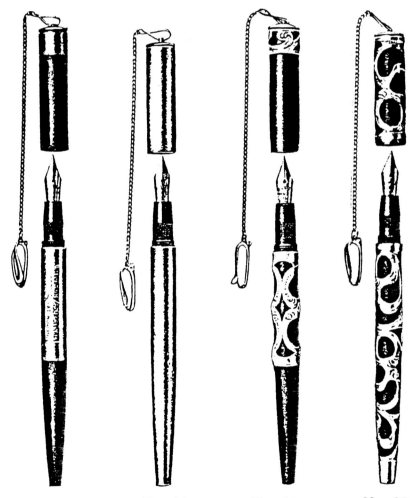

No. 23	No. 24	No. 26	No. 28
Baby Grand	Baby Grand	Baby Grand	Baby Grand
$5.00	**$10.00**	**$5.00**	**$10.00**

Other Titles From Schiffer Publishing

The Book of Fountain Pens and Pencils Stuart Schneider and George Fischler. Over 700 pens and pencils, pictured in full color, with valuable information from two of the world's leading authorities. They also deal with pen company advertising, pen repair, decoration, and valuation. Hundreds of manufacturers are represented.
Size: 9" x 12"   Value Guide   276 pp.
ISBN: 0-88740-394-8   hard cover $79.95

Collecting Writing Instruments Dietmar Geyer. From the flint tool to the stylus, from quill pen to fountain pen and felt-tip marker, this book invites one to develop or deepen one's love for beautiful old writing instruments. Contains 100s of contemporary engravings, illustrations, advertisements, photos, and catalog and brochure excerpts.
Size: 9" x 12"   Price Guide   176 pp.
ISBN: 0-88740-272-0   hard cover $49.95

The Illustrated Guide to Antique Writing Instruments *Second Edition* Stuart Schneider & George Fischler. This is the kind of guide collectors need for quick and easy reference. Both handy and beautiful, it shows over 500 pens and pencils in nearly full-size color photos and provides short histories of the 19 main companies. Concise, helpful information with each photo includes a guide to the price of each.
Size: 6" x 9"   556 color photos   160 pp.
ISBN: 0-7643-0251-5   soft cover $19.95

Pens & Pencils, A Collector's Handbook Regina Martini, Photography by Harald Grotowsky. The limited and standard production pens of the famous makers Montblanc, Parker, Pelikan, Shaeffer and Waterman are presented along with their particular numbering systems. Many smaller companies' pens are also included, as well as period advertisements. Clear drawings and patent applications from 1884 to 1994 show what is inside the pens and how they work.
Size: 8 1/2" x 11"   1,313 pens & pencils   148 pp.
Price Guide
ISBN: 0-88740-942-3   soft cover $24.95

Zenith Radio: The Early Years 1919-1935 Harold Cones, Ph.D, and John Bryant, AIA with Martin Blankinship and William Wade. Presents the documented story of Zenith radio and company from 1919 through 1935. Tells the story of Zenith's impact on early radio history with photographs, documents, and information, as well as color portraits of many Zenith radios of the era.
Size: 8 1/2" x 11"   Value Guide   192 pp.
ISBN: 0-7643-0367-8   soft cover $29.95

Antique Typewriters: From Creed to QWERTY Michael Adler. This new book by the renowned typewriter expert is sure to stimulate enthusiasm by bringing you new insights into the origins of the invention itself and in a detailed history of the machine. 279 photos illustrate this definitive text, which includes comprehensive directories of typewriter inventions, makes, and models, and a guide to values with advice on buying and collecting.
Size: 81/2" x 11"   Value Guide   208 pp.
ISBN: 0-7643-0132-2   hard cover $39.95

Philco Radio: 1928-1942 Ron Ramirez, with Michael Prosise. A superb reference book on Philco, the leading radio manufacturer during radio's "Golden Age." Specifications for each model given. A year-by-year look at Philco's radio line each year between 1928, when the company began to make radios, and 1942, when World War II put a halt to radio production.
Size: 8 1/2" x 11"   828 photos & drawings 160 pp.
Price Guide
ISBN: 0-88740-547-9   soft cover $29.95

Radios by Hallicrafters Chuck Dachis. This book includes over 1000 photographs of radio receivers, transmitters, and speakers, early television sets, electronics accessories and advertising material produced by this Chicago-based firm. Technical descriptions are provided for every known Hallicrafters model, including dates of production, model numbers, accompanying pieces, and original prices.
Size: 8 1/2" x 11"   1000 photos   225 pp.
Price Guide
ISBN: 0-88740-929-6   soft cover $29.95

Telephones, Antique to Modern Kate Dooner. Over 500 color photos cover the development of the telephone from Bell's first experimental equipment. Exquisite examples of wooden box phones, vanities, upright "candlesticks," and desk stand or "cradle" phones. An important reference for novice and avid telephone collectors alike, with full descriptions of the numerous telephone companies and manufacturers.
Size: 8 1/2" x 11"   Value Guide   176 pp.
ISBN: 0-88740-386-7   soft cover $29.95

Telephone Collecting: Seven Decades of Design Kate E. Dooner. Here, in text and over 250 color photographs, a history of the design of the telephone is presented from Art Deco years to novelty phones of the 1980s. The largest telephone companies are discussed, including Western Electric, Automatic Electric, Stromberg-Carlson, Kellogg, and North Electric. Plus there's information on European telephones.

Size: 8 1/2" x 11"   Price Guide   128 pp.
ISBN: 0-88740-489-8   soft cover $24.95

One Hundred Years of Bell Telephone Richard D. Mountjoy. From the Coffin sets of the 1870s to the Princess phones of the 1960s and beyond, this book explores the technology and the history of the telephone. Provides detailed information which will help identify a piece and will take the guess work out of dating equipment. This book will make it easy to match pieces correctly for historical accuracy.

Size: 8 1/2" x 11"   350 color photos   176pp.
Price Guide
ISBN: 0-88740-872-9   soft cover $29.95

Cigarette Lighters Stuart Schneider & George Fischler. Over 500 lighters are illustrated in full color. Shown in alphabetical order of their makers and by date within each company. The available historical data is presented. Lighters include examples from well-known companies like Dunhill, Ronson, and Zippo as well as companies whose names are lost in smoke.

Size: 8 1/2" x 11"   525 color photos   196pp.
Price Guide
ISBN: 0-88740-952-0   hard cover $39.95

ZIPPO: The Great American Lighter David Poore. This book is a must for all collectors and lovers of Americana. It contains a sequential history of Zippo series, cases, inserts, fluid cans, flint packages, and sundries. It is richly illustrated in full color with many of the most highly prized Zippo lighters that people collect. Information was based on original Zippo salesman's catalogs, leaflets, advertising brochures, and the study of thousands of Zippo lighters. Prices are provided with each picture, and a complete price guide is located in the back of the book.

Size: 8 1/2" x 11"   500 color photos   196 pp.
Price Guide
ISBN: 0-7643-0203-5   hard cover $39.95

Tobacco Tins: A Collector's Guide Douglas Congdon-Martin. This book is the first full-color reference on tobacco tins. Over 1000 tobacco tins illustrated in full color, reveal the designer's and the lithographer's art. In addition, it contains advertising and other ephemera.

Size: 8 1/2" x 11"   Price Guide   160 pp.
ISBN: 0-88740-429-4   soft cover $29.95

Tobacco Advertising: The Great Seduction Gerard S.Petrone, M.D. With illustrations of antique artifacts, old photographs and contemporary advertising, the reader is taken through the rapid growth of the tobacco industry and shown a wide-range of promotional ploys and gimmickry that evolved. This highly acclaimed book combines a well-researched text with photographs and price guide to study a hot topic.

Size: 8 1/2" x 11"   Price Guide/Index   264 pp.
ISBN: 0-88740-972-5   hard cover $49.95

Chewing Tobacco Tin Tags, 1870-1930 Louis Storino. Most of these beautiful little pieces of art are over 100 years old and come in various sizes, shapes, and colors. With a listing of over 6000 tin tags described and priced, 2000 illustrated tags, plus the many other illustrated and related features, this work will delight the collector.

Size: 6" x 9"   2000 tags in color   128 pp.
Price Guide
ISBN: 0-88740-857-5   soft cover $19.95

Antique Cigar Cutters and Lighters Jerry Terranova & Douglas Congdon-Martin. For the pleasure and convenience of cigar smokers a wide variety of smoking accessories were manufactured, including cigar cutters and lighters. The text places the cutters in their historical context and contains helpful information.

Size: 8 1/2" x 11"   613 color photos   176 pp.
Value Guide
ISBN: 0-88740-941-5   hard cover $69.95

Great Cigar Stuff for Collectors Jerry Terranova and Douglas Congdon-Martin. This is a compendium of cigar related "stuff,". Here is the breadth of advertising, ashtrays, matchsafes, cigar boxes, dispensers, and holders that have adorned homes and shops for 100 years and more.

Size: 8 1/2" x 11"   Over 500 photos   160 pp.
Price Guide
ISBN: 0-7643-0368-6   soft cover $29.95

Camel Cigarette Collectibles: The Early Years, 1913-1963 Douglas Congdon-Martin. This book celebrates the first fifty years of Camel advertising and packaging. Color photographs capture the rich images used to promote Camel goods. The images are accompanied by useful captions and an informative text.

Size: 8 1/2" x 11"   450 color photos   192 pp.
Price Guide
ISBN: 0-88740-948-2   soft cover $29.95

Camel Cigarette Collectibles: 1964-1995 Douglas Congdon-Martin. In 1988, R.J. Reynolds began one of the most clever and effective campaigns in advertising history. On its 75th anniversary a suave, new character appeared in the Camel Advertising: Joe Camel, a figure which now has international recognition. In addition to traditional posters and signs, these years saw the introduction of hundreds of premiums and merchandise bearing the Camel logos. Joe was retired in 1997 and the collectibles with his image are more desirable than ever. This is the reference guide with color photos and helpful information.
Size: 8 1/2" x 11"   500 color photos   176 pp.
Value Guide
ISBN: 0-7643-0196-9   soft cover $29.95

Match Holders: 100 Years of Ingenuity Denis B. Alsford. The historical influences, patents, marks and photos shed light on the developments of match holders from their early years in the 1850s to their use as commonplace household items. A wide variety of match holders are depicted including pocket, "candle-in-a-box", stand-alone and wall hanging models. Discussions of major manufacturers, and copy from the British magazine "Punch" add dimension as well.
Size: 8 1/2" x 11"   689 color photos   160pp.
Price Guide
ISBN: 0-88740-633-5   soft cover $29.95

Pocket Matchsafes, Reflections of Life & Art, 1840-1920 W. Eugene Sanders, Jr. and Christine C. Sanders. Matchsafes are presented here as a microcosm of life and art from 1840 to 1920. Each is described with details of its pertinent artist, patentee, manufacturer, materials, construction, and value, all complementing the brief and conversational general text.
Size: 8 1/2" X 11"   398 color photos   176 pp.
Price Guide   Index
ISBN: 0-7643-0324-4   soft cover $34.95

Creative Variations in Jewelry Design Maurice P. Galli, Dominique Rivière, and Fanfan Li. Step-by-step instruction through the creative drawing process for twenty-five different styles of jewelry sets, with four variations for each style.
Size: 9" x 12"   100 color drawings   204 pp.
ISBN: 0-7643-0330-9   hard cover $69.95

The Art of Jewelry Design: Principles of Design, Rings & Earrings Maurice P. Galli, Dominique Riviere, Fanfan Li. Beautiful and practical step-by-step format teaches how to create drawings used to manufacture jewelry. A fully illustrated discussion of design principles and metal and stone rendering techniques is followed by detailed sketches and finished drawings of many varieties of ring & earring designs.
Size: 9" x 12"   104 color drawings   224 pp.
ISBN: 0-88740-562-2   hard cover $59.95

Theodor Fahrner Jewelry... Between Avant-Garde and Tradition Ulrike von Hase-Schmundt, Christianne Weber, Ingeborg Becker. Stunning Art Nouveau, Art Deco, and modern jewelry by the firm of Theodor Fahrner is displayed in this detailed chronological study. Sections include advertisements, original design sketches, all known marks, pictures of the important people, and hundreds of pieces of jewelry.
Size: 8 1/2" x 11"   Price Guide   288 pp.
ISBN:0-88740-326-3   hard cover $69.95

The Power of Jewelry Nancy Schiffer. Color photos of magnificent jewelry and fascinating legends associated with the different gem stones are combined to form a fresh, new approach to antique and modern jewelry. European and American jewelry styles spanning 300 years proclaim the social, political, and financial power of their owners.
Size: 9" x 12"   480 color photos   256 pp.
ISBN: 0-88740-135-X   hard cover $75.00

European Designer Jewelry Ginger Moro. Documents the trends, sources and makers of innovative 20th century designer jewelry in 13 European countries. The evolution of artists' limited-edition creations, as well as fashion and costume jewelry, are explored through the well-researched text, photographs and vintage prints. Biographical sketches are provided for the artists and couturiers who worked closely with the fashion designers.
Size: 8 1/2" x 11"   707 photos   304 pp.
Price Guide
ISBN: 0-88740-823-0   hard cover $79.95

Georg Jensen: A Tradition of Splendid Silver Janet Drucker. A new study of the designs of Danish silversmith Georg Jensen (1866-1935) and company. Covers jewelry, hollowware, and flatware designed and produced from 1904 to the present. Jensen's life and the company he founded are thoroughly researched and interpretation of the marks used on Jensen silver is provided.
Size: 9" x 12"   737 color photos   312 pp.
Price Guide   Index
ISBN: 0-88740-978-4   hard cover $79.95

Copper Art Jewelry: A Different Luster Matthew L. Burkholz and Linda Lichtenberg Kaplan. This is the reference that collectors, appraisers, and art dealers have been seeking for twentieth-century designs. Over 300 color photos show hundreds of examples. Original art work, advertising, identifying marks and anecdotes round out this exhaustive study.
Size: 8 1/2" x 11"   300 color photos & illus.   176 pp.
Price Guide
ISBN: 0-88740-419-7   hard cover $ 49.95

Beads of the World Peter Francis, Jr. Written to encourage collectors and clarify the origins and uses of beads in their native settings, this book is the best and broadest reference available to date. Beads of organic, stone, and glass materials are individually discussed, and certain types of beads are traced to their origins in Europe, the Middle East, India, the Far East, Southeast Asia, North and South America and Africa.

Size: 8 1/2" x 11"   272 photos   144 pp.
Price Guide
ISBN: 0-88740-559-2   soft cover $19.95

Glass Beads From Europe Sibylle Jargstorf. The various worldwide uses of glass beads, from antiquity to the modern time, are presented along with the fascinating evolution of the beadmaking industry. Phoenician, Celtic, Viking, Venetian, African, Bavarian, Bohemian, Dutch, French, and Russian styles that were made for symbolic, fashion, magic, and controversial uses are shown.

Size: 8 1/2" x 11"   475 color photos   160 pp.
Price Guide
ISBN: 0-88740-839-7   soft cover $29.95

Baubles, Buttons and Beads: The Heritage of Bohemia Sibylle Jargstorf. This groundbreaking book exposes the jewels, craftsmanship, technological development, and history of Bohemia. Gorgeous color photos show the area's artistry, its most significant designers and manufacturers and their contributions to the art of jewelry, button, and bead making.

Size: 8 1/2" x 11"   384 color photos   176 pp.
Price Guide
ISBN: 0-88740-467-7   soft cover $29.95

Glass in Jewelry Sibylle Jargstorf. A guide to the great variety of beautiful glass jewelry and glass beads created from the 16th to the 20th centuries for the European and North American markets. Text explains the origins of filigree and alabaster glass, the lovely variety of bead types, artificial gems, glass cameos and incrustations, millefiori, mosaic and aventurine jewelry, and even applications in modern jewelry designs.

Size: 8 1/2" x 11"   400 color photos   200 pp.
Value Guide
ISBN: 0-88740-295-X   soft cover $29.95

Costume Jewelry: The Fun of Collecting (Revised) Nancy Schiffer. The delight in owning colored and large-stone costume jewelry is imaginatively conveyed through the appealing photographs of 1593 pieces of jewelry and factual text in this book.

Size: 8 1/2" x 11"   color photos   176 pp.
Price Guide
ISBN: 0- 7643-0005-9   soft cover $29.95

Rainbow of Rhinestone Jewelry Sandy Fichtner and Lynn Ann Russell. Over 450 color photographs display thousands of signed and unsigned jewelry pieces arranged by color and design. This book brings fact and practical advice to the joy of owning beautiful rhinestone jewelry. The suggestions for care result from the authors' experience caring for their own collections so that you, too, can learn to carefully clean, repair and store your jewelry.

Size: 6 "x 9"   over 450 photos   160 pp.
Price Guide
ISBN: 0-88740-895-8   soft cover $19.95

Rhinestones! (Revised Price Guide) Nancy N. Schiffer. Illustrated with nearly 300 color photos of hundreds of examples of gorgeous jewelry never published before, this study focuses on the industry, personalities, and designers who gave women affordable jewelry made with rhinestones. The photos show innovations in the designs of the stones and the technical achievements that produced a wide variety of visual effects.

Size 6" x 9"   Price Guide   160 pp.
ISBN: 0-7643-0269-8   soft cover $16.95

Costume Jewelers: The Golden Age of Design *Second Edition* Joanne Dubbs Ball. Personal glimpses of that elite core of artists responsible for establishing the costume jewelry industry in the United States. Hundreds of color photographs of their jewelry illustrate the expertise in design and manufacture of such masters as Chanel, Dior, Joseff, Haskell, Boucher, Lane, Trifari, and many more.

Size: 8 1/2" x 11"   150 color photos   208 pp.
Price Guide
ISBN: 0-7643-0212-4   hard cover $39.95

Jewelry of the Stars Joanne Dubbs Ball. Journey through the art of Joseff of Hollywood, whose extraordinary design talents contributed to over 90% of the jewelry supplied for the movies during Hollywood's golden years. His jeweled masterpieces are shown in new color photographs made especially for this book and in black-and-white stills of yesteryear showing the stars, men and women alike, wearing them.

Size: 8 1/2" x 11"   Value Guide   192 pp.
ISBN: 0-88740-294-1   hard cover $44.95